Thirsty Animals

RACHELLE ATALLA

Thirsty Animals

HODDER &
STOUGHTON

First published in Great Britain in 2023 by Hodder & Stoughton
An Hachette UK company

1

Copyright © Rachelle Atalla 2023

A CIP catalogue record for this title is available from the British Library

Hardback ISBN 978 1 529 34215 4
Trade Paperback ISBN 978 1 529 34219 2
eBook ISBN 978 1 529 34216 1

Typeset in Plantin by Manipal Technologies Limited

Printed and bound in Great Britain by Clays Ltd, Elcograf S.p.A.

Hodder & Stoughton policy is to use papers that are natural, renewable
and recyclable products and made from wood grown in sustainable forests.
The logging and manufacturing processes are expected to conform
to the environmental regulations of the country of origin.

Hodder & Stoughton Ltd
Carmelite House
50 Victoria Embankment
London EC4Y 0DZ

www.hodder.co.uk

For Sheila

Sheep, like people, are ungovernable when hungry.
John Muir

SPRING

I

It was just before 8 p.m. when we pulled into the Welcome Break service station. Mum came to a stop near the entrance, letting the engine idle, an obvious rattle under the frame of the Defender that neither of us felt the need to mention. Outside, a man was sitting on a stool between two parked cars, cooking on a disposable barbecue, while a woman squatted beside him, scrubbing clothes in a small basin.

They're not staying here, are they? Mum asked, nodding towards them. Surely they're not sleeping in the car park . . .

Unclipping my seatbelt, I noticed a squashed insect on the passenger window. On closer inspection it looked like a mosquito – its legs spread out, a diluted smudge of someone else's blood. Had we always had mosquitoes in Scotland, or had they migrated with the warmer climate? I had no idea, but it worried me. There was something in my blood mosquitoes couldn't get enough of.

Aida, Mum pressed. Will these people give you trouble during the night?

I shook my head, opening the passenger door. They usually get moved on after a couple of hours, I said.

She looked at me then, went to say something before changing her mind.

I'll see you in the morning, I said.

I'll be here. Don't be late.

I nodded, slamming the door shut, mortified that at the age of twenty-one I was struggling to master the skill of driving and still had to rely upon her for getting me to and from work.

As I walked away, dirty water from the woman's basin spilled over, running in a zigzagging line across the tarmac towards me. I could feel this stranger's gaze, a penetrating stare, but I held strong and refused to make eye contact. The stragglers always wanted to talk, tell you their woes and struggles of making it across the border. There used to be hundreds of them, maybe thousands, but they'd dwindled in number, only handfuls at a time now.

The double doors to the service station opened and closed with a whoosh behind me. I passed the different kiosks in the food court and made my way to the staff room, placing my bag in a locker and pinning my name badge to my shirt.

Aaron, my shift partner, was already waiting for me in our concession. He smiled as I settled in beside him – his face familiar and beautiful. He didn't know how beautiful he was.

Thought I'd see you at Joe's last night, he said.

Was there something at Joe's? I wasn't aware . . .

His face reddened. Sorry, I . . .

It's okay, I said. It's not your job to keep my social life afloat.

Above our heads there was a television suspended from a metal frame. The local news was on, and a reporter was speaking to an engineer wearing a hard hat. They were discussing the increased numbers of desalination plants being built across the country to counteract the water shortages. The man in the hard hat was trying to be positive about their progress but the reporter was quizzing him on the cost and timescale. It sounded bizarre to me, gathering up the sea and removing its salt – how was that even possible? They cut back to someone in the studio who had been wheeled out to represent an opposing opinion. It was a dumpy wee man that was talking now, sweating at the temples, moaning about the unnecessary money coming from the tax-payer's pocket. I'd seen his type before, usually called Nigel or Clive, mid-sixties, consumed with economic growth and GDPs – the ones who took videos of water running from their own taps just to prove there weren't any shortages. Nigel would no doubt be mortgage-free with an immaculate garden that he was no longer allowed to water, or own a black Mercedes that was really letting him down now he couldn't get it washed by some twelve-year-old for £5. He probably had a rental property too that was sitting empty. The Met Office had said we'd had the driest five-year period since records began, but for Nigel the drought was one big fucking inconvenience. And as he carried on speaking I imagined him running out of water first; savoured the image of his shock.

People are saying that they might close the border, Aaron said, nodding out towards the corridor, as if the border to England were right there and not seven miles south. Not let anyone over at all, he added. Not even the folk with visas.

Who's saying that?

He shrugged. People on Twitter.

Can we watch something else? I said.

He reached up and changed the channel, settling on a repeat of a cheap reality-TV programme about people who worked on luxury yachts.

We used to watch this when we were hungover, he said. Do you remember?

I nodded, smiling.

Aaron had been the year above me at school but when his dad had taken ill, he'd had to defer his place at university, and then we'd both ended up studying in Edinburgh at the same time, him architecture and me English literature. We'd developed something of a friendship which involved us occasionally sleeping together and, like an unspoken rule, this arrangement only existed in Edinburgh. Now, because of the drought, we were stuck together once again, two to three night shifts a week depending on the rota.

Do you think they *will* close the border? I finally asked.

He paused. Maybe . . . I mean, if the government decide too many folk are crossing over, then why wouldn't they?

Out in the corridor I could see a boy eyeing up the dough-nut stand. Lewis, the manager, had fitted a lock to the cabi-net a few weeks ago because doughnut-looting had become a problem. But now we were never very sure who was meant to have the key. It was awkward more than anything, especially in the middle of the night, when a customer asked for a dough-nut and you had to do the rounds, locating a key from some-one who was usually on a break, while acting as if it was the most natural thing in the world to want a doughnut at 4 a.m. And I was never here when the doughnuts got delivered so I half-suspected that it was the same stale ones that sat in the cabinet day after day, saved from decay only by their obscene sugar content.

If they do close the border, Aaron said, then they'll likely close this place too. And the outlet shops.

A laugh snorted out of me. Not exactly a tragedy, though, is it?

My mum and sister are both working at the Mountain Warehouse.

I fell silent then. Sorry, yeah, it's just, you know . . .

No, I know. They're awful. Total shit.

I placed my elbows on the shelf I was standing in front of, dislodging the plastic strip that displayed the price of chocolate bars. The strip fell to my feet, and I bent to retrieve it. The clip-pings to secure it back into place kept buckling in my hands and eventually I dropped it again, kicking it under the stand. Half the shelves were empty because of supply issues anyway. So really, what did it matter?

When I turned, the teenager from the doughnut cabinet and a man, perhaps his dad, were hovering by the drinks aisle. They were debating something in whispers, picking up one bottle at a time before putting it back and lifting another. They made their way to the tills, and I greeted them, offering them my most hospitable smile because it was still early enough in the night that I felt as though it mattered.

The man placed one half-litre bottle of still spring water and a large bag of crisps on the counter, while the boy retreated to the doughnut stand.

I scanned the crisps through first. £1.19. But it took me a moment to remove the security tag from the bottle of water. Eventually, after I'd fought with the tag, the item rang through at £14.99.

That'll be £16.18 total, I said.

The man stared at me before pulling out a wallet from his back pocket. Happy to exploit the desperate, I see.

Sorry but I don't set the prices.

He began rummaging through the folds of his wallet. I think I've only got my card, is that okay?

The card machines are down at the moment, I said. They've been down for a while. But there's a cashpoint outside if you need it. It does charge, though, I added, still smiling.

The man's shoulders slumped, and he glanced at the boy. Of course, he said. I'll be back in a minute.

Aaron waited until they were out of view. No way he's coming back . . .

But the man and boy did return. They paid their money and as the man slid his wallet back into his pocket the boy cracked open the seal of the water. He gulped mouthfuls in front of us, his jugular moving, all jagged and repetitive.

Are you just passing through? I said, surprising myself for even asking.

The man looked up, holding my eye for longer than seemed natural. My wife has relatives near Fife, and they sponsored our visas.

Have you visited before?

He shook his head, perhaps embarrassed, his eyes shifting momentarily to the floor. And I wanted to laugh: the number of people making it across the border who had never thought to venture into Scotland before.

Are you a golf fan? Aaron asked.

The man stared at us blankly. Sorry?

Golf, Aaron pressed, completely straight-faced. St Andrews, in Fife, is the home of golf.

Oh, the man replied, I never thought to bring my clubs . . . It was as if he was in a fog, disorientated not only by us but by the environment we inhabited. He stared at me, his lips parted. You still have running water, yes?

I nodded.

He licked his lips. I was told that Loch Ness . . . it has more water than all the lakes in England and Wales combined. Is that true?

This wasn't the first time I'd been asked this. It was like some rumour, an urban legend spreading between those making their way north – maybe it gave people hope. But it was weird. And always Loch Ness. I had seen a piece of art somewhere that highlighted the loch's depth – deep crevices making their way to the centre of the earth. I tried to visualise the empty and exposed space; it all seemed so unnatural and disturbing. But, if Loch Ness was to be everyone's saviour, then I was yet to see it come to fruition. The treatment of water, logistics and distribution – those were the terms thrown at us in the government briefings. It had barely rained here in over a year, but this man was looking at me so earnestly, and it felt as if he really needed this, so I nodded and said, Yeah, it's true. It actually has nearly *double* the volume of water of all the lakes in England and Wales combined.

We watched them walk away, the boy once again gulping at the water. Slow down, Jamie, the man said. Save some for the rest of us.

Aaron came round to where I was standing and placed his elbows on the counter, cupping his chin in his hands. How long until he realises we're charging double the going rate for a bottle of spring water?

I laughed but it was half-hearted.

Aaron straightened, something solidifying in his voice. Every time I go into the stock room there seems to be less and less. If they close the land border, how will they get goods in? Will they still let things come by boat, even if they won't let people?

How the fuck should I know? I said. I'm not the border police. I've no idea how these things work.

Have you been seeing all the stuff on social media about what it's like south of the border? Proper Third World shit . . .

I'm trying not to look, I said. My socials are already a mix of the horrific versus perfectly poised selfies.

How can you not look? he said. I can't seem to switch it off.

The internet on the farm is chronic, I said. And anyway, terrible things have always been happening to people. We just never really wanted to look at them until now.

It was never so close to home until now, he said.

The next few monotonous hours were filled with some straight-to-TV movie Aaron had picked, while the hum of the fridges and the occasional customer's voice echoed out from the corridor.

After scrolling through my socials for a while, I took to reading magazines off the rack.

Don't you have coursework to be doing? Aaron asked.

What's the likely chance that I'll be graduating this year? That any of us will . . .

What, so you've stopped even trying?

I don't see you out with your pens and tracing paper, marking up some building, I said. Where's those pretentious postcards you used to bring in as inspiration for your sketches and models?

I take your point, he replied, somewhat aggressively.

I shrugged, making my way through an interior design magazine that was several months old, all Christmas table centrepieces and homemade wreaths. I paused, placing my fingers over the happy faces of those sitting around a festive table, a false family. Christmas on the farm was not usually a particularly joyous day: Great-uncle Bobby would be trying too hard, shattered from tending to the livestock, his partner Sam passive-aggressively preparing the food, grumbling about not getting enough help yet simultaneously demanding we vacate his vicinity. And then there would be Mum, hating every minute. Bobby had bought her one of those SAD sunlamps the year before deciding her problem was down to a lack of vitamin D – that her Egyptian DNA wasn't cut out for Scottish winters despite her having lived here for over two decades.

I closed the magazine. I might nip to the loo, I said, rising from the stool I'd been sitting on, pins and needles suddenly shooting through my feet.

Aaron nodded absently, not bothering to glance up from his phone. Have you seen this video? he said, holding up the screen. It's pretty fucked up. Some guy was killed swimming in a dam. They're saying he was thirsty and jumped in since the water wasn't too deep, but he got sucked down by the turbines and never surfaced again. The whole thing's been filmed.

The fluorescent lights shone brightly in the toilets, and an electronic screen that asked you about your customer experience was still flashing – a smiley emoji for complete satisfaction. I had a strong desire to wash my face, but they'd closed off the taps to stop people who were only coming in to fill up their water bottles. The antiseptic hand gel screwed to the wall bubbled away instead.

The drought had been threatening us since last summer, but it had still seemed to take us by surprise – a once-in-a-thousand-years sort of thing, they kept saying. I'd gone on climate marches, attended rallies, but the jet streams were still threatening to collapse, moving as far north as Iceland, leaving the majority of Europe in a situation it had never really experienced before. We'd had our mildest, driest winter, with almost no rainfall, and now it was Easter – summer would soon be approaching, and we had no idea when rain might arrive. With nothing growing, Bobby was constantly wondering how we'd continue to feed our livestock, having resorted to paying extortionate rates for hay imported from Norway. And it didn't help that we were a salary down, the community hospital where Mum had been employed as a midwife having closed its doors.

There must have been warning signs long before last year – maybe the explosion of dandelions taking over verges, or the lack of badgers and moles for Bobby to contend with compared to other years. And now a country with a population of sixty-odd million had essentially run dry and was attempting mass migration into a population with one-tenth its numbers, curbed by little more than a physical border, controlled by the military, while

patrols monitored our choppy waters, turning the boats back
that hadn't already capsized.

I brought my blood glucose meter out from its wallet and
pricked my finger. I had toyed with getting one of those con-
tinuous glucose monitors that were embedded in your skin but
the supply of them had become so unreliable, plus I would have
had to go on a course, and I couldn't really be bothered. While
I waited for the meter to calibrate, I checked my phone again.
There were two messages – one was from Mia working at the
Premier Inn around the corner, claiming that some weirdo had
left a shit in one of the beds. The other was from Dad, asking if I
had any plans to visit him in Glasgow. Ignoring both, I took out
my short-acting insulin pen, set the dial to six units and lifted my
shirt, injecting myself in the stomach. After, I just kind of stood
there, not really needing the toilet but not really wanting to go
back. I thought about everyone trying their best to use as little
water as possible, growing dehydrated and straining to remove
urine from their bladders, toilets everywhere neglected and
underused – and stupidly this made me feel sad, as if they had
their own feelings. To be honest, I was surprised that the toilets
here were still running in the service station, or that they hadn't
started charging people for the privilege. Instead they were running a chemical through the cisterns that made the water flush
blue, stopping people from drinking it. Bizarre to think that,
until they went out of their way to add a chemical, the water had
been otherwise drinkable. You couldn't flush it right now, though:
the mains water was turned off everywhere between 9 p.m.
and 7 a.m.

All the doors to the toilet cubicles were swung shut on
their hinges and I pressed the door closest to me. A shriek
escaped from me as I jumped back, startled by the sight of a
woman. She was perched on the closed toilet seat, feet off the

floor, her knees raised so they were touching her chin. She was filthy, and the stench of her was suddenly overpowering. For a moment I was confused, as if I was misunderstanding a perfectly reasonable and rational situation. She brought her index finger to her lips and when she spoke, in a hushed tone, it was in a language I did not understand. Instinctively I backed away, my hipbone bumping painfully into a basin. She rose, one shoeless foot accidentally pressing down on the pedal of the sanitary bin, so the lid flapped wide open like a set of lips. She was speaking again, an urgency to her voice, but still I couldn't understand her. And then I saw that her wrist was bleeding, droplets landing on the floor, while she pressed the wound to her chest.

I ran out and down the corridor towards our concession. Aaron, I called out, but my voice appeared muted. Aaron . . .

He looked up at me. What is it?

There's a woman . . . In the toilets . . .

And?

I can't understand her. But I think there's something wrong with her. She's bleeding.

I'll get Lewis, he said in an almost inconvenienced tone.

I went back towards the toilets but found myself suddenly stalling, taking reluctant steps. The woman was standing over the threshold of the cubicle, still clutching her arm to her chest.

What happened? I asked, but she looked at me vacantly. I ushered her forward, droplets of blood falling with each step she took until we were out in the open corridor.

Aaron and Lewis were waiting for us.

Who's the first-aider tonight? Lewis asked.

It's meant to be me, I said.

We took her into our concession and ushered her down on to the footstool I had not so long ago been occupying. She couldn't have been that old, maybe a few years older than me. Lewis left and returned almost instantly with a first-aid box, opening it and handing it to me. I put on a pair of white latex gloves and tore open an antiseptic wipe before trying to pull the woman's arm towards me, but she did everything she could to resist my touch. I placed my hand on her knee, hesitantly, and tried to smile.

We only want to help, I said.

Slowly she offered her arm out towards me and I peeled back the blood-soaked sleeve. Blood began to ooze, almost bubble, the gash deep, and Aaron stepped back, while I tried my best not to gag. I covered her wrist with the antiseptic wipe, but I couldn't imagine it having much effect.

Get me a dressing pack, I said, nodding towards the first-aid box.

Crouching down, Lewis fumbled through all the different things: gauze, plasters, little scissors. He offered me up a selection and I grabbed this thin padding stuff, forcing it on to the woman's arm before taking a bandage and asking Lewis to rip it from its plastic packaging. I was trying to be careful and meticulous, having previously prided myself on my first-aid skills, but the blood was still seeping through. I kept wrapping the bandage around her arm, tighter and tighter, tucking the fabric in at the top.

Afterwards, I rose from my crouched position and stared at my bloodied handiwork.

Do you think we should call a doctor? I said. She probably needs stiches.

Lewis shook his head. No one will come. She's clearly here illegally . . . If she needs a doctor, she'll have to take herself to one.

What do we do with her, then? Aaron asked.

Lewis was quiet for a moment. Give her something from the shop, he said. Some food, milk. I'll square it up with your supervisor.

And then what? Aaron said.

Well, she can't stay here, he replied, that's for sure. God only knows how she ended up here in the first place.

Aaron grabbed a packet of crisps and a banana-flavoured milkshake, handing them to the woman, but she didn't seem to know what to do with them. She just continued to stare, her eyes glazed over.

Aaron shrugged. I don't know what she likes . . .

Lewis turned to face me. You should show her the door, he said.

Me? Why me?

You're a woman . . . She'll understand better, rather than me or Aaron trying to take her out. We'll scare her. He paused. It should be a woman.

Are you serious? I said.

No one replied.

Slowly I guided her out of our concession, back along the corridor. We continued until we reached the front entrance, and I pulled open one of the double doors, ushering her forward with me until we were over the threshold and staring out at the near-deserted car park.

A dilapidated picnic bench was in my sight, and I pointed to it. You can't stay here, I said too loudly. You need to find some-where else to go.

She continued to stare, her eyes burning into me.

I gave a firm nod, pointing again at the picnic bench before retreating and closing the doors over, all the while checking that she wasn't attempting to follow me back inside.

The cleaner took care of the mess that was left in the toilets, and then she arrived at our concession with her mop. I suddenly felt very weak and lethargic. I fumbled for my blood glucose meter again, pricking my finger and shaking as a droplet of my blood landed on the test strip.

Are you okay? Aaron asked.

I was still trembling, but I nodded, inserting the test strip into the reader.

You need to look after yourself, he said, and I stared up at him, irritated, as if he thought he was telling me something I didn't already know. It hadn't been him who had been injecting his body several times a day since the age of five.

As suspected, my blood sugar was low, and I forced a dextrose tablet out from its packet and into my mouth. There were beads of sweat on my forehead but within minutes I was feeling better, more like myself, and, although he didn't say anything, I knew Aaron was relieved too.

The last four hours of our shift passed silently but by the time we were doing handover things felt more jovial, Aaron telling me about some expensive coffee he'd tried in Bali the summer before, where a cat-like creature eats the beans, shits them out and then you drink them. We were laughing as he spoke, really considering the process, but I was also wondering if I'd ever get the chance to see Bali, or if things like that were behind us now. I'd spent my last free summer in the Berkshires of Massachusetts, working for minimum wage as a counsellor at a rich kids' summer camp, while my ankles weeped from mosquito bites.

As we headed out into the foyer Aaron offered me a lift, knowing fine well that Mum would already be waiting for me outside.

How's the driving lessons coming along? he said.

They're not.

He headed right, for the toilets, and I turned left for the double doors. Casually, as I walked out, I glanced at the picnic tables, only to see the woman with the bleeding arm still sitting there, the crisps and milkshake appearing untouched.

I approached the Defender, quickening my pace, and climbed in, the woman watching me the whole time.

How was your shift? Mum asked.

The Defender was warm. The dead mosquito was still stuck to the window and I just stared at it, paralysed.

Is something wrong? Mum said.

I turned to look at her. She was wearing one of Dad's old waxed Barbour jackets.

I hate that jacket, I said. Smells like wet dog.

Stop that, she said firmly.

And we settled into our well-practised routine of silence then, until we arrived back at the farm, the reservoir that fed most of the villages and beyond to our left, parts of its banks exposed. The hills and browned grass were to our right, while the morning sun shone through the windscreen, the heat of the day already upon us.

2

My boots lay out across the doormat in the kitchen, the tread in the soles filled with dirt, compact and solid, and I had this desire to pick them clean but refrained, forcing them on instead. I strode out across the yard, past the broken-down Corsa that Bobby had bought for me at auction, while his and Sam's cottage lay to the left, sitting perpendicular to ours. The doors to the largest shed were open, and I could see Bobby leaning over a rail towards the back, peering down at a lambing ewe. I went to where he was, folding my arms over the metal bar of the pen, my shoulder nudging against his. Most of the sheep were lambing in the sheds now because we had little grass left, needing our assistance more than ever before.

Are you here to help me? Bobby said, a puff of air escaping through his nostrils. It was the closest thing to a laugh I was going to get.

If you want me to.

And you don't have some essay to be doing?

I'm not even sure they're still reading or marking our work, I said.

He reached out and squeezed my hand, his face crinkling into a sad smile. I'd never really been able to place my great-uncle's age. From childhood I'd assumed he was in his sixties, but his general appearance had changed little over time. Maybe his face was thinning, skin-tags lining the collar of his shirt, his body weaker with illness, but his hands were thick and calloused, still powerful.

There was the memory of being thirteen and sitting at his kitchen table and him storming in. His overalls were on, but his arm was lost, stuck inside a lambing ewe. The other hand cradled the animal, its size eclipsing his torso. Aida, for the love of God, he'd shouted, while the sheep bleated out in discomfort, will you pick up that bloody phone and tell the vet to get his arse over here. I'd stared at him, startled. Aida! My hand's stuck. Get the bleeding vet. And I'd sprung into action then, aware of the intensified bleating, gripping the phone and dialling one of the few numbers I knew then by heart.

When was the last time you were here for lambing? Bobby asked now, looking at me with a neutral expression.

It's been a while, I suppose.

Edinburgh always more exciting, was it?

I'm sorry I never came back to help, I said.

Well, you're here now.

I had been so desperate to leave the farm, so desperate to move to the city that I'd never really given much thought to what I was leaving behind. I had enjoyed parts of lambing season: liked the orphaned pet lambs, liked feeding them with those giant, comical red teats screwed on to glass Irn-Bru bottles, the little lambs gulping the milk, chugging it away. There was just something incredibly sweet and reassuring about them. But the rest of farming life I wasn't so fussed on – the hazards, the muck, the isolation. Once you reached the reservoir road, and passed the gates to the waterworks it was only us and the land – the outside world forgotten.

Bobby pointed to one of the ewes. She looks like she's getting ready, he said, his voice full of experience. I watched as she dug her feet into the straw, her mouth twitching. It seemed cruel that they were expected to bear more than one lamb at a time. All those limbs and heads. Bobby had paid someone earlier in the year to come and scan the ewes, so we knew what to expect, were able to separate them so that the ones carrying two or three got more nutrition. Bobby would hold each sheep in place, while the man probed with his ultrasound, counting these indistinguishable blobs. Afterwards, he'd spray their rears – a blue dot on the shoulder for a single, no marking for twins, and a dot on the rear for triplets. An empty womb resulted in a red line across the back, like a mark of shame. If it was their first time, they'd be given a second chance the following year, but if that still failed there'd be nothing else for it but slaughter. Their ability to breed was their worth – they held no other value.

Bobby climbed into the pen, struggling a little, and crouched down by the labouring ewe. He patted her stomach affectionately, the wool looking coarse and itchy to the touch.

What do you think? I said. Does she need help too?

Bobby started to examine her. Sam's cooking a leg of lamb for tea tonight, he said, his eyes raised to the roof of the shed as he felt his way around for lamb limbs.

Clearly irony is lost on you, I said.

Don't worry, potato and leek pie for you, lass.

Sounds delicious.

Mum approached us in her overalls, clearing her throat. You shouldn't be making separate meals for her, she said. Just because she's decided to be a vegetarian, it doesn't mean Sam should be burdened by her choices.

Oh, come on, he doesn't mind, Bobby replied, a strain to his voice now as he got ready to pull. Really, what else is he going to do?

I stared at Mum, irritation growing inside me, and I wondered if I should start up the great ethical and moral debate again just to annoy her. It usually resulted in her telling me how much water it took to make each pair of jeans hanging up in my wardrobe – seven and a half thousand litres per pair apparently, from growing the cotton to retail distribution.

Come on, lady, let's get them out of you, Bobby said, the tension of his pull on the lamb's front legs infiltrating his voice. And then, almost instantly, he was holding a fresh new lamb in his hands, swinging the little body gently from left to right. Aida, love, he said, why don't you grab me a piece of straw for this wee guy's nostrils? Need to get the gunk out before he suffocates.

I climbed into the pen and grabbed a handful of straw on my way towards him. He placed the lamb on the ground, I handed the straw to him, and he poked a long strand into both nostrils. The lamb started to sneeze, raising its head slightly. Bobby was prodding the little thing in the stomach, hurrying him to hunker on to his knees, and eventually, almost amazingly, the little guy was on his feet, while his mother began to lick him.

Bobby was already reaching back in to retrieve the next lamb.

I backed away, climbing out of the pen and to where Mum was now standing. This ewe's ready for you, she said, pointing.

I stared at her. No . . . It's been ages since I pulled one out myself. You do it and I'll help.

Don't be ridiculous, she replied. It's like riding a bike.

I hesitated. Can I put on a glove?

Sure.

I reached for the box of gloves on the shelf above the old Belfast sink. They were rarely used, more for the vets than anything else. Bobby had never used gloves when lambing – you can't get a good purchase on the thing, he'd say. And he was probably right, but still I couldn't imagine doing it without one.

When I got to the ewe, traces of blood and mucus were coming out of her. Is this like childbirth, I asked Mum, or is it totally different?

There are similarities, she said. But ideally we don't want the limbs coming first with humans. She paused then, staring at me. You ready?

I placed my hand inside the ewe and shuddered, the warm sensation travelling up my arm.

What can you feel? Mum said.

I began to have a rummage about, feeling for the head, the nose, then I began to work my way down to the front legs, feeling for the first and then second foot.

I've got them, I said.

Are you sure? You don't want to pull on the wrong part.

Thanks, Mum, you're really helping here with the nerves, I said.

The shed was warmer than outside, and I rubbed my forehead against my upper arm. I'm pretty confident it's the front legs, I said.

Okay, good, good, she replied. Ready? Pull.

I straightened up on to my knees and centred my balance, a vacuum pressure pulling against my body as I tried to break the membrane. I pulled harder but nothing seemed to be happening.

It's stuck, I said, urgency creeping into my voice.

No, it'll be okay, Mum replied.

I could feel the tension refusing to unplug.

It's a gimmer, Bobby called out. Maybe ringwomb . . . ?

Mum exhaled then, coming forward and nudging me out of the way. She was quick in her actions, examining the ewe the same way she'd done a thousand times before. It's like doing a sweep, she said to me over her shoulder, and I just stood there, shrugging.

Suddenly, the feet were out and the front legs visible. I visualised Mum feeling up for the lamb's shoulders and neck, as I'd been taught, to ensure nothing was caught. Then the head was out, eyes still closed, and finally the hind legs, slipping out behind the rest of its body. The ewe relaxed from the pressure and pain that had been inside her, taking a breath before the next one arrived. But the fresh lamb lay lifeless and slimy against the concrete of the shed.

Mum started rubbing its coat, poking at its nostrils, but it seemed to have little effect. I looked up at her, panic rising in my throat.

Swing it, she said. From its hind legs.

Me?

Quickly.

I did as instructed, thrusting the animal from side to side, but it remained limp, like a dead rabbit flung over Bobby's shoulder, ready to hand to Sam for gutting and stewing. What should I do? I asked, still swinging the little creature. It's not working . . .

Suddenly Mum was grabbing the lamb from me and swinging it more forcefully, no concern for breaking or dislocating its legs. And finally the lamb was taking a breath, Mum's hands now rubbing its belly.

Did I do something wrong? I said, tears suddenly threatening to sting my eyes.

No, Bobby said, standing behind us. You know, sometimes they just take a little longer to come round.

I began to climb back over the railings of the pen, my head down, feeling stupid and unable to keep the tears away.

Look, there's no point getting upset, Mum said. You did well.

I ignored her, making my way out of the shed.

The best thing to do is carry on. The next one will be easier, she said, attempting a soothing tone.

I'm fine, I said. I'm just going to check on the hens.

The lamb's okay, she called out behind me. It lives and breathes.

I stopped at the wire-mesh hen house and crouched to get inside, inspecting the frame to ensure there were no holes or openings. The only thing I could do was to pretend I wasn't upset, and anyway, we really couldn't afford to have another hen savaged by a fox. Mum had been quick to remind me that the stock value of a laying hen had climbed significantly – a valuable commodity I was responsible for. My diet consisted mainly of eggs, aside from the vegetables grown in a plot further up behind the sheds, which we were still secretly watering despite the hosepipe ban.

I managed to gather three eggs, placing them delicately inside a pocket of my overalls. We were down to four hens and three eggs, and I knew they were prone to occasionally skipping a day but still this unsettled me.

Are you sure you're okay? Bobby said, his voice startling me.

Wrong-footed, I pressed up against the frame and before I could correct myself I heard the crunch of an eggshell. Down to two eggs just like that. I looked up at him. I'm okay, honest, I said, slipping my hand into my pocket, suspecting I'd touched the yolk, its texture so different from the whites.

Bobby cleared some phlegm from his throat. Is it the night shifts?

I shrugged.

They're messing with your circadian rhythm, Aida. I don't like it.

Well, we need the money, I whispered, attempting to gather the mass of egg leaking out from my pocket, its sensation repulsive as I scooped a handful out and dumped it on to the ground.

Bobby stared down at his feet, uncomfortable with the topic of money that had come to loom over us. He'd never liked talking money; left all the book-keeping and bills to Sam.

The worst of the world happens at night, he replied. If it gets too much, will you tell me? We'd figure something out. I don't want that place getting the better of you just for the sake of money.

Should I have told him about the woman I'd abandoned outside on the picnic bench? Maybe I was worried he would tell me I hadn't done enough.

I cleared my throat, staring up at him. Should we be scared? I asked. About the rain . . . ?

You have such little faith, lass, he said. There's water here, on this land. So don't fear. We won't be going without.

Okay, I said, a little uneasily. It's just, I was reading his article—

I don't know why you're trying to punish yourself for things you can't control, he replied. Stop reading those fearmongering things. I swear, the internet is the worst invention ever realised. We didn't have half these problems before the internet.

Okay, Bobby, fair enough.

Have you been noticing all the beautiful birds we're getting at the moment?

I shook my head.

We had the binoculars out last night and they're everywhere: blue tits, swallows, swifts – robins too . . .

I thought robins were a winter bird.

No, don't be daft, he said, spluttering a laugh. You can come and watch with us later, if you like?

I smiled. No, you're okay, I'll leave that to you guys.

He shrugged. Your loss, lass.

*

I entered the kitchen through our back door and placed my two intact eggs into the little holder in the fridge. I could hear Mum in the living room and followed the noise, pushing open the door, the view from the window overlooking the depleting reservoir.

Mum was removing a key from a chain around her neck, aware of my presence but not bothering to acknowledge me. There was a large storage cupboard recessed into the wall, a windowless space that could have housed a single bed, and it reminded me of the tenement flat I'd stayed in a couple of years ago, where a large cupboard had been converted into a kitchen and the original kitchen made into another room, so that they could advertise the property as a *two-bed*.

Mum opened the cupboard with her key and crouched down to inspect her emergency supplies. She'd crammed the shelves from floor to ceiling with produce: huge bags of rice, dozens of packets of dried pasta, tinned goods, herbs and spices, baking soda, preserves of jam, marmalade and chutney. There was long-life milk and bags of flour and sugar, dextrose tablets and Lucozade for me, Bobby's aniseed balls, Sam's gingersnap biscuits, coffee, and a bag with more than one thousand teabags. There were sanitary pads that she'd stolen from the hospital, thick and long, and packets of paracetamol, a first-aid kit, toothpaste, and stacks of baby-wipes. There was an industrial-sized roll of toilet paper I'd nicked from the supply cupboard at the service station. And at the bottom of the cupboard sat rows of recycled plastic bottles filled to the brim with water. This had been going on for months, maybe longer, silently and quietly, ever since the Co-op in the nearest village had run out of spaghetti. After that, whenever Mum went anywhere, near or far, she'd return home with something that could be saved and stored. And, like someone proud of their achievements, she liked to survey her stockpiling regularly. Plus, we often got mice in the winter so there was that to think about too, although we hadn't really been troubled by them recently – not cold enough maybe for them to bother coming inside.

I crouched down beside her and lifted the nearest bottle of water, turning it on its side to inspect its clarity against the brightness of the room.

Don't worry, she said. I've stashed water-purifying tablets above the frame of the door in case the water does begin to run dirty or get contaminated.

Do you really think this is necessary? I asked.

She was silent for a moment. My *baba*, he was a devoutly religious man. Actively prayed for the world to end so we could all have our judgement day. I have always been planning, worried that what he wished for would indeed happen, and needing to feel prepared for its arrival. She paused then. Perhaps his prayers are now being answered.

I'd seen online that much of Africa had no water left. Not that Mum and I ever talked about it. She discussed little about her past and when she did it was sudden and abrupt in its content. I knew her youth hadn't been easy, and there was no contact with her family. She'd defied her father by coming to finish her mid-wifery studies in Scotland, staying then to marry Dad. We never mentioned that I was conceived out of wedlock; that maybe they wouldn't have got married otherwise.

What is the worst that can happen? she said. That it doesn't get used? That some things go out of date?

Doesn't it bother you that some people will go without, while we have all this? I said. What if we're taking away from others?

You've always worried too much about others.

I got to my feet. I'm going for a shower before I forget and they turn the water off.

Aida . . . she called out.

I stopped. What?

You need to cut your hair short.

Why?

It reduces your time in the shower.

So you are worried? I said. Because Bobby doesn't appear to be . . .

Just cut it, okay?

Fine. Whatever.

I walked into the bathroom and locked the door. Sun was still streaming in through the frosted glass, and I looked at myself in the mirror, taking a bobble out of my hair and letting it fall to past my shoulders. I stripped out of my overalls and underwear and stood there naked, enjoying the warmth on my skin. I opened the bathroom cabinet and found the hair scissors, snapping them through the air a couple of time before chopping off a chunk of hair, letting the strands fall to the floor. It was cathartic, my head feeling lighter as I continued to chop, guessing at the length at the back of my head. Afterwards, I turned on the shower and stepped into the basin we kept in the bath. The government had issued guidance on how to take a sustainable shower, which was to only let the showerhead run until the basin you were standing in was full. I washed my hair under the water, working quickly with the shampoo and rinsing before the basin filled. Reluctantly, I turned the water off then and used a sponge to wash myself. But as I crouched, squeezing the sponge back into the basin of water, cuttings of my hair floating on top, I didn't feel particularly clean. The murky water lapped around my ankles. I stepped on to the bathmat and dried myself before lifting the basin out and pouring some of its contents down our toilet, flushing away that day's urine.

Out in the hall I could hear the kettle whistling gently on the hob as it boiled, and from Mum's whispered tones I knew she was on the phone to Dad. And, sure enough, the cream slimline phone had been stretched into the kitchen, the door closed over the spiralling cord.

I stood there, in my dressing gown, my ear pressed up to the door. There was a lot of agreeing and I imagined her nodding her head. I was looking at baby pictures the other day, I heard her say. Do you remember that padded baby carrier we used to cart Aida about in? There was a pause. I kept it, you know. The carrier . . . There was another pause before I heard her say, She's fine. Bobby will take her with him when he goes for his next hospital appointment, and you can meet her there. The whistle on the kettle began to blow. I suppose that's our time, she said.

I pushed open the door. Are you leaving that for me? I asked, nodding towards the kettle.

No, she replied, appearing startled. She set the receiver down on the cradle, the cord still entwined around her index finger. I'll make the tea.

But I was already turning off the gas and lifting the kettle, heavy in my hands, having been filled to the brim to keep us going for the night. I began pouring the boiling water into the teapot, noticing that there was just one tea bag inside. Don't you think we can stretch to two bags? I said.

Just trying to be economical, she replied, staring at me now, really taking me in. Your hair is nice. Suits you.

It's not even, I said, bringing the teapot over.

Our little table was pressed up against the wall with two chairs – one next to the wall and one facing it. There were scorch marks in the pine – we didn't bother with coasters any more. I glanced around the kitchen as I waited for the tea to brew. The whole cottage was cramped and dated, all hand-me-downs and charity shop furniture. Had it always been this unkempt, or was it only after Dad left? I couldn't really remember. It had only been three years.

As I poured the tea, Mum lifted my book off the table and began flicking through the pages. *Animal Farm* . . . she said.

I'm revisiting it.

For coursework?

For life.

She smiled. The youth are so angry all the time. Maybe you should read something more uplifting.

I take it you were speaking to *him,* I said.

And by that do you mean your father?

Yes, the man who left us.

Correction, she said. He left me, not you. You were at university before he left.

Admittedly, much like myself, Dad was not a natural farmer, but he was Bobby's successor, the farm having been in their family for generations. Bobby still couldn't say his name without getting angry, believing Dad's behaviour to be an act of abandonment of both his wife and his responsibilities.

Do you expect him to come back? I said.

She shook her head. I just like to keep him informed.

But how can you be so nice?

I'm grateful to him, she said. He gave me so much.

Whatever.

You have such little understanding, she said.

I wish you'd explain it better then, I said, already twisting the dial of my insulin pen, pressing it into my thigh.

Ignoring me, she said, I've ordered you more insulin from the chemist.

I nodded, taking my seat by the wall. We should sort this place out, I said, not particularly expecting an answer. It's disgusting.

What's the point? We only bring dirt back in with us.

It was just an idea, I said, opening my book at the page where I'd turned the corner down.

Aida . . .

What? I said, irritation creeping into my voice.

Would you like me to even out your hair?

I placed my book down. Yes, okay.

She left the room, before returning momentarily with the same pair of scissors I'd used, a handheld mirror and a few hair-pins. Ushering me to stand, she moved my chair away from the table before instructing me to sit again. She worked quickly, pin-ning different sections of my hair, fully focused on the job.

You're starting to get some greys, she said.

I'm aware.

Does it bother you that you inherited my hair? she said.

What do you mean?

I just think it would have been easier if you had had your father's.

Do you ever get lonely? I asked. Without him . . .

She paused. No, I have you and Bobby and Sam.

It just feels like we could so easily be forgotten here.

I would think that under the current circumstances that is the ideal situation to be in.

But if something where to happen to us, would people even realise? What if one of us goes insane? Like those lighthouse-keepers you hear stories about . . .

Don't be ridiculous, she said, straightening my head. When your father and I lived in Glasgow, before you were born, there was a man in the flat above who hung his washing out on the communal line, and he left it hanging there for nearly a week. The other neigh-bours were furious at his selfishness. And I remember thinking then, I wonder if he's dead? Right above us, and we don't even know.

And was he?

She laughed. No, he was fine. Just lazy and forgetful.

I shook my head. Sorry, so what's the point of your story here?

She stopped my head from moving. Just that people can die or go mad in plain sight and people still don't notice. So, really, it makes no difference whether we're here, or in a building with hundreds of people.

3

It was too early to be up but still I sat in Bobby and Sam's cottage, waiting. Their place was immaculate and had a nice open-plan layout that you walked straight into from the front door, a large family dining table separating the modern kitchen from the living space. It wasn't particularly grand in size but had clearly always been the farmhouse. Even the details: the dado rail on the walls, the flagstone flooring, the traditional fireplace – they were things to envy. And despite the weather a fire was always burning, Sam constantly troubled by a phantom chill to his bones, Bobby forever hacking down dead trees, chopping them into logs.

But, this morning, the fire was at risk of petering out. As I stared at it, I was filled with anxiety. It was like a bad omen, and there was no one present to rescue the situation apart from me. I crouched down to tend to the embers, taking the fire poker from its holder and prodding the ash, wanting to make a success of my attempt. Keeping a fire alive had never come naturally to me and I took the task as a personal failing. It felt like a rite of passage, like learning to drive, something else I hadn't quite mastered. I prodded the poker around, but it did little to what remained of the burnt logs, and I wondered if I should throw some kindling on – if that was the right thing to do.

What have you done to my fire? Sam said, his hobble a familiar noise across the flagstone flooring.

I'm the only thing stopping this fire from dying out, I said, my voice thick with defensiveness. He tutted at me, but his smile was one of affection, while Rusty, their Jack Russell terrier, practically an extension of Sam, jumped up to greet me.

A silence filled the room then as Sam crouched with some difficulty to resurrect the flames. He'd always been a man of few words, nodding and saying *uh-huh* instead of yes. In his late sixties now – a *toy-boy* to Bobby, he'd say – his strawberry blond-turning-grey hair was thinning on top, his cheeks a ruddy red. On the mantel was a happy picture of them both from years ago, before Sam's knees got the better of him. Having always been hands-on around the farm, he was now near enough confined to the house, occasionally visiting the lambing and calving sheds, but kept busy mostly by the book-keeping and by his passion for cooking. There had been talk for a while about knee replacements, the balls and sockets having worn down to nothing, but there was a heart condition the anaesthetist was worried about, the doctors assessing the risk of surgery to be too great. So he just carried on hobbling everywhere, like a man turning to stone. He would go through bouts of depression, hiding away for days at a time, none of us allowed to talk about it.

What time do you think you'll get back? he asked, interrupting my thoughts.

I shrugged. I don't know, but I'm working tonight so hopefully not too late.

He nodded. I'll make us something special to eat tonight, he said. What do you fancy?

I don't mind.

What about my special mac and cheese from the Nigel Slater cookbook? That's something we all enjoy . . .

34

Bobby came in from the back hall with a pair of shoes in his hand and sat down in his usual armchair. You look nice, he said, taking in my floral summer dress.

He tried to put on his shoes but struggled. They weren't his usual boots or wellingtons – instead they were light brown brogues with wee dimple marks across the toes. And I realised then, taking him in, that he was wearing his Sunday clothes, not that he bothered with church any more – a well-made tweed suit he'd had for years. Seeing him out of his overalls, I had no choice but to acknowledge how frail his frame had become. I came to where he was sitting and took the shoe from his grip, loosening the laces before sliding one on to his foot and then the other, tying the laces too.

All set, then, Sam said, shuffling himself to the door. I'll check on your mum once you're on your way. I think she's been having a long night with the lambing.

Are you sure you don't want to come? I said. I could always stay with Mum instead.

Sam shook his head, bending with effort to retrieve Rusty. I'm hopeless with these sorts of things, he said. And anyway, I've more than enough to keep me busy here. There's a whole pile of invoices with my name on them needing to be paid.

Bobby headed for the door, pausing to stare at Sam, their eyes suddenly locked in a serious expression. Bobby reached for Sam's free hand and planted a kiss on the back of it before walk-ing away. As I followed, Sam reached out and tugged my arm, pulling me closer.

Look after him for me, okay?

I nodded. Of course.

Bobby was already in the driver's seat of the Defender. I climbed in beside him, and from the wing mirror I could see Mum coming out of the shed to watch us leave. But as we drove away, bumping over the cattle grid, she didn't wave, only stared at us before retreating into the shed.

The closest village was four miles away, and as we drove through it we saw that the windows to the little café were boarded up, graffiti decorating the plywood. I wasn't convinced the drought had been the cause of its closing; had heard rumours of an affair, that the couple were getting a divorce after twenty-something years together. They lived in the stone cottage next door on the main road, a huge television sitting in their front bay window, blocking out most of the natural light.

Bobby changed gears and I stared at the signet ring on his pinkie. It looked shiner than usual. Did you polish that? I said, touching it lightly.

I did.

Why the effort?

He shifted his shoulders, straightening his posture. I always wear this when I go into the city, he replied.

For a brief moment, it felt as though I could have asked him anything. There was so much we didn't talk about, and I had no idea where to start.

So, I hear your old man is meeting you while you wait on me, he said.

That's the plan.

Aren't you a bit old to be having your mother arranging your parental visits? He shifted gear again, that familiar rattle under the frame returning.

Doesn't that bother you? I asked.

What?

The rattle.

He shrugged. It's just a bushing.

When we made it on to the motorway, the roads were practically deserted. In the distance the trees were withering, roots struggling underground, newly planted trees dead already, the land varying shades of brown.

Where is everyone? I said.

People will be scared to travel, Bobby replied. What with the fuel shortages. He shifted up a gear, the engine revving, and looked in his rear-view mirror despite nothing being there.

They've put the fuel prices up at the service station, I said.

He laughed. They've always enjoyed a monopoly. But maybe not for much longer . . .

Do *we* have enough fuel? I asked.

What, for the journey?

Generally, I mean.

We've plenty enough red diesel so this thing should be able to chug along as long as the polis don't cotton on to our tampering . . . He paused then. Look, the road's straight enough – why don't I pull over and you can practise your driving?

I shook my head. No way. I hate driving this thing.

He paused, contemplative. I'm sorry I've never managed to fix your wee car, he said.

That's okay.

I know, but I am sorry. He gained on an old Volvo packed to the roof with possessions and switched lanes. As we overtook, faces peered out at us from the windows. I smiled, offered a half-hearted wave, but they turned back to face ahead, suspicious, as if we were capable of taking everything from them.

I wonder where they're going, I said.

Bobby shrugged. At least they're on the right side of the border now.

We made it to Glasgow's city limits just before nine and, to be honest, all appeared as you'd hope, making it easy to pretend that no drought existed. The streets were busy: people going to work, parents dropping kids off at school, shops still trading – it was as if the life we all wanted would continue without any interruption by sheer will. Even an antiques shop on the corner was busy, pieces of furniture sitting outside while a handful of people inspected objects in the windows. It was oddly comforting and a complete contrast to what I'd been witnessing in the service station. Maybe it was only those close to the border who were aware of the realities. Or maybe people were so sick of thinking about it – had grown desensitised. The broadcast news certainly tried their best to keep everything as normal as possible, filtering out anything particularly distressing, never shifting their focus beyond Scotland, leaving social media to fill in the blanks.

We carried on down the never-ending Great Western Road and stopped at another set of traffic lights. We could see the cancer centre towering over us, with its grey colouring and tinted windows. This was my first visit to the hospital with Bobby; Mum usually went with him. And it was only as we approached that I saw a change in him – a tightness of his grip on the steering wheel, his shoulders ridged. The positivity he exuded at home was eroding before me.

The car park was quiet but despite this we still had to pay. Bobby counted the coins in his pocket, handing them to me. As I glanced upwards, the sky was a piercing blue and for a moment I thought I saw a plane, but my eyes were deceiving me; there was nothing but empty sky. Only haulage travel was permitted now – the airlines screaming at the government for compensation, the whole world having come to a halt.

I jumped out of the Defender and slotted the parking money into the meter, waiting for each coin to register. When I looked back, Bobby was slowly easing himself out of his seat, discomfort manifesting across his face. And it was perhaps the first time I realised that he was in real pain. Had he been hiding it from us this whole time? Or had his medication been keeping the pain at bay? There was so much we didn't talk about.

To our left a man in a winter coat was foraging around on the grass. As the man bent, his face close to the ground, his coat tails folded in on themselves across his back.

Are you okay? Bobby said. Have you lost something?

The man looked up in our direction. Don't speak to me, he said. He was sweating, filthy. Under the coat he wore a suit, shirt and tie – all unkempt and torn.

Sorry, Bobby said. But . . .

I can't find my wallet, the man said. I'm sure I left it around here somewhere. He reached up to scratch his forehead and there was a tear in the armpit of his coat.

I grabbed Bobby's arm, willing him to move on with me.

Do you need money for something? Bobby said. To get home?

The man grew perfectly still, and I had this strange suspicion that he might try to dart straight towards us like an animal, take Bobby down and destroy what was left of him. The man's eyes were dark and hollow and honestly, I resented Bobby's act of kindness.

Home? the man said. I don't have a home.

Sorry to hear that, Bobby replied, while my eyes fixed on the sliding doors to the entrance only metres away. Was Bobby capable of making a run for it? I wasn't even sure any more: this stranger had the stance of a panther.

Bobby reached into his pocket. I've some spare change if it's of any use to you?

The man tugged on his coat, beads of sweat on his forehead; it was far too warm for him to be wearing so many layers. Stop talking to me! he shouted. Throw the money over but please stop speaking. I can't stand it.

Bobby threw the money across to him, the coins landing in the dying grass. We watched the man scurry on to his hands and knees, his palms pressing into the dry ground. Bobby turned and nodded, as though he was finally allowing us to make our way to the entrance.

Why do you always have to talk to everyone? I said. The guy's clearly not all there . . . He could be some psycho.

Bobby let out a weak laugh. What's the harm in trying to help him?

I was shaking my head, but we'd reached the reception.

By the lifts, a porter was gripping the handles of an empty wheelchair. Bobby fixed his attention on it. I wondered if he'd get so weak that he'd need one, couldn't really imagine it. There was a strange smell coming from the lift – disinfectant but something else too – a ripening of sorts. The porter and wheelchair were headed for the sixth floor and, when the doors parted on level three, we stepped around him to leave from the other side. From there the clinic was straight ahead. The waiting room was a bright, friendly yellow colour, with a clear view of the city's West End. A receptionist checked Bobby's letter and typed something into her computer.

You can just take a seat, she said. Someone will call you through shortly.

Bobby nodded, and we turned to the full-length window panels, where we could see the dots of people moving in the distance below. When we sat down, I reluctantly took in the other waiting patients. They were sick, obviously, but most of them were really ill, like deathly ill – jaundice, spitting into tissues, some vomiting without effort into sick bowls. A few people were hooked up to drips that had been rolled along with them. The sight of it all made me feel nauseous. I couldn't imagine Bobby ever being as ill as these people. The only time I could recall him taking a day off was when a shard of glass got impaled in his arm, but even then I think he went right back to calving the day after. Aaron's dad had died from cancer, and I remembered him talking about the treatments: the claustrophobia of radiotherapy, moulds and masks for pinpointing targets, and then chemotherapy destroying everything, cancerous or otherwise. It was easy to forget on the farm that Bobby was actually sick – discussions around illness were only pragmatic – the logistics of doctor's appointments and clinics.

Suddenly it felt as if the room was airless, and no windows could be opened. One woman fanned a magazine in front of her face, while a sickly-looking child played with wooden beads on a table. The beads were strung on pieces of bent wire, and they could only be moved backwards and forwards. How had this kid not grown bored of the mundane, repetitive task? I watched on, the anticipation of the beads knocking against each other at every turn almost too much to bear. I stood then and stared out again at the tiny dots of people.

That you all set? Bobby said.

I nodded. How long do you think you'll be?

A good few hours, he said. Sometimes longer if they're running behind. I can text you . . .

So you remembered to bring your phone?

Indeed I did.

Okay, well, message me and I'll meet you at the bench next to the entrance.

Okay, my lass.

I hesitated for a moment before reaching forward and hugging him.

The lift on my descent was empty and the smell didn't seem to bother me half as much. And outside, the man in his filthy suit was nowhere to be seen. The air was thick and polluted compared to on the farm, but I still took gulps of it, my lungs inflating and deflating, the feel of the hospital still on my skin.

I sat down on the bench. I'd brought a book, *Amongst Women*, but I couldn't really concentrate, and before I knew it I was down a social media rabbit hole – images of people in South America sitting in these makeshift refugee camps, not enough water to go around. Then there were the wildfires in Australia that couldn't be contained. Eventually I closed my phone and just sat there, wishing I'd thrown the thing away, wishing I could just forget my password and only have to think of what was directly in front of me.

I could see Dad approaching, offering me a wave when we were only metres apart. I'd have recognised him anywhere, despite his hair having grown long, his appearance dishevelled. I stood and, when he was close enough, he leaned in and embraced me, my body limp in his arms.

You look well, he said. Healthy.

Thanks, Hugh. You too.

He smiled, something concealed behind the eyes. His stature was broad, and he looked a lot like Bobby – you would have known they were related.

I thought we could do a wee bit of shopping, he said, then grab a coffee or something to eat . . .

What do you need? I asked.

No, I want to buy you something. I haven't seen you since before your birthday.

Are you working now?

That's not for you to worry about, he said.

We walked back the way Bobby had driven and the morning sun forced me to keep my gaze low.

So, how's the service station? he asked, walking in stride beside me.

It is what it is.

Your studies . . . Are you looking forward to graduating this summer?

I haven't heard anything about graduating.

He fell silent for a moment. And Bobby . . . Is he keeping okay?

Does Mum not fill you in?

She tries. Cancer is a nasty business . . .

If you hang about the hospital long enough, you can probably see him for yourself.

Dad cleared his throat. Well, if anyone can take cancer on and win, it's Bobby.

It's not about winning or losing, I said.

Dad nodded. Of course.

We arrived at a row of charity shops. In one window there was a rail full of retro denim jeans, skirts and jackets. I thought this was maybe your type of thing? Dad said, nodding towards them. Why don't you have a look?

I barely wear anything other than my work uniform or overalls.

Well, you're not wearing them today.

A bell above the door rang as we entered the small shop, and a woman glanced up at us with a smile before returning her attention to her phone.

Just have a look and see what you like, Dad said.

There was actually some pretty nice stuff. An old frayed Levi's skirt that I could imagine wearing. A leather satchel with tassels, a pretty funky pair of black suede eighties boots. I tried on the skirt, which fitted nicely, and the woman took it from me, keeping it behind the counter until I was finished. The boots were a little too tight, but the bag I decided I definitely wanted. There was a whole section of fur coats and although I

43

didn't really believe in wearing fur there was something about their touch and luxury that I was drawn to, an endurance of sorts.

Dad was behind me, running his hand along the sleeve of one.

How old do you think this is? I asked.

Who knows . . . he said, gripping the sleeve. Would you like it?

I shook my head. I doubt I'll ever need to wear anything this warm again, I said. I shrugged then. It's horrible being at the end of something, isn't it?

He bought me the skirt and satchel without any protest and handed me the bag, the purchase causing him to perhaps appear more confident in my company. Clearly I was quite easily bought, enjoyed having nice things. I couldn't remember the last time someone had bought me something just because I wanted it. Bobby and Sam gave me money on birthdays and at Christmas, while Mum gifted things she considered necessities: bed sheets, toiletries, pyjamas or slippers on occasion.

We entered another charity shop where one whole side was filled with bookshelves, and Dad was immediately drawn in. He had a good eye, often picked books I'd never heard of like *Wake in Fright,* which I thought about on an almost daily basis. And the whole thing just made me sad again, despite it being three years since he left. Mum and I had always been too alike, too volatile and stubborn, with an equally impressive ability to hold a grudge, and Dad had been the one to balance us all out. But now Mum and I were stuck together with little option, no buffer between us, while Dad got to live the life he wanted.

When I turned, he was holding a stack of five or six books. Have you read any of these? he asked.

I glanced at their spines and shook my head.

Excellent, he said.

I followed him to the till, where he spoke somewhat flirta-tiously with the woman behind the counter. An irrational wave of jealousy washed over me; it felt as if his attention was never fully on me.

As we made to leave, I noticed a woman inspecting baby clothes, flicking miniature coat hangers from left to right. When I looked at her, I could see no obvious bump. It was amazing how long a baby could be growing inside you before it became obvious to the world. Although I'd never left it long enough to properly find out.

When we arrived at the coffee shop, one of the windows had been fractured; great silver cracks radiating outwards from a central hole. It still held together, though, the number *130* spray-painted in black across the fissures. I'd seen this elsewhere – protesters targeting mostly chain coffee shops. I hadn't known that it took one hundred and thirty litres to har-vest the beans for one standard cup of coffee, but then I was learning new facts about water every day. I laughed, because I'd thought I was doing my part by carrying around a reusable plastic cup.

We sat down opposite each other and there was a fork on the table. I pressed my fingers into its prongs. A waiter arrived with a notepad in hand. What can I get you? We're still serving coffee, but we can only get robusta beans.

How much? Dad asked.

£5.20.

What's the cheapest thing you've got on the menu? I said.

We have some fruit-juice cartons with a short expiry date, the waiter replied.

I'll take one of those, I said.

Dad clasped his hands on top of the table. No, he said. We'll take two lattes. You still like lattes, don't you?

I'd prefer a flat white . . .

He smiled, a tension on his face. One latte and one flat white, please.

We can't pay that, I said.

It's fine, he replied.

The waiter went behind the counter, and I watched him turn on the grinder, tamp down the grounds of coffee before locking them into the machine. The smell was incredible. When was the last time I'd had a coffee in a proper coffee shop?

So . . . Dad said.

But I was already getting up from my seat. I need the loo, I said.

The only toilet in the place was in a cupboard with a hook for a lock. The noise from the coffee shop flooded through from the other side of the door and I kept thinking that if I could hear them, then they would certainly hear me and my nervous bowels. Afterwards, I tried to flush, but there was hardly any water running through the cistern and I pressed the button down again but it didn't change anything. I folded toilet paper over and placed it delicately into the pan, ashamed of what I'd left, imagining the queue that was perhaps already forming outside. Even the antibacterial gel I rubbed across my hands couldn't remove my shame.

When I returned to the table the coffees were waiting. I pulled back my seat, scraping it across the floor. Sorry, I said sensing a blush of embarrassment travelling across my face.

That's okay, he said, bringing his coffee to his nose and sniffing it. He took a sip, and I watched his jaw move as he let the liquid circulate around his mouth.

How is it? I said.

It's good. He paused, a little foam on his top lip. So, he said, again. I'm really glad we were able to see each other today.

Why do I have the feeling that you've got news . . . ?

He took another sip of his coffee before speaking.

I've met someone, he said. I wanted to tell you myself before word got out.

I was quiet for a moment.

Does Mum know?

He nodded.

I could feel tears behind my eyes and tried to blink them away. I felt stupid, a child once again. So that's it, then? I said.

What do you mean?

You're not going to come back to the farm? Even now . . . with everything that's happening.

I can't go back to the farm, Aida, you know this.

It's just . . . what a normal thing to attempt.

What do you mean?

How can you even be bothered with a relationship when everything is going to shit?

He stared at me, almost in disbelief. People still need love, Aida. What else is there?

Minutes seemed to pass without either of us speaking, only the background noise of other customers filling the static. When I took a sip, my coffee was cold.

Does it make you happy, being here, with her? I asked.

He ran a hand through his hair, tugging at a strand as though he wanted to pluck it from his scalp. I'm happier now than I was before . . .

I get that you never wanted to take over the farm, but how could you leave *us*?

He almost laughed. Aida, you're an adult. I stayed and played my part until you were old enough to leave yourself. He paused. At some point we all need to do what's right for us . . . Your mother understands this. Your mother understands me.

I was shaking my head. *You* don't understand. We won't be able to cope without you on the farm.

Aida . . .

I pulled at a ragged nail. You just don't get it, I said. We can't both leave now.

He stared at me. You could never have stayed in Edinburgh, he eventually said. The east coast is only getting drier.

That's not the point. Am I just to accept that the farm is my future when you didn't want it for yours, Hugh?

He banged his palm off the table. Stop calling me Hugh. I'm Dad. I've always been Dad.

I flinched, forgetting that occasionally he could lose his temper. I'm sorry, I whispered.

He exhaled. No, I'm sorry.

I pushed my coffee cup and saucer away from me.

The farm is the safest place for you to be while we ride out this storm, he said.

I got to my feet then. Are you walking me back?

Slowly, he got to his feet too. It's probably best we just say our goodbyes here.

I nodded. What's your woman like?

Do you want to meet her?

No.

When I returned to the hospital grounds Bobby was already waiting for me on our bench, much sooner than I had been expecting. As I got closer, I noticed his eyes were closed, his face pointing up towards the sun, and it was as if he was in a trance.

How did it go? I asked, startling him.

He smiled, seeming genuinely happy, and I relaxed, already more settled for being back in his company. I could ask you the same thing, he said.

It was fine, I replied, showing him my carrier bags of goods.

Let me ask you something, he said, and as he pushed the sleeves of his shirt up past his elbows I could see the mottling and bruises on his skin, all the various points where they'd attempted to take his blood. Do you think cancer only progresses once its host knows about it?

I don't think it works like that, I said.

He shrugged. Maybe if I didn't know, my body would be fighting it better. He paused. They want to start me on this new treatment . . . A prostate trial. Nothing else is working.

He'd never said anything like this to me before.

Bobby . . .

The doctor that saw me, he looked about twelve.

I'm sure he was more than qualified.

He said that the trial might give me more time but that the cancer isn't going away now. That it's terminal. Its type is too aggressive or something . . .

I felt winded, bile rising up my throat. It was instant and yet seemed as if it had been there forever, waiting for me.

He smiled at me again and all I could manage was, What are you going to do?

That, lass, is a good question. It's all so toxic. I don't want to be treated like some test subject or experiment any more – not for a matter of a few extra months . . . And all this traipsing into the city and leaving your mum during lambing season – it's not worth it.

My body tightened, a contorting. But, Bobby, I said, pleading, surely any chance is better than doing nothing, no?

49

He tried to laugh. They'll probably just give an old-timer like me the placebo anyway.

Bobby, please . . .

I just wish the timing was better on the farm.

We don't care about that, I said. We care about you.

Well, he said, taking my hand in his big, calloused palm, I'm going to die, but then we all have to die.

He glanced around the car park then as though it was all the evidence he needed.

It's funny, he said: they called my name three times, and I had this urge just to ignore them. There's something so unnatural about not responding when someone calls your name. Like being at your own funeral.

4

Sam started taking to his bed, missing whole chunks of the day, leaving us to fend for ourselves in the kitchen, while Mum's way of coping was to turbo-charge her pragmatism, her organisational skills going into overdrive. The only person behaving like their usual self was Bobby – it was as though he'd compartmentalised himself, completely separated the person he was here on the farm from the one who told me he was dying in the hospital car park.

He sat next to me at our kitchen table, a pet lamb on his knee, while I attempted to focus on the horror that was *Tristram Shandy* for an essay I wasn't even sure would be marked. He took a sip of what must have been his third cup of tea. Do you think we should give this wee fella here a name? he asked, laughing through his nostrils, a bottle of milk for the lamb in his hand.

I didn't answer, kept my focus on the page.

Wee Sammy, he said, his laugh intensifying. Do you think Sam would appreciate that?

I looked up from my book. Bobby, is Sam going to be okay?

Bobby began feeding the lamb. You know what he's like. He'll snap out of his pity party soon enough.

Sam has a right to be upset . . . I said.

He made a puckering noise as the lamb continued to chug its milk, the teat of the bottle stretched and elongated. Let's call him JoJo, he said.

Fine, I replied.

Mum appeared then over the threshold of our back door, her arms arching out between the sides of the frame. I think the heifers will be starting soon too, she said. Matter of weeks, I reckon.

Bobby nodded. Aye, Miriam, it'll be a busy, busy time, my lass.

We'll manage, Mum replied, almost sternly, as if the mere idea of not managing was a personal insult to her. We've always managed, she said.

She came forward and placed her hand on my book, pulling it from my grip. Why don't we try and get another driving lesson under our belts before things get too hectic around here? she said. Just down the reservoir road and back again.

No, I said, shaking my head. I'm not learning to drive any more in that Defender. I'd rather stick my hand up a sheep again.

That can be arranged, Mum said. But, in all seriousness, the longer you leave it, the harder it will be.

Please . . . I said, aware I was sounding like a child. Can't we just let things be for today?

You have to learn, she pressed, a sternness once again settling into her voice. I can't be your chauffeur forever. You need to be able to carry some of the load.

Wild to think this was the closest we'd got to openly discussing Bobby's health.

Bobby rose to his feet then. I'll take this wee guy back and settle him down. He looked at me, attempting a serious expression. Do what your mother says. We should all do what your mother says. Miriam knows best.

Silently, Mum and I headed out into the yard. I climbed into the driver's seat of the Defender, while she jumped into the passenger seat, sitting bolt upright, her focus on the windscreen. And I knew what was coming; had been living with Mum's temperament my entire life. She was spoiling for a fight, desperate to be cruel, and it didn't matter what I did next, it was coming.

I turned on the engine and it hummed, the rattle under the frame intensifying.

Ready? she said.

I've told you this thing is too heavy for me to drive.

Nonsense, she said. Mind over matter.

What are you talking about?

The day I went to sit my driving test in Cairo there was a big football match taking place. She spoke seriously, as if she was giving instructions. And I had to wait for the game to be over before the examiner would even consider taking me out for my test. I waited and waited, and I was so nervous. But in the end my examiner's team won, and in his elation he signed my paperwork to say I'd passed and sent me on my way.

I shook my head. And your point is?

That I managed to survive driving in Cairo without passing a test and this is a walk in the park in comparison.

I placed my hands on the steering wheel.

So, handbrake off, foot down on clutch and into first.

I struggled to push the gearstick into first gear, finding third instead. Eventually, Mum had to nudge it into place for me.

Remember the bite, she said.

Why is it even called that?

I don't know . . .

I lifted my foot slightly off the clutch, but the Defender jerked forward, and the engine cut out.

Right, okay, she said. Let's try that again.

I manoeuvred myself into first gear. Ahead of me I could see someone in a hi-vis jacket coming out of the waterworks at the top of the road.

Okay, good, Mum said as I began to roll the Defender forward. Now keep her nice and steady as we get over the cattle grid.

We made it over the metal bars, but as I moved it up into second gear the car began to shudder as if it was about to sneeze.

Keep your speed steady, she said.

The reservoir was to my right, ripples passing through the margin of water that remained. Have you ever seen the water this low before? I asked.

Mum didn't answer.

High wire fencing was the only thing separating us from it. I used to worry about it flooding, the banks bursting and wiping us all away. And sometimes I'd imagine us driving into it. I'd even watched these YouTube videos about what to do if your car were to be submerged in water. The trick was to open your windows as quickly as possible, before the whole vehicle went under. And I really tried to visualise it, even now, make sure everyone else had their seatbelts undone.

Steady, Mum's voice was saying. Keep it steady.

But I was still thinking about the water. If I'd kept the baby that had begun to grow inside me, would it have got stuck in a car seat? I was aware suddenly of the Defender veering to the left, as far from the water as possible, but everything was happening in slow motion.

Suddenly, Mum grabbed the steering wheel and pulled on the handbrake; it made a clicking noise that seemed unnatural and damaging. Our heads were thrust forward, our bodies pinned back by our seatbelts, and the engine cut out.

What the fuck were you doing? Mum shouted. We were going to clip the kerb.

Sorry . . . I don't know what happened. I was trying to keep it straight.

That's enough, she demanded. We're switching over.

No, I said. I can try again.

Is it your blood sugar? she asked. Did you check?

Yes, I checked, I said, practically shouting. I'm fine.

I rolled down the window. The air in the Defender was static; the fans had never seemed to work – it was always either too hot or too cold. I unbuckled my seatbelt and we both just sat there for ages saying nothing.

Sometimes I think it's you that doesn't want me to learn to drive, I said. That you went out of your way to get Bobby to buy something that was never going to be roadworthy.

What would the point of that be? she said.

When I was seventeen, I asked for lessons, and you said they were too expensive.

They *were* too expensive.

But you liked having that control. I couldn't just leave and go where I wanted to, without you having to know.

She kept her gaze straight ahead and I knew she was trying to remain calm.

You *did* leave, she said. And it suited you not to be able to drive when you lived in Edinburgh – stopped you from feeling like you had to come back; it was never convenient to come home.

Until this fucking drought brought me back, I said.

You're behaving like a spoiled child, Aida. It's embarrassing and pathetic.

I cast my eyes up to the roof, exhaled, could feel my breath rattling through me.

Can I ask you something? she said.

What?

Did you at least try and talk Bobby into joining that drug trial?

Excuse me?

Did you really try, Aida? Or did you let it pass over you like you let everything else pass over you? And each word hung there, a bite to them that felt physical.

I gripped her arm, practically begging her to look at me. Do you really think anything I could have said would have changed his mind? When has he ever listened to anyone else once he's made up his mind?

She closed her eyes, and I could see she was fighting tears. I couldn't really recall ever seeing her cry, even when Dad left.

Think of all the times you've tried to implement change around here, I said. Be more environmentally minded. He would have none of it. So why should this be any different now?

What are we going to do? she whispered.

I don't know. I asked Dad to come back, but he told me about his new woman . . .

She shook her head, willing me to stop.

We swapped seats and she drove to the bottom of the road, reversing at the entrance to the water works, and then we were back to where we started.

It was late into the night when I got back from helping with the lambing, leaving Bobby and Mum to carry on. I struggled to get my boots off as I came in through the back door, and in the glow of the kitchen two moths fluttered past me, drawn to the light above my head. I stared up at them, these creatures of dust, and I gauged how settled they were before daring to move below. I'd had an irrational fear of moths since childhood – ever since I'd left my bedroom window open with the light on. By night, a mass of them had gathered on my bedroom ceiling. Mum had refused to let me sleep in with her and Dad, so I'd been forced to pull the duvet up and over my head for protection. In the morning, some had fallen dead on to my covers, resting on top of me. A violation of sorts.

By the table, I pressed the toes of my left boot on to the heel of my right, managing to force it off, a skid of cow shit spreading across the linoleum. I just stood there then, surveying the state of the place, the cluttered, sticky countertops. I was hungry and I thought about making an omelette, but I couldn't really be bothered, plus the dirty frying pan would have been something else to add into the mix. I decided on some toast in the end and a cup of tea, the kettle full as per usual, already sitting on the cooker. The ignition button didn't work any more so I lit a match, and the burner came to life. While I waited, I checked my bloods, gave myself some short-acting insulin and instinctively attempted to scroll through my phone but there was nothing but buffering.

I turned the phone off and stared out into the darkness, thinking about Edinburgh. I'd spoken to hardly anyone from there since coming back, except for Aaron. The whole experience, on reflection, had been pretty superficial, but then really what had I been expecting, trying to move somewhere like there? There was that rich bitch from my class who dominated time and space, asking me: *where are you from?* when I'd dared to give an opinion on the loneliness of Mrs Dalloway.

The whistle on the kettle blew, startling me, and immediately I was turning it off. Even here, I didn't have that many friends, except for Mia and I wasn't even sure she liked me, or I her for that matter. She had been popular at school in a way I suspected was no longer relevant and I think part of her resented me for trying to get above my station – for attempting to leave. And stupidly, I'd been arrogant enough to think that I'd never be back. On reflection, maybe I was always destined to return home, regardless of the drought – Mum's question forever haunting me: *what exactly are you going to do with an English literature degree?*

A rattle at the window jolted me from my thoughts and I looked up to see Bobby standing outside, the buttons of his overalls pinching at his neck.

What? I mouthed, before coming to the back door and opening it.

Quick, he said. I hear something down on the reservoir road.

It'll be the men from the water works; they've been coming and going all day . . .

He was shaking his head, listening, face turned towards the darkness of the road. Get the shotgun, he said. Now.

Are you serious?

Just get it, will you?

Where is it?

Miriam says it's in your hall cupboard, he said, ushering with his hand for me to move.

I ran into the hall and opened the cupboard door, retrieving the shotgun from where it rested next to a shovel and an old plastic sledge. Running back, I said, Is this not a bit much?

He was already forcing cartridges into the barrels. Stay here, he said.

But . . .

Just stay here, he repeated, moving as quickly as he could out into the yard.

I followed him, regardless. The sheepdogs were going ballistic now, barking from their wee gated outhouse.

An old, battered campervan was approaching the gateposts, slowing almost to a stall as it rattled over the cattle grid.

Who is that? I said.

I told you to stay in the house, Bobby spat.

But there was no time to retreat. Mum stepped out into the middle of the road, blinded somewhat by the van's headlights. The vehicle was in a bad way, rusting evident on the bodywork, the windows looking as though they could fall out of their frames.

The passenger seat window was slowly rolled down, and a woman with wispy blonde hair peered out, her hands creeping over the window's frame.

Please, she said. Can you help us?

Turn off your lights, Bobby called out.

The lights immediately went dead, and we could see her better. She looked as if she could have been Mum's age, perhaps a few years older.

This is private property, Mum said.

We mean no harm . . .

I could see a younger man in the driving seat. He was attractive, broad, with short, dark curly hair. The woman reached across to say something to him, and he turned off the engine so that the yard was suddenly quiet. Her head appeared again out of the window.

As I said, we mean no trouble . . .

There's nothing for you here, Bobby said.

Please . . . she pleaded. A soldier at the border told us a midwife lived here.

What of it? Mum said.

The woman paused. My daughter . . . she's pregnant.

I don't work as a midwife any more.

She's had a bleed, the woman said.

Mum paused, taking them in. You should go to a hospital, then. She'll need to be checked over – the baby too.

The woman was already shaking her head. No, they told us the local hospital was closed. We don't have enough fuel to get to the city . . . We won't get much further without daylight and our bearings.

You have visas to be over here, do you? Bobby barked.

The woman nodded again. Please. I can show her to you, if you don't believe me.

No one spoke for a moment.

Fine, show us the girl, Mum said.

The woman rose from her seat and entered the back compartment, slowly ushering someone into the cramped space of the front cabin. A young woman appeared, and we squinted to get a better look. Her head was lowered, hair falling in front of her face. It was difficult to tell her age.. The older woman began pressing her hands in around her daughter's stomach, trying to show us the bulge of a baby. See? she said. Do you see it now? The undeniable swell of a pregnancy protruded from the daughter's skinny frame. There seemed to be nothing else of her, her filthy loose-fitting kaftan-style dress swamping her.

Are you still bleeding? Mum asked the daughter.

She didn't answer, and the woman reached up and brushed a loose strand of hair away from her face. Rebecca isn't one for words, she said, patting her stomach, which the daughter seemed to read as her cue to retreat, disappearing into the back cabin again. The woman looked out towards us with concern etched into the creases of her face. She won't speak any more, she said. I should explain that.

I nodded, feeling shame then at the spectacle of having had her paraded out in front of us.

Is anyone else following you? Bobby asked.

The woman shook her head. My name is Evelyn. And this is my son, Peter, she said, pointing to the man in the driver's seat. His features were quite prominent and angular, a well-defined nose.

Bobby and Mum looked at each other, as if they were capable of exchanging unspoken thoughts.

Mum's expression was pained; one of reluctance. I still have a pocket Doppler, she said, but it won't be as accurate at detecting a heartbeat as one in the hospital.

Will you check for it . . . ? the woman, Evelyn, asked.

Who told you to come here? Mum pressed.

Please, she begged. Will you help us or not?

Mum stared at her. The boy stays in the van, she said.

Evelyn nodded.

Bring your daughter into our cottage and I will assess her, and my daughter will act as a witness.

Evelyn nodded again, already opening the passenger door to climb out. She came around to the back cabin door and opened it, ushering her pregnant daughter down, gripping her tight around the arm.

Aida will show you into the living room while I get what we need, Mum said.

Both mothers looked at me then as if I was holding up the whole operation. This way, I said, and Evelyn and Rebecca followed me across the gravel until they were through the front door. I guided them into our unkempt living room, pointing to the corduroy sofa that I hated.

Evelyn pressed her daughter down into our sagging cushions, lifting her legs up and swivelling her until she was flat, hands resting by her sides.

We waited, my eyes darting around the room.

You have a nice home, Evelyn said.

Thank you.

The daughter, Rebecca, appeared completely vacant.

We heard Mum out in the hall. I'll be with you in a moment, she said. And then I could hear her in her bedroom, rummaging about in drawers. Moments later she joined us with her Doppler, a tube of lubrication and a roll of toilet paper. She stared at

Rebecca. I'll need to see her stomach, she said, but by her tone it wasn't exactly clear if she was speaking to herself or making a request.

Evelyn began lifting the dress that swamped Rebecca. And then her fragile limbs were exposed, a longstanding scar visible across her thigh. The fabric of the dress ballooned out in Evelyn's hands, until she was holding the bulk of it above Rebecca's chest line, tucking it in around her, while Rebecca lay in off-white cotton pants, a little bow stitched on the front. And before us was the large swell of her stomach, her skin stretched so thin. And it was mesmerising and bizarre, almost otherworldly to me. Looking at a body expand – the visible image of something that I had stopped my own body from doing, through choice, with no regret or remorse.

When is she due? Mum said.

We're not sure, Evelyn replied.

Has your daughter . . . sorry, what's her name again?

Rebecca.

Has she seen a doctor or midwife before?

We haven't always had good experiences with doctors, Evelyn said. We believe in *free birth*.

You're joking? Mum said, but it didn't sound as though there was anything to laugh about.

What's that? I asked.

It's a natural practice, Evelyn replied.

Mum kept her gaze on Rebecca. It's when for an entire pregnancy there is no medical supervision or intervention. There isn't even documentation of the pregnancy.

It's how babies have been brought into this world for thousands of years, Evelyn replied, defence thick in her voice. Before we became obsessed with medical intervention.

You think so? Mum countered.

We wouldn't have evolved as a species without the natural wisdom of free birthing.

Yet, here you are, seeking my help . . . Mum said.

No one replied.

Mum got to work, rolling up her sleeves, squeezing lubricant across Rebecca's stomach, handing me the plug of the Doppler, and me feeling grateful to be somewhat useful.

The echoing noise of the Doppler held a rhythm I began to nod my head to. It sounded like being underwater, blowing bubbles through your mouth. I had no idea how Mum did it; how she knew what she was listening for, I suppose in the same way that I couldn't understand how you could decipher the blob of a growing lamb inside its mother's stomach. Suddenly there was a change, a solid, rapid beat, and instinctively we knew she'd found the baby's heartbeat. Whether Mum realised it or not, a smile settled on her face. Did all midwives smile instinctively when they found a heartbeat? Did all expectant mothers?

That's your baby's heartbeat, Mum said, softly. It sounds strong.

So, the baby is okay? Evelyn said.

Yes. For now, Mum said, reaching forward for the toilet roll. She began to wipe the gel off Rebecca's stomach, carefully lowering the ballooning dress down delicately around her waist, while Rebecca remained perfectly still.

So, things are fine . . . Evelyn said.

Tell me more about this bleeding, Mum replied.

It wasn't too much, Evelyn said. Her pants stained, like the start of a period, but it got us worried . . .

Mum was quiet for a moment. You can return to your campervan now.

Evelyn got her daughter on to her feet, and they followed Mum's lead, while I trailed behind them back out into the yard.

Bobby was chatting to the son through the driver's window, the barrel of his shotgun pointed towards the ground.

The baby is okay, Evelyn said as she approached them.

Her son nodded.

Glad to hear it, Bobby said.

Evelyn opened the back cabin door, ushering Rebecca inside, before turning to stare at us once again.

Bobby cleared his throat. There is petrol at the Welcome Break service station, he said. It's about eight miles back from where you've come. I'm amazed you didn't see it – it's the first port of call once you're through the border, at the big round-about. He turned and flashed me a smile. Our Aida works there, although not tonight, obviously.

We did see it, Evelyn replied, but we have little money left. It's so expensive.

Bobby cleared his throat, sizing them up. We don't have much fuel, he said, if that's what you're after. But what does this thing drink? he added, nodding his head towards the camper.

Diesel, she replied.

I could see him weighing it all up in his mind, visualised the stockpile he kept for the generator. Maybe we could take some from the tractor, he said, not that we have much ourselves, mind.

Mum cleared her throat. Bobby . . .

Where are you trying to get to? Bobby asked.

Glasgow, initially, and then northwards, Evelyn replied. But, as you can imagine, this van is not the most fuel-efficient.

Bobby paused. I doubt we'd have enough to get you to Glasgow in that thing . . .

There really is nothing else here for you, Mum said, inter-rupting whatever it was she was anticipating him saying next. We have no money either.

Evelyn stared at Mum. Will the baby be okay . . . ?

I still think you should take your daughter to a hospital, in Glasgow. Her bleeding will need to be checked.

What will they do? Evelyn asked.

Monitor both mother and baby, I expect. Normal practice would be to continually check the heartbeat throughout the next twenty-four hours and track a pattern of movement to ensure it's okay. And, for Rebecca, try to determine why she has had a bleed, monitor her blood pressure, take some urine samples. It'll all be routine stuff.

Are these things that you could do yourself? Evelyn said.

Mum grew defensive, as if she was being forced into something against her will. What are you asking me?

It would be one night, Evelyn said, almost begging. Monitor what you can and then we'll leave . . .

Mum was shaking her head. No, I'm sorry, that won't work . . .

But I was already thinking about Rebecca and the heartbeat of her baby. I wasn't sure why I was drawn to her, or to any of them really. They were different from the others I saw passing through the service station – as if they'd really endured, had seen things perhaps I'd only witnessed through social media. It intrigued me; I thought I'd suffered, was suffering, but I hadn't, not compared to these people. And maybe the woman I'd abandoned at the service station was still bothering me – perhaps I was seeking some form of salvation.

Maybe they *should* park their van here for the night, I said. What's the harm in checking on the baby again tomorrow before they leave?

Mum looked at me, anger burning through her. Aida, I don't think . . .

Bobby drew Mum towards him, attempting to converse unsuccessfully out of earshot. What do you think? he said.

65

I don't like it, Mum said, not even attempting to whisper.

But what if something does happen to the baby? I pressed.

We have our own supplies, Evelyn interrupted. We wouldn't need anything else from you aside from a place to park our vehicle. My son is strong and willing. If there is labour to be done, he can help as a means of repaying the favour.

Bobby was quiet for a moment, his eyes narrowing in contemplation. You can park around the back of the shed, he finally said.

Bobby . . . Mum said.

He shrugged, as if the decision was out of his hands. It's one night, Miriam.

Evelyn exhaled, a breath being released. Thank you, she said.

And I worried she was going to cry with relief. We wouldn't have known what to do with a stranger crying – even the thought of it filled me with anxiety.

Mum stared on as Bobby waved the campervan forward, guiding it into a space around the back of the shed, out of view.

Once parked, Peter emerged from the van to join his mother, taller than I had been expecting. There was something unnatural about them just standing there, staring at us. I was aware of Mum's grip suddenly on me, hurting me, the warmth of her breath on my neck.

I'm Bobby, this is Miriam, Bobby said, pointing to Mum, and my great-niece Aida.

They nodded in unison.

Okay, time's getting on and we still have a night of lambing ahead of us, so let's pick this back up in the morning, he said.

Collectively, we began to retreat towards our cottages, Sam peering out from their front window. I turned then to see Peter stretching in front of the campervan. He was exchanging words with his mother that I could not hear. Despite his leanness he appeared strong and fit. He was incredibly attractive; so good at looking sad.

Sam was opening the door for Bobby from the other side, while Mum and I walked into our kitchen. Closing the door, she rested her head against the back of it. Why did you do that? she said.

I shrugged, coming to stand by the window. I felt sorry for the girl, I replied.

What are they doing? she asked, nodding her head towards them.

They're removing something from a compartment on the outside of the van . . .

She straightened and came to where I stood. They're emptying their toilet, she said. Here. In our yard. She exhaled. I hope you realise that none of this is a good idea.

You're a midwife, I said. What if something happened to that baby? Wouldn't that have troubled you?

Well, we'd never have known. Their situation is not our problem.

You would care, I whispered.

I'm surprised *you* care so much about that baby, she replied.

And I didn't know what to say to that, my mouth parted but empty.

The phone began to ring in the hall and Mum retrieved it, bringing it through with her. She sat down and brought the receiver to her ear. Are we taking it in turns to watch them? she said.

I could hear Bobby's voice down the phone but couldn't quite make out what he was saying.

Well, they're still strangers, regardless of how genuine you think their need appears, she replied.

I turned again to watch the son out of the window.

So how do you want to do it? Mum asked. Alternate in shifts between us all? Aida and Sam take the reins when one of us is out with the ewes . . . She nodded at whatever Bobby was saying in response. Yes, and keep the gun with you in the shed, just in case.

She placed the phone back on the receiver. Sam will take first watch while Bobby goes out to lamb and then we'll swap.

Okay . . .

Lights out now, she said.

I was already reaching for the switch.

And lock the door, will you? Just to be on the safe side.

I clipped the Yale lock down. It was the first time we'd locked the back door since Dad left. Perhaps we had both been hedging our bets, believing that he might some day actually want to come home.

5

I watched the campervan all through the night, imagined these strangers in their cramped environment, wondered if they were staring back in the darkness. People used to turn up at the farm all the time, and Bobby would welcome them, relished the opportunity even – a weird assumption between farmers that you'd always be free to stop for a chat, a cup of tea; that you couldn't possibly be busy or indisposed. Bobby had done it to me once when I was in Edinburgh, the weekend of the Highland Show: just rung my buzzer, assuming I'd be there, expecting to be invited up, never mind that Aaron was still in my bed. I'd been horrified at the time, but now there was something nostalgic about the innocence of it all. At what point in the drought's progression did we grow to become suspicious of new arrivals? When had we decided that someone unknown driving towards us merited the shotgun?

Maybe it was rooted in loneliness, but there was a feeling of excitement settling in me. The appeal of having new people here, even if only briefly – you could recreate yourself in the eye of a stranger and they'd never be able to question your past. I'd been trying to do that the entire time I was at university, and at Camp America too – pretending to be a good role model to spoiled twelve-year-old girls from wealthy families. There had been a camp counsellor in my team called Danielle whom everyone called Dani, and I remembered mocking her, as she phoned her new college roommate and introduced herself as *Elle*. The audacity at her obvious attempt at rebranding was astounding to me, despite my own exactly similar attempts.

As the sky got lighter, I saw movement, someone parting a curtain, before closing it over again, the van swaying slightly. The walls no doubt paper-thin, not an inch of privacy or space to swing a cat. Bobby and Sam used to take me with them on their annual week's holiday to the same static caravan way up in Nairn once the lambing and calving season was over, and even as a child I'd struggled to see the attraction of sleeping in something like a caravan. The weather was usually always shit, the sea freezing. Perhaps I had inherited Mum's ability to so bitterly feel the cold, my body built for the Egyptian climate it had never had the opportunity to experience. Why were farmers so bad at taking half-decent holidays anyway? Why were they always reluctant to leave Scotland? I doubted if Bobby or Sam even had a passport.

I stretched, still staring at the campervan. Walking into the hall, I could see Mum's bedroom door ajar. She was sleeping on top of her covers, curled on her side, having been up half the night lambing. I stood over her for a moment, listening to the rhythm of her sleep.

Mum, I said. They're up.

She mumbled something into her pillow.

I walked back into the kitchen, and she followed me through in her dressing gown, her collarbone protruding out, pointy and sharp. Are they doing anything strange? she asked.

No, I said, sitting, pricking my finger, inserting the test strip automatically into my meter.

Without asking, Mum handed me my long-acting insulin pen from the fridge, and I set the dial, fourteen units, lifting my T-shirt and injecting it into my stomach.

I don't want them wandering around, she said. Poking their noses into things.

So, what's the plan? I said.

I'll check the baby again and then they can be on their way.

It was only then, as I stood, that I saw the son, Peter, out in the yard, peering under the bonnet of my Corsa.

Mum came closer, our shoulders touching. What *is* he doing?

We watched him circle the vehicle before his head disappeared under the bonnet again, like a salesman trying to appraise its value.

The phone began to ring, and Mum picked it up immediately. Well, she said. What do you think? She gripped the collar of her dressing gown as she listened to Bobby down the line. No, nothing suspicious. You? There was a pause. I'll get Aida to go and offer them a hot chocolate, she said, matter of fact. See what they say.

Me? I said.

But Mum was already placing the receiver down on the cradle. Well, that might be something the daughter can have, she said. I don't have any decaffeinated tea or coffee. Bobby swapped some beef ribs with John Watson for too much milk, so it needs used up anyway before it turns sour.

Why should it be me that goes out?

They'll be more natural around you, she said. Less threatened.

Thanks . . .

Will you just go? I want to know what they say.

Isn't that milk unpasteurised? I said. Can you have unpasteurised milk if you're pregnant?

Uh, Mum said, rubbing her face. Well, I've got some normal blue milk too. Just go and ask them . . .

As I made my way out across the yard I turned briefly, catching the curtains in Bobby and Sam's cottage twitching. I attempted a wave, but the curtains grew still.

Our guests seemed pleased to see me, leaning against the van, except for the pregnant daughter, Rebecca – she was out of sight.

Did you sleep okay? I asked.

Yes, Evelyn replied. I think that's the best sleep we've had in a long time. Just to know we're somewhere safe.

Mum is asking if you'd like a hot chocolate . . .

Please don't go to any effort for us, she said.

I pointed back towards our cottage, unsure whether I should push the invitation further. It's no trouble, I said. We're making some anyway . . .

Evelyn paused. I'm lactose-intolerant but I'd devour a black coffee. Everyone else is fine with milk though.

I'd need to check if there's still enough water in the kettle, I said. The taps don't come on until 7 a.m.

So, the taps *are* still running?

I nodded.

She glanced up at the sky. It must be close to seven now, surely . . . she said.

What are you doing with the Corsa? I asked, turning my attention to Peter.

He's just seeing what's holding it back, Evelyn replied. Is it yours?

It's meant to be.

I ushered Evelyn towards the kitchen door and, as she walked with me, she pointed in the direction of the reservoir. Where does it feed?

Here, and the nearest towns, I said. And further, I think. Some parts of the Clyde too.

Will it last?

We try not to think about it, I said. Hope for rain.

As I crossed the threshold, I noticed with fresh eyes that our dirty dishes and cups were still lying out next to the sink, a fly having landed in some of yesterday's curdled milk in my cereal bowl.

Mum smiled at Evelyn, but it was taut and unnatural. Good morning, she said.

Is there any water left in the kettle for coffee? I asked. Evelyn is lactose-intolerant.

Mum hesitated. Yes, I think there's enough for a cup or so. Would the others still like some hot chocolate?

Evelyn smiled. Cold milk will be fine. No need to spoil them – save the powder for yourselves. But thank you.

How is your daughter? Mum asked.

She's still sleeping. She'd probably sleep for a week if I let her. Evelyn glanced back towards the yard and Peter, who was still inspecting my car. The rest is doing her the world of good. It's so quiet and peaceful here.

I'll check her again, when she wakes, Mum said. You'll want to leave with plenty of sunlight in front of you to help you keep your bearings. She paused. Bobby is seeing what he can do to help you with fuel for the journey.

And you're sure the baby will be well? Evelyn said.

The baby's heart is strong, but I cannot be sure of anything, Mum said, an edge of hostility creeping in.

Okay, I understand.

Apparently, Peter is very good at fixing cars, I said.

Is that so? Mum replied, laughing, but there was still a falsity to it.

You'd be amazed at what he can do, Evelyn said. We wouldn't be able to go anywhere in that rust bucket out there if it weren't for him.

Well, I suspect that Corsa has had its day, Mum said.

Bobby did order some new parts for it a while back, I said, but they're still sitting in boxes.

Perhaps Peter can take a look, then. Even if it means leaving the car in a better state than its current one.

Mum shook her head, having always had a real issue with accepting anyone's generosity. Honestly, we can't possibly . . . We would never expect that.

Evelyn reached out and placed her hand on Mum's arm. Let us do this for you, Miriam. For your daughter, she pressed, turning to take in my nervous smile. It's the least we can do. Think of it as payment for your kindness.

I cleared my throat. We're driving into the nearest town this morning to go to the pharmacy. If there's anything you need . . . before you leave . . .

Okay, thank you, Evelyn said. Peter is prone to hay fever so it might be worth us getting some antihistamines. She turned her attention back to Mum. And what pain relief can I give to Rebecca if she needs it? She's occasionally prone to headaches.

Headaches . . . Mum said, the word lingering there. Paracetamol is basically all you can offer pregnant people without seeing a doctor.

Evelyn nodded. Can I send Peter with you?

Okay, Mum said. We'll be leaving as soon as the shops open.

Perfect, she said. That'll give him enough time to see if the car is salvageable.

I walked back out into the yard and hovered by the car for a moment, waiting for Peter to acknowledge me. He was crouched down, oblivious, pieces of my car in front of him. Well? I said. What's the verdict?

He stood up, towering over me. I wouldn't say it was in the grave yet. Maybe worth attempting resuscitation.

Thank you, I said.

He shrugged, not really meeting my eye. It's a puzzle, he said, crouching again, brushing his hand against the side of the car as if it was something to admire.

74

I smiled at him, but it made little impact, his manner so aloof. At uni, I'd found it quite easy to attract men – had a way that seemed to draw them in, perhaps with my own aloofness. But I was getting nothing from Peter, not a sniff of flirtation. It was probably what I found most attractive about him.

I'll tell you something, though, he said, his head back inside the bonnet, it'll take longer than a day. Definitely not a quick fix.

Mum sat up front in the driver's seat, while I sat next to her, Peter in the back cabin, the fold-down seat clearly too small for his frame. And when he tried to click his seatbelt in, it wouldn't work. Sorry, Mum said, shouting over her shoulder as she turned on the engine. The back seatbelts are broken so you'll just need to hold on.

I glanced over to take Peter in, trying not to laugh at the absurdity of him balanced on that wee seat, the cabin appearing cramped around him, his legs spreading out, hands on his knees. And the mess of the back compartment: tools for fixing various things, boxes of useless, random shit that Bobby was forever trying to trade, sheets and blankets. And there was the strong stench of the sheepdogs too.

Turning, I could see Mum staring at the dashboard. The fuel gauge is in the red, she said. Do you think it's been like that for long?

I shrugged. Do you want me to nip out to one of the sheds and get some from Bobby's supply?

She gave me a look, and I knew immediately that I'd overstepped the mark, given away something I shouldn't.

As we drove down the reservoir road, I glanced at Peter again, his gaze off in the distance. His lips were extremely chapped, painful-looking, and I wanted to dribble drops of water on to the cracks and watch them seep through. As if he was reading my mind, he licked his lips.

Is it only paracetamol and hay fever tablets you think you need? Mum asked, peering into her rear-view mirror.

We have no money, he replied, his words a mere whisper, his tongue doing most of the work. There isn't really any point in me going to the pharmacy, because we can't buy anything.

I don't understand, Mum said. How will you continue on with your travels without any money?

He shrugged into his seat. Good question.

I hesitated, shifting slightly to face him. I have some money, I said. I can get you your medicine.

Really?

Paracetamol is like what, 20p or something? It's nothing . . .

He nodded, mouthing a silent thank you.

We parked up a side lane beside the pharmacy and Mum stayed in the Defender, while Peter followed me inside. Behind the counter, the shop assistant Shirley was pricing up heartburn tablets. She looked up and smiled, her eyes showing familiarity, but I doubted she could remember my name. She wore a badge that read: *Ask me about nasal sprays.*

Hello, I said.

Hi, she replied. How can I help?

We need something for hay fever, I said. And there should be a prescription ready to collect for myself. Aida Sinclair.

Of course.

A young woman I hadn't seen before, who I assumed was the pharmacist, glanced out from behind the dispensary.

So, for hay fever, Shirley said. Are you on any other medication?

Peter shook his head.

Drowsy or non-drowsy?

Drowsy, he said, almost instantly.

Shirley turned to inspect her selection on the shelves, gathering a rectangular box and placing it on the counter. £3.99, she said.

Can we get two packets of paracetamol too, please? I said.

I'll need to check if I can sell two packets together . . .

It's one for each of us, I replied. We're two different households.

She rang everything through, and I handed them to Peter. Can you take these out and give my packet to Mum, please?

He hesitated, as if he was going to ask for something else before deciding against it and leaving the shop, the tinkle of the bell over the door still reverberating. It was probably the most assertive I'd been since his arrival, and I wondered if he found it attractive. Most people found assertiveness attractive, didn't they? Mostly, I just didn't want him having to wait while I got my insulin or hearing the questions they sometimes asked. It wasn't that I was ashamed; it was more that he didn't know that side of my life and I liked feeling like I wasn't totally exposed. I'd been with guys who found it uncomfortable watching me inject and I just didn't want to know yet which way he would fall.

Shirley smiled at me. I think your prescriptions only came back this morning, she said. They should be ready shortly.

I nodded, before shifting my gaze to a *Stop Smoking* poster on the wall, thinking the pharmacist behind the counter could only have been a few years older than me. Maybe I should have thought about doing something more practical, like pharmacy – jobs that helped you get a mortgage, apply for a car loan. Were these things still worth lusting for now? Did a job like that offer some form of stability? Make you content, with purpose? The pharmacist behind the counter didn't look especially happy, though, and I took comfort from this.

My phone vibrated in my pocket, my notifications catching up with me now there was signal. I almost didn't want to check but it was an addiction, the farm the only thing saving me from it. I started scrolling, getting caught up on WeRateDogs for a while, which was one of the few profiles I hadn't muted: this wee pup, with paws too big for his body, looking as though he was off on his own wee mission. 13/10.

I saw an empty chair and sat down, still scrolling through the dogs, the woman sitting next to me shifting awkwardly. I came to the end of my unseen content and accidentally caught a drought headline: reports of mass shootings in drought-ravaged America. Immediately, I closed my screen and pocketed the phone. I focused on another poster on the wall, of a mother holding a baby in her arms. *Why breastfeed? The benefits.* Mum liked to remind me of the sacrifice she'd made in breastfeeding me for a whole eighteen months. There were bullet points down the side of the poster: *good gut bacteria, immunity from infections, health benefits to baby and mother.* I couldn't imagine it – the sensation. If I'd kept my baby, I think I would have felt compelled to breast-feed, prove to Mum that I could be the type of mother she had been to me. I wondered about the bottle-fed babies then – if the drought continued, would their mothers have enough water to make up formula? How was it all going to work?

The woman sitting next to me was muttering under her breath, her feet tapping the floor. I followed her gaze to the door of the consultation room. There was a handwritten sign taped to the outside: *If you consume medication on the premises, you MUST bring your own water.*

Are the rumours true? the woman whispered.

I had no idea who she was speaking to.

Are they? she repeated, louder.

Sorry, what?

Are they going to run out of my methadone?

I . . . I don't know, I replied.

People are saying it'll happen. That they're struggling to get all sorts of medicine across . . .

Another member of staff came and stopped in front of us, a plastic cupful of green medicine in her hand. That's you, Natasha, she said.

Natasha got to her feet, the muttering still audible. I could see the fear of it settling in. She blinked several times, looking at me for reassurance before being guided into the consultation room.

For Aida Sinclair? a voice finally said. The pharmacist was standing out on the shop floor by the counter.

Yes, sorry, I said, slowly getting to my feet.

She was holding my bag in one hand and the paper prescriptions in the other. Can I double-check the address please?

I recited it.

Lovely, she said.

The bag was cold and refreshing in my hand and I wanted to bring it to my cheek. Thank you, I said, distracted, still thinking about Natasha and her methadone.

I climbed into the Defender to find Mum and Peter sitting in silence, the news on the radio.

Mum began fumbling with the dial, trying to turn it down.

What are they saying? I said.

That we might be due rain.

I looked up at the blue sky through the windscreen.

They're saying what they want us to believe, Mum said. There's no rain coming.

When we returned, Bobby and Evelyn were sitting at our kitchen table sipping cups of tea. The door was wedged open, letting the morning sun stream in, and it looked as though they'd been sitting there a while, comfortable, like two co-conspirators, revelling in each other's company. Bobby was relaxed, smiling at Evelyn, showcasing his yellow teeth, his arm leaning back against the chair as if he didn't have a care in the world.

How did you get on? he said, straightening in his seat to take us all in as we approached.

Good, Peter replied, holding up the medication he'd acquired.

Excuse us, Evelyn said, laughing. Sitting here, making ourselves at home in your absence.

I weaved past them and opened the fridge, placing my bag of insulin inside as if it were a large carton of milk.

Bobby drained his mug before standing, seeming unsteady as he gripped the table. I better get back to it, he added. It's a busy time of year for us, Evelyn. A lambing ewe doesn't care if there's a drought or not. And the calves will be coming soon . . .

Do you want some help with anything? Peter asked.

No, no, Bobby replied. You're alright, lad.

I don't mind, Peter pressed. I've worked on farms before. I really would be more than happy to help. He spoke with real enthusiasm, perhaps the most animated I'd seen him.

Bobby paused, contemplating. Well, I actually do have a few jobs needing done that require some heavy lifting. What do you say? Are you up to the task?

Peter nodded. Absolutely.

Okay, well, follow me, then. And as he made to leave, he stopped and turned to look at Evelyn. Look, if I've got Peter here helping me for the day, you might as well stay on another night and join us for dinner, he said, a command rather than a question. It doesn't really make any odds to us if it's one night or two.

Evelyn paused. Are you sure?

Aye, Sam's always cooking too much anyway. We'd be glad to have you, wouldn't we, Miriam?

Mum nodded slowly, hesitantly. Of course, she said, the words practically having to be forced from her mouth.

And then Bobby and Peter were gone, and Evelyn was swivelling in her chair, a smile settling on her face. Is there anything I can do to help? she said, glancing around. I'm good at cleaning . . .

Mum cleared her throat. If you don't mind, I really would feel more comfortable being able to check on Rebecca and the baby . . .

Evelyn nodded, sombrely, and then she too was leading Mum out into the yard, and I was alone. And suddenly it felt as if I was surplus to requirements – a rare moment when there was no expectation on me. What was I meant to do? Would it be ridiculous to put on a terrible DVD and fall asleep to its comfort on the sofa? It was difficult to tell what was appropriate any more. The extra box of paracetamol was still sitting on the kitchen table. Instinctively I wished Mum had taken it, had already incorporated it into her hoarding cupboard – as if the world would only feel secure once something else had been added to her supplies. In the end, I did put on a DVD, *The Apartment*, and, pulling a blanket up over me, thought about Peter, touched myself, and eventually fell asleep.

Sam was making a parmesan and pea risotto for dinner, deciding that it was easier to feed everyone veggie, while I was tasked with setting the table. He instructed me to take the good plates and glasses out of the sideboard, and the fancier cutlery too, with the bone handles.

Are you feeling a bit better? I asked.

Uh-huh, he said, nodding.

Bobby arrived then, coming through from their back hall and into the open plan in his socks. The first heifer looks like she'll drop sooner than we thought, he said to no one in particular. He paused, smiling at us. Miriam's just cleaning up; she'll be in in a moment.

Sam and I nodded.

Well? he said, turning on the tap to fill a glass of water, before gulping back the contents. What are your thoughts on our guests, then?

Sam was quiet for a moment. They certainly look as if they've been through a war zone to get here. And they don't appear to want anything from us, aside from a safe place to park their van and Miriam's help checking the baby.

Bobby nodded, stopping to acknowledge Mum, who had arrived through the front door.

Rusty jumped out of his bed, looking for affection, but Mum brushed him off, almost oblivious. She'd always been this way. It was as if she couldn't accept that people took pleasure in animals as pets – that they weren't just there to serve a practical or financial need.

How's the baby? Bobby asked, directing his attention to Mum.

The heartbeat continues to be strong.

Well, that's good news.

She nodded. But . . .

But you're still concerned, he said.

Well, of course, she replied, seeming conflicted. I mean . . . the stress and trauma of what that girl has been through . . . It will certainly have an impact on her pregnancy.

Of course trauma and stress have that effect, Bobby said. It makes me think of our poor ewes when they're traumatised – we've seen enough miscarriages and stillborns to know the damage stress causes.

The thing is, Mum said, I see no signs of bleeding . . . I've checked and there's still nothing.

Surely that's good too, Bobby said.

What if she lied to us about it? Mum said.

No one responded.

What's their plans for moving on? Sam asked.

I think there's family living somewhere along the northwest coast, Bobby said. That's what the mother, Evelyn, told me earlier.

He cleared his throat, staring at Mum in the same way he'd done the night before, when the strangers arrived. It was as though I could see the cogs of his mind turning. You must admit, he finally said, rubbing his face with his giant hands, that big lad Peter, he was a right good help today. Some strength to him, honestly.

Sam stopped stirring the risotto.

Bobby, tread carefully here, Mum said, her words spoken clearly and firmly. We have no obligation to them. We have our own problems to be contending with.

Bobby exhaled. I'm just saying there are certainly benefits to having a strong young lad about. And we could do with the help, no?

Again, no one responded.

There was a knock on the door then, exactly at the time we'd suggested they arrive. Peter entered first, followed by Evelyn and Rebecca. He wore the same clothes from earlier, but Evelyn had changed into jeans and a bobbled jumper. She wouldn't have been obviously beautiful, but there was something interesting about her face, unusual. And Rebecca – her painfully thin frame was swamped in another kaftan-style gown, her head hanging low, while Evelyn guided her forward, a hand wrapped affectionately around her shoulders.

Bobby ushered them towards the large dining table. This is Sam, he said. I don't think you've properly met yet.

Sam nodded, hobbling towards them, extending his hand out to shake each of theirs. When he got to Rebecca, she turned further into her mother, practically shaking at the idea of having to touch him.

I'm sorry, Evelyn said. Rebecca is *very* shy. Particularly with men.

Sam smiled, perhaps embarrassed. That's okay, not to worry. Please, make yourselves at home. Are you okay with risotto? he asked.

Absolutely anything is better than the chunky tinned soup we've been living off, Evelyn said, trying to laugh.

83

Please, grab a seat, Bobby said. Aida, can you give everyone a glass of water?

I began to fill tumblers, water hissing out of the fancy tap head they'd had installed. It was like a hose you could pull out from the tap, and for some reason it really impressed me, something to aspire to.

The water in these parts in the nicest-tasting water you'll ever have, Bobby said warmly. Truly it is. I defy anyone to disagree with me.

I placed the tumblers down on the table, two at a time. Glancing up, I was suddenly aware of Peter sitting next to my empty chair, waiting for me, with Evelyn and Rebecca positioned on the other side.

Mum placed the bowls of risotto down in front of everyone. It looked and smelled wonderful. But then everything Sam cooked was wonderful.

Mum took the empty seat next to Rebecca, and finally Bobby and Sam settled at the top and bottom of the table. Bobby smiled, his teeth on show, plaque visible around the edges. And instantly I was running my fingers along my teeth. I'd been scolded in childhood for being too aggressive with my toothbrush, the dentist warning me that I was causing my gums to recede, that they wouldn't grow back.

Evelyn raised her tumbler. We should make a toast, she said. And she waited for us all to follow. To kindness, she said.

Bobby smiled, taking a sip. Tuck in. Don't let it get cold.

Rebecca remained motionless as we all began to eat, and Evelyn nudged her to start.

There was a quickness to their pace once they got going, forcing forkfuls in as if the food was at risk of being taken away. It really is delicious, Evelyn said with her mouth still full. Honestly, divine.

Glad to hear it, Sam said.

Bobby brought a forkful to his mouth and swallowed. Is there no meat in this? he said, already disappointed.

You'll survive one night, Sam replied.

Do you enjoy cooking, Sam? Evelyn asked, wiping her mouth with her finger.

He nodded and inserted a forkful of risotto into his own mouth before responding. Yes, he said. It's a hobby that has perhaps become an obsession.

A silence fell upon us, eyes shifting around the table, an awkwardness identified. Evelyn cleared her throat.

We're incredibly grateful for your kindness, she said. It's more than we could have ever expected.

Can I ask, what's the border like? Bobby said. Is it as bad as they say?

Evelyn stopped. I don't think I have the vocabulary to describe it, she said, looking down. It's not a place I ever want to see again.

I'm sorry, Bobby said. I shouldn't have asked that.

She shrugged, attempting to smile.

I noticed Peter playing with the grains of rice, searching for peas and shifting them to the side of his bowl.

You don't like peas? I asked.

It took Peter a moment to realise someone was talking to him and he looked up, his fork stationary. Sorry . . . I've never been a fan.

You would think, after everything we've been through, he would have overcome his aversion to peas, Evelyn said, attempting a laugh.

That's okay, Sam replied. For me it's cucumber. I've never been able to stand the stuff.

It's mostly water, Mum said, irritated. Tasteless. I don't get the aversion at all. In Egypt we put cucumber in everything.

If you don't mind me asking, what brought you to the farm, Miriam?

I married into it, Mum replied. And now Bobby is stuck with me.

I think she had intended for her tone to be filled with humour, but it fell flat. Like me, she had never really been good with jokes, always missing the tone, or the rhythm of laughter. Hugh, my husband, Mum pressed on, is Bobby's nephew. He left me shortly after Aida went to university. Didn't like being a farmer.

Well, his loss, for sure, Evelyn said. I don't know why anyone wouldn't want to be here, with all of you.

And then suddenly we found our flow and were all chatting, laughter spilling across the table. And it was nice, having these people here, bringing the place to life. It felt like being on holiday, even though I knew Bobby and Mum would be heading back out to the sheds once the meal was finished. But in that brief moment everything felt lighter – that things weren't unbearable. Maybe all of us thought we were delaying the inevitable, because these people didn't know about Bobby's health, and, if they didn't know, then maybe it wasn't happening.

Afterwards, when the plates were cleared away, Bobby brought JoJo the pet lamb inside, resting the wee guy on his knee, and Rebecca seemed to come to life for the first time, feeding him a bottle. I caught Peter watching me, smiling when he caught my eye. Even Mum relaxed, telling us about the time she and Sam decided they wanted to watch the *Mamma Mia* DVD, except what they'd bought and put in the machine turned out to be just the soundtrack. They couldn't understand why they were hearing the music but not seeing anything. And laughter erupted, Miriam the introvert momentarily becoming the life and soul of the party.

6

I stood with a hose in my hand, watering the vegetable plot. Bobby had put a tarpaulin around its perimeter in an attempt to disguise it, but I didn't see the point – it was a trek from the cottages to where the soil was good enough to sustain crop growth, and it wouldn't have stopped something like a drone from flying over to investigate. I had applied factor 30 sunscreen to my shoulders and nose that morning to stop them from burning. I couldn't remember ever having used sunscreen as a child, my skin so alike to Mum's, but now it seemed essential.

Glancing back down at the surfacing onions, I was surprised to see how well they had come in, the potatoes too, but the lettuces were feeling the effects of too many slugs surfacing for moisture, our finely balanced ecosystem clearly disturbed by the drought. I never expected to be someone who took pride in growing my own food; hadn't anticipated taking pleasure in compost bins and water butts. I'd been fussy as a kid – turkey-shaped dinosaurs in breadcrumbs, meatballs in tins, all the questionable meats that got power-washed off carcases and mashed together. I thought about those mass-produced foods a lot now, wondered why Mum had ever let me have them, why I hadn't eaten the freshest cuts of meat from the farm. Maybe it was just easier, these processed foods distancing me from the food chain.

I looked upwards into the sun, my eyes turning funny, spots in my vision, before bringing my attention back to the vegetables. It occurred to me then that if we were caught watering them, we'd be unlikely to pay the fine.

Pressure in the hose suddenly ran down to a trickle and I stopped, inspecting it, a twinge of panic running through my body, before I looked up to see Peter standing with one foot over it.

You'll damage the rubber doing that, I said.

He took his foot off.

The hose was limp in my hand, water now pouring out in no targeted direction.

Peter shifted from one foot to the other, appearing out of place. Miriam has asked that you come and help . . . he said. Show me how to castrate some of the lambs from yesterday.

I turned off the tap, coiling the hose around my arm, while Peter inspected the vegetables.

Are you impressed? I said.

He shrugged.

I dumped the rolled-up hose on the ground, and he led the way back down towards the yard. As we made for the shed, I could see Rebecca sitting in the back of the Corsa, her head resting against the back seat, eyes closed, all the windows rolled down.

What's she doing? I said.

Peter looked in Rebecca's direction. She likes sitting in it, he said. Makes a change from the campervan.

Won't she be too warm?

She'll come out when she is.

We walked into the main shed, and inside, the place was stifling and sickeningly hot. The sheepdogs were milling around, lapping up water from their bowl, looking sorry for themselves, while Mum watched over a ewe who was giving birth without needing any assistance. And it still amazed me that most of the time they were meant to do this completely unaided – just settle down and force a creature out of their body as if it were nothing.

Mum nodded to me as I approached, hanging over the rail of the pen. She looked exhausted, a tiredness that penetrated her whole body.

Do you remember what you're doing? she asked.

I picked up the castrating device, something that resembled pliers, and the little bag of orange elastic bands. It had never really bothered me, doing castrations – it was painless for all involved.

I climbed into the pen with Peter in tow. Are you happy for me to show you one and then you can do the rest? I said.

Sure.

I placed an elastic band over the pliers and opened them up so that the band was stretched into a wide circle. I reached for the lamb then, and, meeting little resistance, turned him on to his back. Carefully, keeping the lamb in position, I brought the stretched elastic band down around his scrotum and released it from the pliers. It was nothing: caused him no harm and was done in a matter of seconds. The lamb was already getting back on to his feet, looking for his mother, and I shooed him along.

I looked up at Peter, wondering if I'd made him uncomfortable. I think I wanted him to be. But he was expressionless, ready and waiting to take over.

Okay?

He nodded again, shrugging as if it was something he'd done a thousand times before. I handed him the device and watched him repeat exactly what I had done, pinning his lamb into place, bringing the elongated band down.

Nice and low, I said. You want to make sure you don't aggravate the skin.

And then it was done, and he was already reaching for the next lamb, looking as if he was in his element.

My mouth was dry, a furring on the tongue, and I retreated from the shed, needing to be outside. Rebecca was still sitting in the car, but she'd moved to the front seat, hands on the steering wheel as though she were going somewhere. I watched her with suspicion before making my way to our cottage.

In the kitchen Evelyn was scrubbing the hobs of the cooker. I couldn't remember the last time I'd seen the place so clean. And as I took a step closer, I squinted, staring at one of the cupboard doors that had previously had a coffee spill trailing down its front. Evelyn herself looked clean too, out of her dirty clothes and into leggings and a fresh baggy T-shirt. I wondered if she'd washed herself – stood in our basin under our shower, used our sponges. How much water had it taken to clean this place? I ran my hand along the surface of our wooden table; the sticky sensation was gone.

She turned to look at me. What do you think? she said.

I nodded, reaching for a clean glass on the drying rack, before filling it with water from the tap. Does Mum know you're doing this? I asked.

She paused. Will she mind?

I gulped down the water. She might.

Evelyn stopped then, the scrubbing brush falling from her hand. I'm sorry, I just thought . . .

The place looks amazing, though, so I think she'd be mad to want you to stop.

I refilled my glass and left, spilling a few droplets on the pristine floor. I wasn't sure why but I found myself walking around to the side of the Corsa and climbing into the passenger seat beside Rebecca. Her eyes shifted momentarily towards me, returning to the windscreen, her hands still on the steering wheel. I settled in beside her, my shorts riding up, resting my hands on my bare knees. I hadn't done a very thorough job of shaving them, and little dark hairs sprouted out from around my kneecaps.

Where are we going? I said.

Obviously, she didn't reply.

I rested my head over the back of the worn seat, the sun beaming across my face. I offered her the glass of water and she stared at it for a moment before taking it. She took a sip, measured and careful, before handing it back.

What does it feel like to have a baby kick you from the inside? I asked.

She looked at me briefly.

Can I tell you something?

She remained perfectly still.

I abandoned someone who needed my help, I said. I think she'd come across the border, just like you. And now I keep thinking that . . . Well, she's probably dead, or has had something else horrendous happen to her. I laughed at the awkwardness of my words. I could have done more, I added. I don't know why I didn't.

We just sat there for a while in silence, and I felt no better for having confessed – I could so easily have been that woman I'd left at the picnic bench. I could so easily have been Rebecca, too.

Peter came out of the shed and, seeing us, made his way towards the Corsa. He lifted the bonnet in front of us, suddenly blocking our view, a shadow descending. I could hear him tinkering, a spanner clanking off something inside the engine, yet we both carried on sitting there. After a few minutes he closed the bonnet and came around to the passenger door, opening it.

Do you really think you could fix this car? I said.

He shrugged. If I had the time.

I can't even imagine it, I replied.

If the car did drive, would you still stay here or leave? he asked.

I paused for a moment. I don't know . . .

He cleared his throat. It's hard for me to do any work on it when you're both sitting inside it.

I walked past Evelyn who was still scrubbing in the kitchen and headed into the living room, realising the carpet was clean, lines running across it from where the hoover had been, the coffee table empty of clutter. It looked unnatural and I felt as though I couldn't sit down. Evelyn had done this weird whacking-of-the-cushions thing I'd seen in some of those home magazines at the service station – like when you puff the cushion up and then karate-chop your hand down on it. I stopped at Mum's storage cupboard and reached for the handle, turning it. It was locked, and relief washed over me; I rattled it a few times to be sure.

Are you okay? Evelyn said, standing behind me.

That was when we heard Mum arriving. I walked into the kitchen to see her looking down at the mess her shoes had made on the clean linoleum.

Isn't it amazing? I said, attempting a buoyancy to my voice. I've never seen the place so clean . . .

Mum began to take her boots off slowly, lining them up on the mat, silent in her actions. It was as if we weren't there.

Mum, I said, don't you think we should thank Evelyn for all that she's . . .

Mum looked at me, ignoring Evelyn. I didn't ask for this, she said.

Evelyn hesitated. I'm sorry . . . I've overstepped the mark. I can see that now.

This is not your home to clean, Mum said.

Evelyn nodded, a sadness creeping across her face that felt like it could spread out and touch me. She left us alone then, the kitchen gleaming.

Was that really necessary? I said.

Mum stopped. We don't know these people . . .

Whatever, I said, walking away. That was brutal and embarrassing.

She smacked her hand on the counter. Don't talk to me like that. You have no idea . . . I would never have spoken to my parents like that. Never.

I went into the bathroom, the tension of it all making me need to pee suddenly. I sat on the toilet for a while, thought about Peter castrating the lambs, thought about Rebecca sitting in that car beside me. It was nice, to have others here, to have young people around.

I wiped and pulled my pants and shorts up, automatically reaching towards the bath and our basin of used water to flush, the cistern dismantled. But the basin was empty despite my having had a shower earlier in the day. I turned myself around in a circle. Would Evelyn have tipped it down the plughole? I stared into the toilet, at my yellow urine, the porcelain the cleanest I'd ever seen it.

In the hall, the phone was now missing, its cord trailing into the kitchen, the door ajar. I could hear Mum on the phone to Dad, but for once I didn't want to know what she was telling him. Suspected she'd be seeking validation for her behaviour, offloading her narrative to the man that left her. I found a pair of trainers in my bedroom and walked past her sitting at the kitchen table. She stopped speaking down the phone for a moment, bringing the receiver away from her ear. She went to say something, but I was already walking away, banging the door behind me.

Bobby and Sam were sitting on the bench outside their cottage, enjoying the early evening sun, watching Peter work away on the Corsa. I'd always found it amusing that they preferred looking out across the yard and sheds, instead of the fields and reservoir seen from the back entrance to their home.

It'll be too late in the day to be sending them on their way now, I said, nodding towards the campervan as I nuzzled in between Bobby and Sam on the bench.

Where's your mother? Bobby said.

She's on the phone to *him*.

Was there a disagreement with Evelyn? Sam asked.

Just Miriam trying to assert herself, I said.

Don't be like that, Sam replied. Don't belittle her.

Bobby crossed one knee over the other, then uncomfortably tried to uncross them again. Laddie, he called out.

Peter surfaced from the car looking in our direction.

Take a break, will you?

Peter came over to where we were sitting, wiping his forehead with oil-stained hands.

Do you know the game Kubb? Bobby said.

Peter shook his head.

Aida will show you how . . . Will you go and get it from the cupboard in our back hall? he added, turning to look at me.

Now? I said.

There's no better time to play. The heat of the day has passed, so why not?

I retrieved the game, which was sitting exactly where Bobby said it would be. I hadn't played it in years, but I loved it, a game that Dad had bought and introduced us to one summer, a nostalgic memory coming to the forefront of my mind.

I set out the wooden blocks in the yard, careful in my spacing, and counted out the batons for throwing. Bobby attempted to explain the rules, but Peter wasn't quite sure he understood so I intervened, suggesting it was probably best if we just started playing and he'd pick it up. And before we knew it Evelyn and Rebecca were coming out of their campervan to watch me kick Peter's ass, his aim terrible despite his strength. Bobby and Sam welcomed Rebecca on to the bench beside them and she sat down without hesitating, while Evelyn perched herself on the front step of Bobby and Sam's door. The only person that didn't join us was Mum.

There was heckling from the sidelines, but they all fell quiet as I drew the game to a close, skilfully throwing a baton towards the middle of the grid, knocking over the king, the only block left for me to conquer. Peter reached out to shake my hand and I was almost certain that he was holding it for longer than what would be considered appropriate.

We made our way into Bobby and Sam's, where giant bowls of penne pasta with pesto or beef ragù were served, looking starchy and delicious. No one seemed to notice or feel the need to acknowledge my insulin use, making me feel much less self-conscious about the whole thing. Peter focused on his bowl, and Evelyn was too busy fussing around her daughter despite Rebecca appearing at ease, while glasses of water were consumed as if there were no drought.

We stayed there for a few hours, the livestock momentarily wiped from Bobby's mind. And still Mum never came to join us, waiting for Evelyn, Peter and Rebecca to retreat for the evening before making an appearance. Then she stalked in, ignoring Rusty as per usual. She made her way across the open-plan space and peered into one of the now cold pots of pasta, scooping a portion on to the plate that had been left for her.

You okay? Sam asked her, cautiously.

She nodded, gripping a piece of pasta with her finger, not bothering with a fork.

Miriam . . . Bobby said. We don't want you to be upset. Aida told us about Evelyn cleaning your place without you knowing. I can see why that might have startled you.

It's humiliating, Mum replied. That woman is implying that I am unable to keep a home for my family.

Bobby paused. I don't think that's what she was saying. I think she was just trying to find a way to feel useful . . . He winced then suddenly, gripping his hip.

Did you take your meds? Sam asked him.

I will, he replied, trying to breathe through a sharp pain until it appeared to pass. Miriam, he said. I think we need to discuss this new situation we find ourselves in.

She stared at him. What situation?

Obviously, we'd all need to agree – it's a family matter, after all – but I was thinking . . . We could offer our guests the oppor-tunity to stay in the yard a bit longer . . . That way we can keep an eye on the girl and her baby. And Peter can lend a hand where it's needed.

Mum went to speak but Bobby raised his hand.

I'm just suggesting they stay until the baby is born – just until we know that Rebecca and the baby haven't come to any harm. You're a midwife, after all. You can't let something avoidable happen if you have the power to prevent it.

You have no right to place that burden on me, she said.

Miriam, he whispered, we need help, and we can't afford to pay for it. You know it and I know it. He paused. Let them help us through the last of the lambing and into the calving season at least, no? He coughed, clearing some phlegm. This way, it gives us the opportunity to get our ducks lined up in a row . . . Get organised for the future. Get our affairs in order.

There was the heaviness of his words again and their hid-den meaning. How long did we have, really? How long before

Bobby's cancer took everything? So much of the farm and the business was just him, our biggest asset his expertise and knowledge, not something that could be written down or placed in a deed.

Do we even have enough resources to keep them? Mum said. Enough food and water for everyone . . .

We can be careful with the water if we need to be, he said. And we've plenty of food. Hell, we could keep them in steaks for a year and it would hardly make a dent . . .

The extra help would be good, Sam said, seeming to really consider it.

Mum was staring at me. How do you feel about all this? she said.

Slowly, I nodded. I like them, I said. And I think it would be good to help them. I'd want to be helped if the shoe were on the other foot.

Mum closed her eyes for a moment. Has this decision already been made without me knowing? Is asking me a token gesture?

No one has been talking about this behind your back, I said. You're being paranoid.

Yet you do all want them to stay?

No one said anything.

She nodded then, crestfallen. If you all think that's best, then I won't go against you, she said. This is not my farm, after all.

This *is* your farm, Miriam, Bobby said. And if you're not happy I'll tell them to go. Really, just say the word.

She paused. I will not have them imposing on our homes, she said. It is not their place. They are strangers, and I want them kept at arm's length.

Fine, Bobby said. We'll set some boundaries.

I mean it, she replied. I don't want them using our things, helping themselves to our resources. Jim White along the way didn't have his fruit-pickers eating dinner with him every evening or taking liberties. He always just gave them their food to eat in their static caravans – their water too.

We understand, Bobby replied. I understand.

There's something about her I can't take to . . . she said.

It's a difficult world out there, Bobby said. We've got to help if we can. Isn't that our basic moral duty?

A pained expression settled on her face. Fine. They stay, but only until the baby is born.

SUMMER

7

At the entrance to the service station there were still hanging baskets drilled into the walls, flanking each side, the mesh-bowled frames completely corroded, the flowers dead. As I pushed through the double doors, I brushed a strand of hair away from my face, feeling the dust on my skin. It was so dry now that, despite washing, I couldn't seem to get away from it; it coated everything and everyone.

In the staff room, one of the women who worked at the noodle bar sat at the communal table – I could never remember if she was called Janet or Janice. She often told me how much she liked my *Egyptian* hair, *so thick and dark*, as if I was the most exotic thing she'd ever seen. Usually she was talkative, but today she was reading a newspaper, her eyes fully focused on its content while she peeled a banana, the tip of it black and bruised. And as if on autopilot, without looking, she tore the bruised section off and laid it down on the table.

In my concession there was no one except for Aaron who was, as per usual, in charge of the TV channels. Honestly, he said, terrestrial television is the pits. It's all cheap documentaries about weirdos on the internet who marry their sex dolls. He kept pressing the button as he spoke, his arm stretched up over his head, flickers of colour flashing before my eyes, until he eventually settled on the news. It was a group of opposing politicians sitting in a semicircle debating the new Drought Act that had just been passed in parliament. Some guy was up in arms about how it was just an opportunistic move from the government to claim emergency powers. Aaron turned to look at me for a moment before returning his attention to the screen.

I walked over to the magazine rack and removed a fitness and lifestyle magazine that looked relatively new. In the background they were now discussing the potential reality of Day Zero – the day when, if left unchecked, the mains supplies would run dry. It was only ever estimations and projections, shifting on a continual basis, no one wanting to actually confirm whether it would become inevitable or not.

How's the reservoir looking? Aaron said.

I flicked through the pages of my magazine, found an article about yoga. It'll be bone-dry soon, I said. The weirdest part is seeing the old washing-line poles exposed from back when my great-granny was alive, before they must have flooded the place.

Are you connected to the mains? he asked. Or do you guys have your own water supply?

I was still focused on the pages of the magazine. There used to be a borehole or a well years ago, but I think it dried up, I said. Plus, there was worry about the old lead mines contaminating it or something. I shrugged. We've been connected to the mains for as long as I've been there.

I turned another page of my magazine, different yoga poses detailed before me, the instructor the absolute picture of health – hadn't there been an Australian woman who had pretended to have every type of cancer under the sun but had sworn that yoga and clean living were healing her? It had all turned out to be a hoax but for a moment I wished for it to be something that would help Bobby. I couldn't imagine him ever entertaining the idea of yoga, though. I'd become almost obsessed by watching him, assessing the way he moved, the way his cheeks would quiver slightly when he was trying to hide discomfort. Sometimes I thought he was disintegrating, shedding before my eyes, yet we still said nothing, pretended it wasn't really happening.

When I glanced back up at the screen, a member of Extinction Rebellion was shouting at the camera, furious at our collective excessive consumption and waste, a preaching tone to his voice, rather condescendingly suggesting that if we had only reduced our individual water to forty litres per day, months or years ago, then perhaps we wouldn't be in the position in which we found ourselves now. I laughed, clicking my tongue in agitation, because, while I didn't disagree, the attack felt personal, and nobody wanted to be told they were responsible. What did forty litres even look like? What did that mean, when we'd never had to account for our water use before?

Under the counter I noticed a note left from Sharon, our supervisor.

The peanut M&Ms are short-dated. Push them for a sale if you can. S x

I checked the expiry date and the product description on the back before tearing it open. I tipped some of the contents into my palm, letting four or five colours roll around, scooping them into my mouth.

Are you allergic to nuts? I said, still chewing.

What? Aaron said, straightening.

I offered him the packet.

Are you allowed these? he said, already taking it from me. I mean with all the sugar . . .

I'd spent most of my life having strangers tell me what they thought I could and couldn't eat. Yeah, it's fine, I said, taking the packet back from him and forcing more into my mouth. You've seen me eat crap before, I snapped. I know how to count what I'm consuming and adjust my insulin accordingly. I'm not stupid.

Okay, calm down, he said. Sorry.

Jesus though, honestly, you weren't showing much concern before . . . All those times we used to get drunk and . . .

Alright. I said I was sorry.

Okay, fine, whatever, I replied, closing the magazine over.

We sat in silence for a moment, an awkwardness present which I relished. There was pleasure to be had in making someone familiar uncomfortable – maybe it gave me some sense of control, to tease and then reward. It was a quality I could see in Mum and hated but knew I had inherited too. And I was also bored out of my mind – felt as if I was making no inroads with Peter – as if I barely existed beyond the Corsa.

Aaron, I finally said, do you ever still think about us hooking up?

I thought I saw him blush then, a redness reaching his ears. He shrugged. It was a while ago, like . . .

True. I looked down at my hand and there was a wonky blue M&M sitting there in amongst other perfectly shaped ones. Its dye had begun to stain my skin.

Why, do you? he said.

I laughed. Yeah, sometimes.

What do you think about?

I pulled the footstool out from behind the counter and sat down.

Sometimes I think about that time we had sex in the hallway of my old tenement flat, three floors up, my skin against those cold ornate tiles.

Aaron popped a few more M&Ms into his mouth, tilting his chin towards the ceiling. I remember, he finally said.

Sorry. That was weird. I don't know why I brought that up.

He smiled, went to open his mouth, words on the tip of his tongue, before changing his mind.

Are you seeing anyone? I asked.

He paused. Not really . . . You?

No, no one.

I waited, but he didn't feel the need to respond.

We have people staying with us, I said. From across the border. They've been here a few weeks.

You've never said anything before.

I suppose I didn't think it was worth mentioning . . . Wasn't sure if they'd be staying for long.

What are they like?

I shrugged. Grateful, I said, looking down at the blue mark left on my hand from the M&Ms. One of them is going to have a baby . . .

What do they say it's like, across the border?

They don't talk about it, I said. At all. Is that strange?

I probably wouldn't want to talk about it either if it's as bad as people are saying online. He paused then. Do you ever think about driving down there and seeing it for yourself?

What's the point? I said. What with the army patrolling the place . . . you wouldn't even get close enough to see anything interesting.

He shifted, removing his phone from his pocket. I read an article about all these dead bodies they found in a secret compartment in a lorry, he said. Some pipe got bent, cutting off their oxygen supply. For all the people that get rescued or helped, there's probably more that don't make it.

I looked up at the screen and realised the news was still on. An expert was explaining how poor our water infrastructure and pipes were – telling us that we were losing billions of litres of water to leaks every year, enough for the needs of twenty million people – that, despite water companies investing heavily in sensor technology, they were never really able to plug the holes. And I tried to imagine all the water, constantly disappearing into the ground, deep down below us – to think of the grief I used to get from Mum for leaving the tap running while I brushed my teeth. Strange to think that until she arrived in Scotland she had never drunk water from the tap – it wasn't clean enough – the absurdity of Coca-Cola or Fanta being the cheapest and easiest thing to access. I reached into my own pocket then and removed my phone. I couldn't stop myself – I started Googling articles about Egypt's water crisis – the famine, people dying in the streets from a lack of food and water. Ethiopia had built a dam years ago that had heavily affected Egypt's water supply even before the drought, having drawn so much water from the Nile. And I wondered then if Mum ever read articles like this, if she worried silently about the implications for her family, or whether she ignored them entirely, the poor internet connection on the farm providing a sense of blissful ignorance. And suddenly I wanted to smash my phone on the counter, stop all the information and its endless stream of worry.

Where's the remote for this thing? I said, pointing to the TV.

Aaron laughed. Oh, come on, that would be too easy. He went over to the television and reached up, his finger tapping a button repeatedly, flickers of colour flashing once again before changing shape. He settled on a film that hadn't aged well. Mel Gibson, before we were born. But Aaron had obviously seen it because, as he retreated, a comforting smile spread across his face.

A man walked into the shop then and traipsed the short aisles as though he was looking for something in particular. Neither of us bothered to ask him if he needed any help, and he left shortly afterwards, empty-handed. Sharon would probably watch the CCTV tapes back and scold us for our lack of engagement, but really, what difference did it make now? If he wanted something, he would have asked.

A little over two hours passed before another person walked in. It was a woman, and she bought a packet of mints from the stack Aaron had just organised. It wasn't even midnight yet.

I went to the refrigerator aisle and picked up one of the security-tagged bottles of water, inspecting it. I'd never been great at staying hydrated – would have subconsciously chosen to drink anything other than water. But then I reasoned that maybe I would fare better now because of it, not like those people who were obsessed with drinking more than two litres a day – carrying around those huge plastic water bottles with motivational time markings drawn on – *11am you've got this!*

They've increased the price of the water since my last shift, I said.

Yeah, and they're still selling. Sharon was saying the rest of the drinks are due to go up in price too.

I took my time walking back towards the front counter, picking up different items: a packet of batteries, a portable speaker, Pokémon headphones – all of it overpriced and never sold. Can I take second break? I asked.

You always take second break, Aaron replied. Why would tonight be any different?

I sat back down on the footstool and tried to watch the film but it was difficult to follow – something about people pretending to be cowboys and gambling, an old American paddleboat, a young Jodie Foster before she came out as a lesbian.

When we finished the packet of nearly out of date M&Ms I checked my bloods, upped my insulin accordingly and opened another packet.

So, what's the plan once this all settles down? Aaron said. You heading back to Edinburgh?

I faltered. I don't know . . .

I thought you'd be desperate to get back . . . *Leave this shit hole behind* I'm pretty sure is a direct quote.

You're making me sound like a bitch.

He smirked, but didn't try to dispute the claim.

What about you? I said. Will you be heading back?

I could tell he was pretending to look at his phone. I don't think I'll ever be able to afford going back now.

So, what, finish your degree here, online?

He tried to laugh. I think a degree in architecture here is as much use as an English literature one.

Well, you could always design me a new house on the farm.

Speaking of the farm, he said, is it surviving okay with the new restrictions?

Restrictions?

He paused. Because I saw, you know, about the government wanting to impose livestock quotas. So, I assume that affects you guys . . .

I stalled, a sudden pressure in my chest. Where did you read that?

He began flicking through his phone again, before handing the illuminated screen to me. An article from a site I'd never seen before filled the page with the title: *Government plans for livestock reductions.* I started reading, skimming the words, my finger hovering over the page. *One kilogram of beef equals 15,400 litres of virtual water* . . . I said aloud. What does that even mean?

I think it's how much water is used to rear one kilo of beef. He paused, staring at me, his face appearing large. You didn't know about the quotas?

I handed him back his phone. No one tells me anything.

Well, maybe it doesn't affect all livestock farms.

Aren't you going on your break? I asked, nodding towards the clock.

He pulled himself up from the counter and retreated, his footsteps echoing off the floor. And I carried on sitting on the footstool, hidden behind the counter, my mind in overdrive. What exactly did quotas mean for us?

I shifted my attention to the television, and the opening credits of another poorly made movie. I turned then to the security cameras, wondering if anyone was staring back, suppressing the urge to wave. It would have been so easy to steal money from this place – to put through returns that didn't exist. Would it be enough to keep the farm afloat? Nearly all of my pathetic wage went to helping Sam balance the books. I wasn't sure how we planned to feed and water the livestock for the rest of the year without something changing, so was this a blessing or a curse?

I tried to focus on something else and began scrolling through my phone again. I found this handle where people sent in pictures of now empty swimming pools from around the world. And it was oddly comforting – comparing tile and mosaic designs – the empty, vast spaces waiting to be filled. When I looked up, I saw Aaron passing by with a burger in his hand, headed for the staff room. What would it be like to sleep with him again? Good, I imagined. It had always been good. He had lovely arms, nice wrists. I had the sudden urge then to leave the shop, to follow Aaron into the staff room, purely for the excitement of it. The thought that he might no longer want to have sex with me never even occurred – the fact that so much had changed since we'd last been together was momentarily forgotten. I didn't move, though; I just sat there thinking about having the weight of a body on mine. And when Aaron returned from his break there was still a tension and energy between my legs.

Are you not going on your break? he said, staring down at me.

Eh, yeah.

My cheeseburger cost me £1.10 more than it did last week, he said. So maybe that's a good thing for your farm and the price of meat.

I shrugged, getting to my feet. Maybe.

He settled back behind the counter, slumping over the surface. Did I miss anything? he asked.

Absolutely nothing.

What are you having for break?

Not much. Breadsticks and hummus.

He raised his eyebrows.

I've eaten too many M&Ms . . .

Will you be okay?

Yeah, I'll be fine, I said, already gripping the zipped pouch with my insulin and meter inside.

There was a questionable aroma in the staff room; maybe it was something within the walls, or under the pelmet of the kitchen units. And one of the strip lights in the ceiling was flickering and buzzing. I closed my eyes and opened them again, as though somehow this would re-set the fault. It seemed to be buzzing even louder and I bit off some breadstick, dry and a little stale, the hummus looking grittier than usual, my appetite gone. The buzzing and flickering got the better of me. How had it not bothered Aaron? I lifted the lid of the bin and threw in what remained of my stale breadsticks. The bin repulsed me – I'd emptied it once, the cleaners not taking any responsibility for the staffroom, and I'd found a maggot wriggling around at the bottom.

I walked through the double doors of the entrance and stood outside, taking a few deep breaths. My eyes caught the picnic table where I'd left that woman. It seemed like a long time ago now. There were a few stars in the sky, but I couldn't find the moon. I'd told Aaron once when we were drunk that I didn't like a full moon; that I preferred the moon when it was only a sliver, as if it was trying to hide, be cheeky. He'd found this endearing, and I liked to think of myself as endearing. But, in reality, I was more settled and secure when I could see the moon, as if only then could I be sure it was doing its job of keeping the waves in rhythm across the world.

I walked back inside, thinking I should find an opportunity to tell Peter the same endearing story about the moon. It was so superficial, guys lapping up all that random philosophical shit.

I had fifteen minutes left on my break and my eyes focused on the flashing sign for the gaming room, now the busiest part of the entire service station and potentially the only reason our doors remained open. It was mostly lorry drivers in flux waiting for their cargo's paperwork to be completed, locals too with nowhere else to go, now that they couldn't just hop over the border to the bowling alley or amusement arcade. It was a demographic of middle-aged men, and there was something a little pathetic about them congregating in this room as if it were a club, inserting endless supplies of coins into slot machines. I doubted they even won anything significant. But then maybe it provided them with comfort, the lights alluring in a way, and I supposed we all needed comforting. I slid my hand into my pocket and felt for a coin. I shouldn't have been carrying any money – all my personal possessions should have been in my locker, otherwise it could be seen as stealing.

A machine where you attempted to catch a cuddly toy with a claw sat at the entrance, almost giving the impression that it was a family-friendly space, and, inside, two men stood at machines next to each other. Towards the back was an abandoned miniature air-hockey table, minus its puck. I inched forward, beginning to wonder what I was hoping to achieve. The men didn't seem to notice me at first, their eyes fixed on the numbers and flashing lights. It was only when I stood in their glow that the men sensed my presence, their heads turning simultaneously to take me in.

Do you know what you're doing? one of them asked.

Sorry?

Do you know how to play?

I revealed the coin in my hand as though it were treasure.

The man that had spoken came and stood next to me, his hand gripping the edge of the machine's frame. What are you doing in here? he said. His hand was worn, and warts decorated the nail bed of his index finger. I flinched, imaging him trying to touch me.

The other man came forward too, leaning in to get a better look at me. Where do you come from? he said.

Excuse me?

You Asian? Did they let you across the border?

I stared at him and then down at my uniform, as if I was already guilty of something.

I work here . . .

He placed his index finger on my cheek and firmly brought it down, like wiping away a smudge. This skin isn't from here, he said.

And it occurred to me then, like a pretty pathetic epiphany, that these men needed someone to blame, the drought perhaps finally exposing their intolerance. Or maybe I had just been sheltered. Had it always been there, hidden behind a false veneer, and I'd never really noticed? Had the whole community been whispering, speaking in hushed tones about me behind my back? I certainly looked more like Mum than Dad, but I couldn't recall being singled out for it before. Was this how Mum had lived most of her life?

And then, instead of being surprised or outraged, there was only a shrugging sense of inevitability, as though it had simply taken longer for people to turn on me than I had expected.

Nothing home-grown about that skin, the other man said.

I tried to turn but they stepped closer, their breaths on my face. How did you get over? the first man asked. I thought they'd closed it off to foreigners. Did you sneak in? Bribe someone?

My face grew hot. I think it's time you left, I said. I'll call Security.

They laughed in unison, a deep chortle of a laugh. Giving the immigrants the jobs, the tallest said. Fucking couldn't make it up.

Rationally I knew I was safe, that we were in a public space, but my body wouldn't cooperate. A tear escaped and rolled under my chin. It was as if I was in shock – couldn't process the genuine distaste they held for me. The one who had already touched my face slid his finger under my chin, flicking the tear away before inspecting the trace it left on his skin.

It's not just the darkies you've got to worry about though, Stephen. Mind I was telling you about the Polish lass in the pub before it closed? The one who was always giving us the *poor little me* eyes? Made out she was practically homeless, coming over here to pull pints and scrape money together for her deprived family. Aye, but then Ryan the pub landlord goes over to Poland on an invite for her wedding and here's the thing – she's from a big wealthy farm and none of them look like they're struggling for a penny. It's an epidemic, I'm telling you.

It's a pandemic, actually, I said, regretting the comment the second it had left my mouth.

They stared at me, and for a fleeting moment I thought I was about to be struck, and braced myself for impact. But instead the men backed off, returning to their respective machines as if I'd never been there.

By the time I'd sorted myself out I was late back from my break. Aaron was stacking some hardbacks on the bestseller chart. Are you okay? he said, stopping to look at me.

Sorry, I said, trying to pretend there was something in my eye. I'm fine.

You don't seem okay.

Honestly, I'm fine.

He looked out past the windows of the shop into the main foyer but there was no one, and I had such a wave of affection for him then. Those men would still be where I'd left them, playing their slot machines in the games room, knowing there would be no consequences for their actions. I had enough understanding to realise where their footing was in the world. Perhaps they'd return home in the morning to wives, be back in time to see their children wake up for breakfast. And, in that moment, I hated those men more than anything else in the world – had an irrational desire to cause them physical pain. And I thought again of Peter on the farm and his size. His strength. And then I was imagining his hands around their necks, squeezing the breath out of them.

8

Sam took one of his turns again, disappearing from view. Was that how depression worked? Was it like a weighted blanket being wrapped around you, without permission, pinning you down, and you just had to wait for it to fall? It was awkward timing because we were basically in the thick of it with calving, and it had been Sam who'd been measuring out portions of food to leave for Evelyn, Peter and Rebecca, water too.

We hadn't shared a single meal together since Mum's stipulations, but then there was hardly any time to spare. Evelyn behaved as though she didn't mind, understood that she was a guest that not everyone wanted. Even when they ran out of gas, their cylinder empty, Mum refused to let them join us, offering them the camping stove instead.

I watched them emptying their toilet system into one of the drains and wondered if they begrudged us for utilising their labour but not wanting them inside our homes. I supposed Mum would argue that we were keeping our side of the bargain – offering safe shelter and her assistance in midwifery. It was all even and fair.

Rebecca continued to grow and swell. She spent most of her time in the campervan now, sleeping, or preferring to be hidden from view, but occasionally I'd see her milling about the yard, keeping her distance from the shed. There was real risk about pregnant mothers being near livestock – diseases like toxoplasmosis spreading to your unborn child. For the brief period last year between coming home to tell Mum about being pregnant and booking the abortion she hadn't let me near the animals, and I'd wanted to laugh, because what did it matter when you weren't planning on keeping the baby anyway?

When I came out of our back door, I could see the Defender parked and ready to go, Peter in the driver's seat, and a float of lambs already loaded in the trailer, bleating out in a call of hello.

I headed towards the cattle shed, feeling Peter's gaze on me. Inside, Mum and Bobby were sitting down on an old bench, talking quietly about something. A cow turned to look at me before deciding I was no threat and carried on licking her newborn calf.

When Mum and Bobby saw me, they stopped their conversation. Here she is, Bobby said, trying to inject humour into his voice.

How are you feeling? I said, inspecting Bobby's face, noticing the gauntness in his cheeks.

I'm fine.

You don't look fine.

Have you always been this rude? he said.

What were you talking about when I came in?

Oh, nothing, lass. Business . . .

Are you going to the abattoir? I said.

Bobby nodded. That's the plan.

Bit early for them, is it not?

Bobby and Mum looked at each other. Well . . . Bobby said. We just thought that it was a good time. We'll be getting a decent price for—

So, you're not going to mention the livestock quotas being imposed? I said.

Where did you hear that? Mum asked.

Does it matter?

Bobby closed his eyes for a moment before opening them. I'm sorry, Aida. We should have told you. You know what the government's like for wanting to leave its mark. It's no great surprise, I suppose.

So, is this the plan: termination? I asked.

That's what we're trying to figure out, Mum said, if you have any suggestions.

Bobby exhaled. I mean, with the cows, there's no way of getting around their passports . . . But I do think we could get away with some of the sheep. Do some de-chipping and send them up and over the hills. No inspector's going to roam the land looking for them, are they?

The sheep would turn feral, Mum said, matter of fact. So, what's the point?

Bobby sighed. Well, what am I to do, Miriam? Tell me, please.

Mum bit her bottom lip. Maybe a reduction in numbers isn't the worst idea in the world. I mean, we are running low on silage and hay, and I heard some of the containers of feed can't even get docked in at the harbours now.

Bobby tried to stand then, weakness flooding through him; he had to grip Mum's shoulder to steady himself. I best not keep that boy waiting too long, sitting in the motor with the heat bearing down on him.

I'll go to the abattoir, I said. You should stay here.

Bobby shook his head. No, lass, it's okay.

Let other people do things, Bobby, I said. I don't mind it. Anyway, maybe you should be spending some time with Sam . . .

Bobby smiled. You mean, coax him out of his mood so we can all eat tonight.

Some people might say he's suffering from heartache, I said.

He coughed in irritation. I'm still here, aren't I?

Maybe you need to take a different tack with this, Bobby, Mum said. I'm not sure tough love is the best response here.

There was silence for a moment.

Evelyn is still looking to make herself useful, I said. Why don't one of you ask her to make dinner tonight?

No, Mum said.

Well, are you going to cook, then? I asked.

She went to speak but stopped again, perhaps weighing up her options.

Maybe you could get her to check on the hens while I'm away, too, I said, already making my way out towards the yard.

I climbed into the Defender's passenger seat as if it was nothing, while Peter just stared at me. I'm coming instead of Bobby, I said. He needs to stay and sort something out.

I hear Sam isn't quite feeling himself, he said.

I nodded.

What's all that about, then? Is he sick?

Something like that, I said. He takes *turns*, but he comes out of them eventually.

Does something trigger it?

It's usually Bobby who triggers it.

Peter turned on the engine. Is it far? he asked as I clipped my seatbelt into place.

Maybe twenty minutes . . .

He nodded, manoeuvring us out of the yard and across the cattle grid without any difficulty. I tried not to look at the reservoir as we passed; a few men from the water works had been coming and going, much more occasionally, their hard hats and yellow hi-vis tabards visible from a distance, but I suspected that one day soon they would stop coming altogether.

Have you seen an animal be slaughtered before? I said.

I've killed pheasants and chickens. And I've done some shooting. But I've never been to an abattoir, if that's what you mean.

I leaned my head against my window. I wish we'd got the wind turbines, I said, practically a whisper. It feels like we're trapped in some sort of purgatory now. We'll never get out of this pit.

You don't like living on a farm? he asked.

I didn't answer.

We drove the rest of the journey to the abattoir in silence, the Defender swerving with the weight of the sheep in the trailer behind us. On our arrival, one of the men in white rubber boots waved Peter forward and he thrust the gearstick into reverse. It took him a few attempts to line the trailer up with the loading dock. The man waved him in one direction and then the other, a stain smeared down the side of his white coat, shouting something to us that we couldn't quite hear.

What are you saying? Peter said, rolling down his window. He was visibly flustered, an agitation in his body.

You've overshot it, the man replied. A little to the left before you turn hard on the reverse.

I'm doing that, Peter snapped.

Do you want me to have a shot? the man asked.

I'll manage, he said, pulling the Defender forward, it jolting in frustration. I'll take it again, he added, while the sheep began to bleat, taunting him from the trailer, and I turned the radio up to drown out their noise.

My phone vibrated with a couple of notifications and I took it out of my pocket. But it was nothing of interest, mostly Dad asking if I'd read one of the books he'd bought me – he never mentioned our guests despite Mum having told him. I tried to log into one of my socials then, but it buffered for so long that in the end there was no point. I was in a reasonably good mood, so why ruin it with sickening levels of anxiety?

The small abattoir was a windowless building filled with shadows – fluorescent bulbs encased in metal shades, fans turning in a breathless heat. I'd been taken to the abattoir for the first time at sixteen because nothing was meant to be off limits and there was no point shying away from the realities of life and death – I'd run into the office toilets and thrown myself down until my face was level with the pan, vomiting. I was used to it now but I still wondered if it was worth it for the men who worked here every day in their overalls and boots, something automatic in their movements, without pause or reflection. What was the long-term effect on a person who continuously slaughtered living things? When Dad had been on the farm it had always been his job to take the livestock to the abattoir, but this was one job that Mum had been unwilling to take on – so used to bringing life into the world, she didn't want to watch it ending. Bobby had always felt that it was our duty to witness the process – to see what happened to the animals we cared for. We had taken real pride in the way we reared our animals; it seemed only fair that one of us stay with them until the end. And, in the opposite way to Mum, I preferred the end-of-life care to the beginning, maybe something to do with it being less hands-on. It felt like a rite of passage, something to be endured and considered. I wanted Peter to see it too, experience the full process, just as I had at sixteen.

When the sheep were unloaded, they sang to one another – a peaceful noise, friendly, as though there was no threat. Premature in their delivery here, they'd no doubt be significantly under Bobby's target weight of forty-two kilograms, but oblivious to their bad luck in not getting to live a fuller life.

The men had known Bobby for years so took no issue with us wanting to stay. However, it took a while for us to get sanitised before we were allowed into the production line. Our suits were paper-thin, with a white zip going from crotch to neck. I scrubbed my hands with antiseptic gel until they were almost weeping, the plastic socks over the rubber boots causing me to slip a little, the elastic pinch of the hairnet irritating the skin underneath my hairline.

There's a queue, one of the workers said. I recognised him from the local pub. I thought his name was Greg, but I couldn't be sure. We're pretty busy at the moment, he added.

So, everyone's getting rid of some, are they? I said.

He smiled. At least it's still an accepted currency.

Do we just wait here? Peter asked.

The man shrugged. You can either hang back or walk through with them. Bobby normally walks through.

I'll walk through, I said, but you're welcome to stay here.

No, I'll come, Peter replied, with perhaps some defensiveness in his voice.

Fine, the worker said but, as he turned, he stopped mid-step and looked back at me. Did Bobby hear about Stuart?

Stuart . . .

Yeah, Ian's son . . . Worked here since he was a boy.

I shrugged. I don't think so . . .

Let Bobby know that he died, will you?

I'm sorry to hear that, I said. I'll be sure to pass that on.

He hanged himself.

My footing faltered, nearly stepping into Peter. Oh, I said, having no real idea of what to say, of what would be appropriate.

He always liked blethering to your uncle. So, I thought I should say.

The sheep were led into the lairage pen, and I found myself waving them off. Their heads turned for a moment, like a fleeting goodbye, and then they skittered on without any protest, followed by the man in overalls. I wondered what sheep said to one another – had there ever been a sheep to escape from an abattoir and spread word of what was happening in these enclosed spaces? The waiting animals couldn't see what was happening to the ones in front, held in blissful ignorance. But, as Bobby said, everything that lived had to die. And our livestock were lucky because their pain and suffering was so contained, so minimal. If only everyone could die in such a way.

*

I smiled at our sheep, who were huddled together in the high care area, and paced back across the concrete floor, my boots making an impressive echoing sound, until I could see other animals, like a conveyer belt hidden behind strips of plastic cold-store curtains. I was thinking – this living, breathing creature will not move shortly. Soon it will be gone.

It was time for our first lamb to meet its fate and the worker passed by clutching a prong device in his hands, swinging it casually like an umbrella or walking stick. He brought it up to the skull of the lamb's head and stunned the creature, watching while it fell to the ground, electric impulses spreading like a disease through its small brain. I wanted to know what it felt like to still be alive but feel nothing. The lamb twitched once, twice, then grew still. A different man from the one holding the prong shackled a chain to one of the lamb's hind legs and then the animal was being hoisted into the air, the clink of metal chains echoing through the building. The lamb was hanging at head height and then its throat was cut in one quick and seamless motion. The man who carried out the final execution had done it thousands of times before. He did it so skilfully that there was not a trace of blood on his hands. The blood was flooding out across the floor and a young lad – one who I hadn't seen before – was hosing the ground with a pressure washer, forcing blood and faeces into the drains, ready within seconds for the next animal to be brought down the line. Our lamb was already out of view, away for its skin and insides to be removed. And I estimated that within ten to fifteen minutes the animal would look only like a piece of meat – to be seen in the supermarket or butcher's window.

And then we'd return in five days to collect our share, already cut in a specific way to Sam's specifications – manageable chunks but ready for the skill of his own butchering hands, while the rest would be couriered away to the butchers we had contracts with, assuming they still wanted the meat.

When we left, the trailer rattled empty behind us, a continual reminder as to what had just taken place. I felt this sudden sense of relief; an acceptance of sorts after enduring an ordeal and for it to finally be over.

What did you think? I asked.

It was . . . straightforward.

Has it put you off meat yet?

He turned to look at me then, held my gaze. Is that why you stopped?

I shrugged.

No, he replied, turning his attention back to the road. It hasn't put me off. What's the point in holding on to any emotional attachment?

His eyes lingered over me, an unfamiliar expression surfacing.

How old are you? I said.

Twenty-six. How old are you?

Twenty-one.

He nodded. Same age as Rebecca.

We were approaching the roundabout and I had no desire to return to the farm. His finger hovered over the indictor. He looked around, placing a hand on my knee. Where are we going now?

I pointed and he indicated, taking us back along the road towards the service station. The radio was on, the jingle of news, but I turned it down. When we arrived at the junction, I told him to take the second turn in and park behind the Premier Inn, the Defender and trailer hidden from obvious view, not that I expected anyone to be looking for us.

We got out in unison, saying nothing to each other.

The sun was beaming down and the few people we passed wore only short sleeves. In the reception Mia was behind the desk. She was on the telephone, and she held up her index finger without looking up at us. Peter rested his elbows on the counter. Paperwork covered the surfaces, and two fire extinguishers were clamped to the wall.

I'm sorry to hear that, she said down the phone. Unfortunately, there will still be a cancellation fee as it's less than seventy-two hours' notice. She glanced up and acknowledged me with a knowing smile. I appreciate that, she replied into the receiver. But we're all in the same boat. She brought the earpiece away from her, rolling her eyes. The line seemed to go dead, and she placed the receiver back down in its cradle.

Who's this? she said, looking at Peter.

Any chance you can give us a room for a few hours?

You know we don't rent rooms by the hour, she replied.

I glanced around. Look, the place is empty, I said. No one is coming. Don't be a dick.

We'd still have to clean the room, though, wouldn't we? She was eyeing Peter up, smirking. Where have you been anyway? Why are you not replying to my messages?

Sorry, I've been busy.

I can see that. Her eyes shifted to me. Look, she said, lowering her voice, a guy checked out earlier and his room hasn't been cleaned yet. He was only here one night. If it doesn't bother you, you can *sleep* in his bed for a while.

Really? I said.

I can give you spare towels.

Is the water still running? Peter asked.

She shrugged. They haven't cut us off yet.

He stood there for a moment, an awkwardness in the air.

Can you give me a minute? I said to him. Meet you by the lift?

He hesitated. Sure . . .

I waited for him to leave before turning my attention back to Mia.

Where did you find him? she said.

Do you have a condom?

Are you serious?

Please.

She rolled her eyes, before opening one of the drawers under the reception desk. Here, she said, handing me two in their little foil wrappers.

A bit ambitious, I said.

Just don't damage anything.

See you soon, I replied, already walking away.

Answer your phone next time, she shouted behind me.

The previous occupant had left the room in good order. The bed was half-made, covering the mattress, a few pillows resting on top, but a purple bed-runner lay crumpled on the floor. Sunlight shone into the room, making it warm and bright, but I closed the blackout curtains, plunging the space into darkness. There was the red glow of the standby light on the television. Peter turned on one of the bedside lamps, the small one for reading, and slowly began to strip off his clothes, leaving them on the floor. He walked towards the bathroom without saying anything and turned on the shower. I stripped out of my clothes too and followed him. He was staring at himself in the mirror. There were bruises on his body. I touched his stomach, brought my hand up to his ribcage, tried to feel his bones.

I put my hand under the water, but it was scalding. Turning the temperature down, I unrolled a plastic bathmat, settling it on the base of the bath, the suckers engaging with the surface below. Peter clutched the handle screwed to the tiles and eased himself over the edge of the bath, while I shuffled in behind him. We stayed under the showerhead until our skin began to prune, the whole time never touching each other. The water that washed away down the sinkhole was dirty and yellowish and I wondered how long it had been since he'd been able to properly clean himself. He closed his eyes and gulped on the water, almost choking.

The towels were white and soft cotton. He wrapped one around himself, tucking it in at his waist. He held my hand as I stepped out over the bath, before handing me a towel. As I wrapped my damp hair up in another one, I watched him work a complimentary plastic comb through his hair. The tap in the sink ran with bubbled water, wrongly textured but clean, and he brought his mouth to it, once again gulping. He walked back into the bedroom and lay down on the half-made bed in his towel. Despite the warmth of the room, I noticed his skin goose-bumping. There was the faint smell of staleness in the air, mixed in with something sweet like dying flowers.

I sat on the edge of the bed, staring out at the stream of light coming from the open bathroom door, dust particles floating in the air. I lay down beside him and he was so still that part of me wondered if he'd already fallen asleep. He moved closer and rested his head in the crook of my neck, before turning and pressing his lips against my skin. I took his hand and guided it downwards, pulling my towel open. His hands were cold and unfamiliar, his body turning and contorting to get on top of me. His breathing grew rapid, his fingers now circling my nipples. He was forcing his tongue into my mouth, eyes closed, and I watched on in the dimness as if I were a separate entity, simply observing, amazed somehow that what I'd longed for was now happening.

A condom, I said, fumbling for one of them in the darkness.

Do I have to?

I can't get pregnant again, I said. I've already had one abortion and I'd like to avoid another one.

He sat up, ripping the packet open.

And then he was on top of me, inside me, and it was all so instinctive. And I could have cried from the relief of how good it felt. There was nothing like it; all else could be forgotten, briefly.

My gaze shifted momentarily to over his shoulder, to the little red glow coming from the television. And I think I thought that if I could keep staring at that little light then it wouldn't have to end.

It was over within minutes, and he rolled away, shoving his face into the pillow beside me. I lay there, feeling suddenly cold, bereft at its end, but unable to move or pull the tucked-in duvet out from my side of the bed.

He sat up again, removing the condom, tying it in a knot before lying back down and focusing on the ceiling, one arm tucked behind his head. Was that okay? he said.

I nodded, focusing on the ceiling too. Yes.

He started pulling the duvet out from his side and curled himself into it. He closed his eyes and almost immediately I could tell he'd fallen asleep. And as I checked my blood sugars, I watched him, and accidentally dropped my used test strip on to the duvet, leaving a trace of blood.

When we got back there was a grubby white gazebo erected in the yard, practically linking Bobby and Sam's cottage to ours, and an old outdoor table positioned in the middle with garden chairs scattered around. Peter brought the Defender to a stop and climbed out. We had barely exchanged a word since he woke in the Premier Inn. I could see Evelyn in our kitchen window, her back to us, peering into our fridge, perhaps taking stock of its contents: out-of-date jars, my insulin, Mum's haemorrhoid cream. She looked peaceful, her movements effortless and light, as if she were in her own home. As I made my way towards the door, she came out, balancing dishes in her hand. Well, hello, she said. Don't worry, I've *permission* to be here.

I held my hands up in a gesture of peace. What's happening outside? I asked, nodding to the gazebo.

Well, no one says we can't all share a meal together outside, she said. And I found that old thing begging to be brought back to life. She paused. It's nice, don't you think?

I nodded.

Despite all the cooking, the kitchen appeared to be in a reasonable order. Occasionally, maybe once a year, Mum would take a notion and spend hours preparing koftas in her spicy Egyptian tomato sauce, but every pan, bowl and plate would be used in its making, and by the end it was never that mindblowing, even to her, and we were left with the debris, amassing to too great a chore. In contrast, Evelyn's cooking seemed so contained, so controlled.

In my bedroom I stared at myself in the mirror – the sun had darkened my complexion further, perhaps to what I would have looked like if I hadn't spent my entire life living in Scotland. I turned then, running my hands along my face and neck. Maybe I was looking for Peter's mark, but there wasn't one. I brought my T-shirt up to my nose and inhaled, but it smelled only of me. I injected myself in a new site, squirted a little insulin across my bedroom floor by accident.

Evelyn called us outside, asking us to take our seats, and sure enough it was bang on five-thirty, exactly when Bobby liked to eat.

I passed Evelyn again in the kitchen as I made to leave. She was wearing our worn oven gloves and removing what looked like lasagne from the oven. She turned to acknowledge me. I've made a small vegetarian one too, she said. I hope you don't mind, but I had to take a few things from your vegetable plot.

I shook my head, feeling as if I was in her way and not in my own kitchen. No, it's okay, I replied, a little on the back foot. Did you manage to check on the hens?

She nodded. Four eggs, in the door of your fridge now.

Outside, I took a seat at the empty table, the warmth of the day sweating on my skin. I was giddy with the feeling of having something forbidden to hide.

Mum arrived, still in overalls, her hands looking filthy, despite dripping with water. Behind me, she stopped, as if she could sense my indiscretions, and pulled my top down at the back where some of my skin was exposed. There was something about my skin being on display that always unsettled her, particularly my lower back. She'd whacked me on the back once as a child when I'd worn a top that exposed too much, and had been horrified, when I came back from Edinburgh, at some of the outfits she'd found in my wardrobe.

How did you get on at the abattoir? she asked.

Fine.

It took a long time . . .

As you can imagine, Miriam, they're pretty busy.

She narrowed her eyes. When did they say we could go back and pick up the meat?

Just whenever we usually do.

Evelyn brought the large Perspex dish of lasagne out and placed it down on the table. It was scorching, the contents bubbling away. As she went back into the kitchen Mum lowered her voice and said, She is too comfortable here.

Some would say she's being a great help, I replied.

A jug and some glass tumblers were already sitting on the table, and I reached up and out of my seat, the skin on my back once again exposed as I poured myself a glass of water.

Mum finally took her seat.

Evelyn returned with my vegetable lasagne, positioning it in front of me before sitting down too. Is no one coming? she called out, her voice travelling through the yard, attempting to rally the troops.

Peter emerged from their campervan with Rebecca in tow. He sat down opposite me, the furthest away he could possibly be, but Rebecca seemed to make an active decision to sit next to me, the bulge of her baby pressing up against the table. Bobby arrived shortly after and settled into another seat, exchanging pleasantries, before Evelyn placed a steaming hot portion of lasagne down in front of him.

Why are we eating outside? Bobby said, in a neutral, inquisitive tone.

I'm sorry, do you not like it? Evelyn said. I just thought it would be nice.

Oh, it's fine, Evelyn. It's just different, but not a bad different.

Still no Sam? Evelyn said, glancing around the yard as if she expected him to appear at any moment.

Bobby rubbed his hands together. He'll be fine, he said, his words flippant in response.

That's a shame, Evelyn said. But there's plenty left, so we can take some over to him after . . .

Maybe, lass, thank you.

I watched Peter gulp his glass of water before refilling it, forcing a forkful of food into his mouth as if he was ravenous, as if he hadn't eaten in days. Everyone seemed to agree that the food was good, judging by the speed it reached people's lips. I took a sip of water, swirling it round in my mouth. The sheepdogs padded about, hoping for scraps.

How'd you find the abattoir, Peter? Bobby asked.

Peter forced a forkful of lasagne into his mouth. He nodded.

It takes a bit of getting used to, Bobby said.

I cleared my throat. Is there coriander in this? I said, addressing Evelyn.

Yes, do you not like coriander?

No, it's delicious, I said.

Evelyn was back up on her feet, offering seconds, and Bobby raised his hand like a schoolboy. She reloaded his plate, then suddenly came to Rebecca's side and wrapped her arms around her shoulders, tenderly kissing the top of her head. Would you like more? she whispered, but Rebecca didn't respond, only stared down at her half-full plate.

When we could eat no more, Evelyn once again got to her feet. She began gathering our dirty plates, stacking them, looking around as if to ensure all our needs were being met. There was a stray fork in the middle of the table and, as she reached across for it, she brushed up against me. A necklace fell from her jumper. It was a gold pendent with a turquoise stone, like a perfectly round ball. It looked so prominent and familiar. Had this necklace been Mum's? There were a few pieces in her jewellery box, never worn. I used to look at them sometimes as a kid when she was out on the land, when I knew I wouldn't be disturbed. Now I couldn't decide if I was looking at something that belonged to Mum or not. Was I being completely irrational? It wouldn't have been the first time I'd wrongly accused someone of taking something.

That's a beautiful necklace, was all I managed.

Evelyn glanced down at the pendant, cupping it in her palm, before tucking it back into her top. Do you like it? she said. I've had it for years. I'm not sure it suits me, being gold. Would go with your complexion better, no doubt.

Afterwards, I took a plate of cold lasagne through to Sam. Inside, their place was quiet, no lights on, the curtains drawn. I walked towards the kitchen counter and heard Sam clearing his voice from somewhere within the darkness. I turned then, trying to make him out. Rusty found me and licked my fingers.

Why are you sitting here in the dark? I said, making out Sam's silhouette. He didn't reply. I turned on a lamp and he flinched, as though the sudden change caused him pain.

I was sitting here, listening to all the chatter, he said. It sounded lovely.

You could have been part of it.

He shook his head.

I brought you some lasagne.

How does it fare? he asked.

I hate to tell you this, but I hear it's good.

He smirked. They're certainly making an impression.

Will I heat it up for you? I asked, already opening the microwave.

I'll eat it the way it is.

Are you sure?

He nodded.

I pulled open a drawer and removed a fork, stabbing it upright into his food. Are you going to be okay, Sam?

He attempted to smile, taking the plate from me, but there was only sadness in his eyes.

Did you always know you wanted to be with Bobby? I asked.

He stared at me, the plate resting on his knee. Why are you asking?

I don't know . . . You never talk about each other.

He chewed on a mouthful, nodding slowly.

What's it like to be in love? I asked.

Painful, my darling.

So, it's not something worth pursuing, then?

He loaded his fork up again. That's not what I said. He lifted his fork to his nose. There's something in this I wouldn't have thought to add . . . He sniffed it again.

You could ask Evelyn, I said.

He laughed. You know I'm not going to do that.

9

In the calving shed Bobby was hunkered down, tending to a newly born calf, its mother taking little to no interest in him, while I peered down, my weight resting against the metal railing of the pen. Bobby was rubbing mucus across the calf's little body, trying to get the cow to take an interest, but it was as though she'd already made up her mind about having a baby. Bobby stopped rubbing the calf's stomach, his hands resting still by his sides, defeated-looking.

Why doesn't she want it? I said.

He just stared at the calf. I'll have to get some colostrum out of the fridge . . . he replied.

Out in the yard, Rebecca was sitting on the bench outside Bobby and Sam's cottage, and I took the seat next to her. She shifted silently, looking uncomfortable and sore. She'd ballooned recently, not so much in the belly but more in her ankles, her face. Perhaps it was the heat; it was almost unbearable. I reached for her hand, and she let me take it, but when I squeezed it there was no reciprocation.

In front of us, Peter worked away on the Corsa – he'd become quite consumed by it since we'd returned from the Premier Inn. He'd also barely spoken to me; perhaps that was why I'd shifted my attention further to Rebecca, needing to feel like I was close to at least one of them. He appeared from under the bonnet and straightened. He made his way into the driver's seat and my thoughts shifted randomly, completely untethered, wondering why it didn't hurt when you cut your hair or fingernails – to think that there was something growing on your body that wasn't really living gave me the creeps.

And suddenly I was aware of the noise of the engine revving, dominating everything. I'd been so sure that he'd never get the thing going. Sam was already hobbling out of the door to stare, and Bobby too emerged then from the calving shed, while Mum was a bit more hesitant in her approach.

Peter turned the engine off and climbed out of the driver's door with something that resembled a smile.

Sam started clapping his hands. I swear to God, he said, I thought that car was sitting in its grave.

I went to where Peter was standing. It was as if he was waiting for me to say something profound, and of course I was grateful, but the moment seemed to fall flat.

Does it drive? I asked.

You can try it?

I climbed into the driver's seat, it warm from his body, and clipped my seatbelt on.

Peter stared out across the yard, no Evelyn in sight. Do you want to go? he asked, turning to address Mum.

Mum shook her head. This is your achievement, she said. You go with her.

I waited, my hands gripping the steering wheel, staring out as he hesitated, appearing reluctant, before climbing into the passenger seat beside me.

They were all watching, and I held my breath, feeling for this elusive *bite* everyone talked about. We began to move, and to my surprise it was incredibly easy, no juddering underfoot, no force required to change gears. We were so low to the ground compared to the Defender but in a good way, as if by being closer to the ground I had more control over what happened. I shifted gear and we carried on. It felt as though we could have gone anywhere, Mum's figure getting smaller by the second. And I carried on until I'd reached the entrance to the water works, their gates closed, no life in the place. Our wheelie bins were positioned in a row to the left, overflowing and abandoned. I kicked the gearstick into reverse, having sat in the broken car so many times, and expertly managed a three-point turn before making my way back towards the yard.

I brought the car to a stop, peering out of my window at everyone still standing there.

What now? I said, a smile beaming across my face.

You were a natural, lass, Bobby said. A real natural.

Mum nodded slowly in silence, her body tense. It's a good start, she said.

Is that all I'm getting?

There's calving to be done, she said. That's where everyone's attention should be. She walked back into the cattle shed, and out of view.

Bobby crouched by my open window. Don't take any notice of her, he said. She's proud of you. And she's grateful to you too, Peter, for making this happen.

You'd think she could be a little more excited, I said.

Bobby glanced back at Sam, before returning his attention to me. Why don't you take a wee trip to the pharmacy for me, he said. There are some pills I need picking up and I don't want to burden your poor mother with it right now.

Is it okay for me to go? I said.

You're up to it, he replied. I know you are. He gripped the frame of the window, more to balance himself than anything else. And you'll look after her, Peter, won't you? Keep her safe on the roads.

Peter nodded, but I sensed his reluctance.

Rebecca was standing now, pained, looking as if she desperately wanted to say something.

Do you want to come? I said.

No, Peter said. Evelyn won't have it.

Okay . . .

Sam retreated inside and returned moments later, hobbling over to place an L-plate sticker on the back of the car, before coming to the front and sticking one down on the bonnet.

Where'd you get those? I asked.

Sam winked. Never you mind.

And then we were off again, repeating our drive down the reservoir road and past the water works, eventually turning on to the main road.

Am I doing okay? I asked, glancing at Peter.

Eyes on the road.

Have I done something to annoy you?

No.

It's just you've barely said a word to me since we . . .

What is there to say?

I hesitated. Did you not like it?

Don't get attached, he said.

I looked at him again. I'm not attached. It was just sex.

I took a corner in too high a gear, everything feeling like it was out of control. He gasped but I corrected myself. Sorry, I said.

What does your uncle need from the pharmacy? he asked.

I don't know.

He straightened in his seat, hands planted on his knees.

If I do well with my driving, do I get a reward?

What type of reward?

I glanced at him again. We could go back to the Premier Inn . . .
Eyes. On. The. Road.

In the pharmacy Shirley was once again behind the counter,
fighting with a till roll that refused to click into place. I'll just be
with you in a moment, she said, appearing flustered.

No rush, I replied, looking out of the window to where Peter
sat in the Corsa.

Eventually, Shirley gave up with the till roll, placing it on the
counter. Jackie, she said, shouting behind her. If anyone comes in
needing a receipt, we'll just need to hand-write it until I get this
thing working again.

There was no reply from anyone in the back and she looked
up at me, attempting to smile, a strand of her fringe momentarily lifting from her forehead as she exhaled. How can I help,
dear?

I'm wondering if I can collect a prescription for Bobby
Sinclair? And there might be a repeat prescription for me too.
Aida Sinclair. Mine will be in the fridge.

Okay, she said. I'll check for you.

When I looked out of the window again, the Corsa was
gone from view and a sudden panic rose inside me. What if
Peter had decided to go? Maybe this had been his intention
the whole time. I came up close to the window, peering out,
my hands pressing into the glass. I caught a glimpse of the car
then, parked further down the street. Weirdly, I think a part of
me was disappointed.

Just take a seat, Shirley called out from the back. We're looking
for them.

Behind me the waiting chairs sat empty, but I didn't bother
sitting. I could hear words being exchanged in the back where
they kept all the medicine. Well, a different woman's voice said,

I'm sorry, Mr Davidson but the supplies are out of stock with that medication and the manufacturers can't give us a date for it coming back in. There was a pause. We check every day, she said, her tone curt. Well, you're welcome to come and collect your prescriptions and take them to another pharmacy if you want to try elsewhere.

Moments later a young woman in a smart dress approached me. Hi, she said, already appearing flustered, holding two separate pharmacy bags. So, for Robert Sinclair, can you confirm the address?

I nodded, doing so.

And do you have ID?

ID? No . . . why?

She paused. We have to ask with controlled drugs.

I'm sorry, I didn't bring any . . . But we live together. The insulin prescription is mine. It's the same address.

The pharmacist hesitated.

He's not well, I said.

I see that. She turned Bobby's prescription over in her hand. Okay, sign here and here, she said, pointing. And as I did so I was suddenly very conscious of how quiet the place was, eerily so. Shirley was back behind her counter, fighting again with the till roll, and on the shelves that surrounded her there were gaps where medication and health products should have been.

The pharmacist then handed me my bag of insulin. A ticket of sorts was stapled to the outside. I stared at it, and it was as if she was reading my mind. We don't have everything for your prescriptions, she said. It's a balance ticket.

Okay . . .

We have *some* of everything but not enough to complete the prescription. We only have one box out of three for your bolus Fiasp, and only two boxes of the basal Tresiba . . .

When do I get the rest?

She paused. We don't know . . . We're trying to order them every day.

Should I try another pharmacy? I asked.

She came closer, lowering her voice. You can try, but you'll not get them anywhere. I've already phoned around.

So, what happens if it doesn't come back? Do I have to go back on to Novorapid? Because actually that would be bit of a pain; taking it twenty minutes before you're meant to eat is not exactly ideal—

We're running out of everything, she said firmly. She looked behind her as if she needed to make sure no one was listening. Look, if anything comes in, you'll be the first to know, okay . . . ? But her words landed slowly, their meaning confusing. Suddenly I was trying to tally up in my head the doses of what I had left. How many boxes were still in the fridge at home? I felt so naïve then, just standing there, that I hadn't ever considered this as a realistic possibility. Why not? There was a comfort in knowing that everyone was affected by the water shortages, a collective suffering of sorts, but no one aside from my loved ones would give a shit if I couldn't get hold of my insulin. It was a burden others didn't have to carry.

Try not to worry, the pharmacist said, placing everything in a carrier bag for me. We'll work something out.

Okay . . . I said. What about my uncle's tablets, then? Will he run out too?

She paused. I doubt he'll need any more than what's been prescribed.

Oh, right, I see . . .

I got back into the Corsa, my mind in overdrive, Peter still sitting in the driver's seat.

Did you get what Bobby needed?

I nodded, trying to remain calm. I didn't know what was worse – the pharmacist essentially giving Bobby an expiry date, or implying that, if they couldn't get any more insulin for me, then essentially I would be going too. Rationally I knew that our fridge was relatively well stocked, that I was holding a bag of insulin in my hand. Nothing was immediate. But still, it wasn't exactly a good sign.

Peter indicated out. Were you serious about going to the hotel? he said.

I shook my head, kept my focus straight ahead.

That's what I thought, he said.

I turned to stare at him. Why did you fix this car?

Maybe I wanted to run away, he said, but from his expression I couldn't tell if he was joking or not. Wasn't really sure he was capable of making a joke.

On our return, there was a silence to the yard that hadn't really existed since our guests had taken up residence. Bobby and Sam were sitting out on the bench, clearly waiting for us, a tension hanging in the air.

Where is everyone? I said, handing Bobby his medicine.

Bobby and Sam looked at each other. We don't want either of you to worry or be alarmed because Miriam is on top of the situation, but Rebecca isn't well . . .

What? Peter said. Is she having the baby?

Something to do with her blood pressure, Sam said. She was sick too. Not long after you left.

Where are they? I said.

In yours, Bobby replied.

Should I go and see if they need anything? I asked.

Maybe, lass . . .

I left my bag of insulin on the bench beside them. Can you put my stuff in your fridge? I said, and they nodded in unison, Peter staying with them as I ran inside.

In our living room, Rebecca was once again lying out flat on the sofa while Mum and Evelyn peered over her.

What's wrong? I said.

I'm worried it's pre-eclampsia, Mum said. But I've no means of being able to check for protein in her urine.

So what do we do? I said.

I want Rebecca to go to the hospital . . . Mum replied.

No, Evelyn said. That isn't an option. No doctors. That was the one stipulation we made. You're a midwife: just tell us what we need to do.

Mum looked at her, stunned. We'll drive you, if it's fuel you're worried about . . . We'll go now, in the Defender.

No doctors, Evelyn said.

But, Evelyn . . . Mum pleaded.

Just tell me what we can do to lower her blood pressure, Evelyn replied.

I've already given her aspirin, but . . .

But *what?* Evelyn shouted.

I'm not sure that will be enough at this late stage in her pregnancy. Aspirin would have perhaps made a difference if there had been obvious symptoms earlier on. Really what I suspect she needs is labetalol, Mum said. But if you're not willing to go to a hospital or see a doctor I don't know how you get your hands on some. You need a prescription for it.

And without it? Evelyn said.

Rebecca retched then, turning on to her side and vomiting a little pool of sick on to the carpet, like something a dog would deposit and then eat again.

Mum crouched down on to the floor and placed a tea towel over it. What is it you want me to say? she snapped. That she'll be okay? That it'll all go away? I don't know that.

Worst-case scenario? Evelyn said. What are we talking?

Mum was quiet for a moment. For Rebecca . . . worst case would be the development of fits or a stoke, although that would be rare. It's the baby that's perhaps at most risk. Poor blood supply from the placenta causes reduced growth. The baby won't be getting the nutrients it needs to thrive.

Evelyn was quiet for a moment. I'll take her to the city, she finally said. Tomorrow, if she's no better. Okay? If that's what is needed, I will take her, on *my* terms.

Mum nodded. Yes, okay.

She's my daughter. I decide what's best for her. You don't get to decide everything for us.

Fine, Mum said. Okay, tomorrow.

Mum and I sat alone in the kitchen. I couldn't remember the last time it had been just us; it felt as if we were always surrounded by others now. Mum's elbow rested against the table while she rubbed at her scalp, asking me to make her a cup of tea.

Would you like it black with honey?

She nodded. I wish they'd never come, she said. I wish we'd never let them stay.

I made her tea, placing the cup down in front of her. Are you okay? I said.

It's too much to take on, Mum said. They're fleeing from abuse. And it's more that we can deal with at the moment.

How do you know that?

Do you think I've never seen signs of abuse before? Do you think I've never had to ask a vulnerable young mother if she's experienced domestic abuse in her home? Evelyn as good as said it to me – they have run from an abusive husband and father.

Is that why Rebecca . . . ? Her pregnancy . . .

I don't know. But I assume.

There was a dribble of honey on the side of her cup, and she licked it away.

I sat down beside her. Did you like being a midwife? I asked.

She stared at me. Why do you ask that?

I shrugged. It was something you did for so long . . . I don't know. I never thought about what you did as a job until . . . until I fell pregnant, I guess. You never really talked about it.

She tried to laugh. It's not so different from caring for live-stock. Maybe except that in midwifery there's the expectation that the children you bring into the world will live long and healthy lives.

But you've obviously seen some pretty horrendous stuff . . .

She exhaled as if I irritated her. I really don't know why you're asking this . . . She stared at me again, hesitating. It's easier with livestock to accept that sometimes things don't work out, that it wasn't meant to be. But with babies, with these little people, there was always the fear – mothers unexpectedly haemorrhaging, an infant starved of oxygen, the placenta failing and the baby inside no longer thriving. You could take all the precautions, have all the experience in the world, but tragedy still happens – still finds a way to exist. It was exhausting, devastating. And that's just the babies. Then I'd come home and have to pretend none of it had happened. Just compartmentalise everything and do the school run.

I'm sorry, I said. I don't know why I never asked you before.

She waved my words away. There was joy too, she said, but I think the sadness was what wore me down. The memories of trying to dress a premature stillborn in a babygro and cardigan, barely the size of my hand, skin so thin and transparent that you could see the veins. The couple who had spent ten years attempt-ing IVF to finally conceive their miracle baby, only to discover there was no heartbeat a week before the due date. That new parents could be joyous in one room, while there were howls of grief in another. Asking a mother to deliver her baby, her partner telling her *you can do it* with desperation in his voice, awaiting the child that would never breathe. All the lockets of hair, and clay handprints. All that misery and sadness before a life had even begun.

I paused. What if Rebecca's baby doesn't survive? What if it's already too late?

Don't say that, she said. We never talk like that about an unborn baby.

Saying something doesn't mean it will come true, I said.

Still, she said. Just don't.

How much longer do you think until the baby is due?

Difficult to tell. Maybe a few more weeks. She took a sip of her tea.

So, we just try to keep her and the baby safe for a few more weeks, I said, matter-of-fact. That seems do-able.

Mum cleared her throat. A few more weeks and then they'll be gone.

I pulled at a ragged nail, and it came away too close to the skin. Have you heard about the medicine shortages?

Don't talk like those people who read conspiracy theories on Facebook. The world is still turning. The hospitals in the cities are still operating.

There *are* drug shortages, I said. The pharmacist told me today when I picked up my insulin.

Mum went to take another sip of tea but stopped. What did she say?

That I wasn't to worry . . .

Mum rubbed her forehead, closing her eyes for a moment. That's all we need, she finally said.

10

I rattled my knuckles on the surface of our kitchen table, a nervous habit I'd struggled to quit. In contrast Evelyn's hands lay flat, so calm and assured in her approach. Evelyn couldn't drive and it was decided without my knowledge that I would go with her and Rebecca to the hospital in Glasgow. There was too much needing done for anyone of particular use to leave. Bobby and Peter were assigned to calving while Mum was tasked with organising the logistics of getting a dozen sheep up and over the hills, hidden from view, anticipating further quotas being imposed. There were already rumours of the butchers defaulting on their contracts, not wanting all the meat previously agreed, demand falling with the increased prices of everything.

The driving practice was intended to do me some good.

You'll be great, Evelyn said. You're already so confident in the Corsa.

Do you think so? I said, bringing a spoonful of porridge to my mouth.

She placed her hand over mine. She had these beautiful long fingers, and I couldn't take my eyes off them. The porridge was hot, burning the roof of my mouth, but I was too embarrassed to spit it out. Okay . . . I said.

She smiled, dipping her pinkie finger into my bowl and scooping up some porridge for herself. It's a day away, Aida. It might even be fun . . .

I've never driven in the city before, I said. What if something happens? What if the car breaks down?

You don't trust Peter's skills?

I shook my head. Of course I do.

I reversed the Corsa, so its nose was facing out. Evelyn guided Rebecca into the back, before clicking the passenger seat into place and sitting down. Mum stood by the driver's door, staring at me, the window having been rolled fully down.

You've enough fuel?

Bobby found half a tank of petrol, I said. Is that enough?

She peered in at the dashboard as though she needed to see it for herself. She opened her purse. I have twenty pounds left. I spoke to your father, and he says there's still fuel in the petrol stations. Cheaper too than what they've been trying to charge around here.

They've just closed the petrol pumps at the service station, I said, because the last tanker never turned up. I think it's only one diesel pump working now.

Well, a half tank should be enough. But fill up anyway, if you can, otherwise this thing becomes useless. And I don't want you chancing it back on fumes.

Okay, noted.

And you have some water? she said. I don't trust the city water. It tastes wrong.

I nodded.

Your insulin?

Of course. You're talking as though I've never been to Glasgow before . . .

She nodded. I know. It's just different now, okay?

I know.

And if you can, if you have time, try and see your dad. She paused, peering in at Rebecca, before focusing on Evelyn. And remember it's labetalol 200mg, okay? I think that's what the doctors will want to give her. But you can check. And you know the hospital we talked about? You know where to go?

Evelyn nodded. We've got it.

If you need anything, I've brought the phone into the kitchen and have left the back door open so one of us should hear if you call. She paused. And your phone is charged?

I nodded again.

And you'll be okay driving?

I'll have to be.

She looked at me, a pained expression on her face.

Evelyn leaned past me to face Mum. Try not to worry, Miriam. I'll look after them both. All will be well.

Bobby came to say bye too. Drive safe and we'll see you tonight, he said.

They waved us off and then the three of us were cruising down the reservoir road, not a cloud in the sky. The roads towards the city were even quieter than before, and I found myself relaxing, resting my left hand on my thigh. Evelyn touched me gently on the arm, asking me to keep both hands on the wheel. Otherwise, she behaved as though she was in safe hands, as if there was absolutely nothing to worry about.

She shifted her knees, pointing them towards me. Are you going to give her a name? she asked.

Sorry?

The car . . .

Do people do that?

Yes, I think so.

I thought about it for a moment before saying, Karen?

Karen?

I shrugged. She just feels like a Karen.

Evelyn laughed. Well, it's your car.

She put the radio on, but the signal kept cutting out, leaving us with only static. There was a CD player, but we didn't have any CDs.

How's your singing? she asked, smirking.

Terrible, I replied.

She reached over and stroked my arm quite tenderly. Thank you for coming with us, she said.

I shrugged. It's fine.

She held a map in her hands, and I wasn't sure if it belonged to her or if Bobby had lent it to her.

I've got Google maps on my phone, if that's easier, I said.

No, it's okay. I prefer to do things the old-fashioned way.

I glanced in my rear-view mirror; Rebecca's attention was fixed on her window.

Can I ask you something? Evelyn said, her eyes upon me.

Sure.

Have you always been a vegetarian?

I smiled. I stopped eating meat about a year ago because I'd read some article about how a vegetarian diet had the potential to control your diabetes better, and I had thought why not? I paused. I'm not sure it made any difference, but the idea of eating meat now . . . it just doesn't appeal.

And it doesn't upset your family?

Bobby doesn't give me any grief, but it irks Mum. I know that. Just wait until I decide to go vegan.

And fish? she said. No fish?

Occasionally, I said. If I have to.

She laughed then. A vegetarian on a livestock farm, though . . . You must admit that's funny.

I laughed too. Yeah, I suppose it is. Clearing my throat, I said, What about you? You've always eaten meat?

I'll eat whatever I can put in front of my children, she said.

I nodded, my cheeks flushing with the embarrassment of my privilege.

And your diabetes . . . she said, turning to look at me. You've lived with it your whole life?

Since I was five.

And it's in the family?

I shrugged. I don't know. No one else in the family has it. Not that I know of.

But you keep well?

I laughed again. I mean, I could probably be better, I said. I'm more reactive to my blood sugars than proactive.

Do you see it as a burden, to have to think about it all the time?

I turned to look at her. It's second nature now. I don't really know or remember any other way.

How often do you have to check your blood sugar?

It varies . . . A lot sometimes.

Your poor fingers, she said, brushing her own fingers over my left hand. Are they all good for getting blood from?

Everyone probably has a favourite finger. For me, it's this one, I said, tapping the middle finger of my left hand off the steering wheel. Even if my hands are freezing cold, it always delivers.

When I glanced back into the rear-view mirror, Rebecca's eyes were closed, her head lolling slightly to the side, asleep.

How is Rebecca feeling about becoming a mother? I asked.

Evelyn tried to smile, but it was pained. As you perhaps already suspect, the baby . . . it isn't something Rebecca asked for or planned for.

I understand, I said. I'm sorry.

Evelyn shifted, looking straight out of the window. So much is out of our control, isn't it?

Everything is, I said.

Are you and your mother close?

I paused; didn't know how to describe our relationship. We're quite different, I said. But then also we share same of our worst traits. We're both stubborn, particularly with each other. I paused. What about you and Rebecca? Are you guys close?

I would like to think so, she said. But she's angry at the world and I suppose, by extension, at me too. She exhaled. Girls are harder than boys. That's all the wisdom I have when it comes to children.

As we approached the city, Evelyn reached forward in her seat to get a better view, her breath fogging up the windscreen. She directed me at a junction, telling me to turn right, barely consulting the map open across her knees.

I don't think that's the way to the hospital? I said.

We're not going to the hospital.

What?

There are people I know who can help me acquire the medicine we need without us having to visit a hospital . . .

But doesn't she need to see a doctor?

What do you think will happen if we go and see a doctor? Evelyn said. They won't let us leave. They'll keep us there and then we have nothing.

But . . .

This way is better, she said. You just need to trust me on this. Now, go left here before you miss the turn, or we'll end up having to do a loop.

Have you been to where we're going before? I asked.

Yes, but many years ago, she said, pointing her hand right this time, intruding in my line of vision.

The street was dark and shaded, positioned underneath the motorway, and she instructed me to park anywhere I could find a space, which wasn't easy; it looked as though most of the cars hadn't moved in days if not weeks, their windscreens littered with fliers warning us of impending doom, some tyres flat.

Do you think it's safe to leave the car here? I said.

It's nice that you're so precious about it.

I reverse-parked into a space I wasn't sure I'd be able to fit into, but somehow managed without asking Evelyn to get out and guide me. She unbuckled her seatbelt while I gripped the gearstick, the engine still humming and vibrating through my hand.

We're all going in, Evelyn said, more of a command than a suggestion.

Do you think we should?

She laughed then. You don't need to be so scared, Aida. Live a little. It won't take long. She glanced at Rebecca sleeping in the back. She just wants to sleep all the time, doesn't she?

Evelyn . . . If you can get Rebecca's medicine, can you get other things too?

She hesitated. Like what?

Insulin. More of my insulin.

She seemed to consider this for a moment. I didn't realise that was something you were concerned about, she said.

I shrugged. Can you help?

Do you have the insulin, so I know what type you need?

I nodded, already opening my zipped pouch from my bag. I showed her my long- and short-acting pens. There was a little card inside that documented what I was currently on, written in beautiful penmanship by the last diabetic nurse I'd seen, nearly a year before. I realised then that I was due a review.

Evelyn took the card from me and stared at it. Fine, she said, I'll see what I can do. But no promises. She turned again to Rebecca and started tapping her knee. Time to wake up now, she said. Come on. Time to put on a show.

Tucked under a concrete bridge of the motorway, the strip club didn't look open from the outside, but a doorman appeared from the shadows and opened the door for us. I'd never been in a strip club but for a Tuesday it was surprisingly busy. It dawned on me that perhaps people needed this distraction more than ever. If the future was bleak, what better way to spend your savings? I'd only ever imagined strip clubs to be like what I'd seen in films, and I couldn't decide if this fitted the bill – there was a coldness to the place, clinical even. Evelyn led the way, settling in at the bar, patting the empty stools on either side of her before ordering me and her a whisky, despite the cost on the menu, and a glass of milk for Rebecca. For her heartburn, she said to the bartender before he walked away.

She had the air of someone who was familiar with this type of environment – behaved as if what we were doing was the most natural thing in the world.

I don't think I should be drinking, I said.

Nothing bad will happen, she said. I promise. The police have better things to do these days. And anyway, does anyone pay attention to them now?

Can we afford this? I whispered.

Do you have any money?

A little . . . For fuel.

She laughed. Don't worry, I won't leave you with the bill. We're not paying.

The barman placed two identical glasses of whisky down, with one large ice cube in each, while the milk came with a straw. I brought my glass to my lips, swallowing some of the burning liquid. God, Evelyn said, doesn't this feel nice? She nudged me then in the elbow before getting to her feet. We followed her towards the stage, settling a few seats back from the front, and we watched a flat-chested girl come down the pole head-first, legs spread apart in the air. As I watched, I was fascinated by her movements, the way the joints at her hips turned. Evelyn knocked the last of her whisky back, Rebecca sipping her milk, while I let my tumbler rest on the table. I'd never really understood the attraction to whisky. Bobby and Sam were fans, but I couldn't imagine myself taking to it. I'd read in one of my service station magazines about a distillery, and how the water was arguably the most important ingredient.

Can we interest you in anything? the hostess asked.

We're waiting to see someone, Evelyn replied, curling her arm around Rebecca. But you might like something, Aida . . . What do you think?

What do you like? the hostess asked.

I shook my head. No, I'm okay . . .

Evelyn stared at me. Have you ever had a lap dance?

I snorted a laugh.

I'm serious, she said. I think it would be good for you. I think it's something everyone should experience at least once.

The hostess smiled. Have you met Nala yet?

I just stared at her, my mouth open ever so slightly.

I'll send her over, she said. I think you'll like her.

A young woman who I assumed to be Nala arrived with a wide, confident smile; she couldn't have been much older than me. Lowering her mouth to my ear, she said, Can I interest you in a dance?

No, I . . .

I'll take care of it, Aida, Evelyn said, her words confident and forthright. You go with the nice girl. I'll settle this with who I'm here to see – the drinks too. So, you don't need to worry.

Honestly, I don't think . . .

She shooed me off. Have a nice time. Honestly, it'll do you the world of good.

I felt only a great sense of confusion. But I was already being led away by this woman and for some reason I wasn't refusing or rebuffing her instructions.

She led me to one of the curtained booths and ushered me to sit down. I did so, somewhat uncomfortably, but her smile seemed genuine, and I began to relax, laughing at the absurdity of it all.

You don't look like someone who is familiar with how this place works, she said, but your first five minutes have already been paid for; after that you'll have to pay for each five-minute period from then on. And there's no touching allowed. Okay?

I nodded.

The music was coming from the main dance floor, but it boomed through me. She stopped in front of me, unclipping her bra. Her arms came up and danced above her head before she lowered them on to my shoulders. You can relax, she said. She moved her hips in a circular motion, as if she was pretending my hands were placed on her skin. She pressed into me and out. It was hypnotic, soothing even.

I closed my eyes, trying to resist thoughts I didn't want to go near: the reservoir depleting, Bobby so thin, his skin clinging to his bones, Mum then, taking me to get the abortion, the look on her face.

I could feel hands on my shoulders again, a mouth close to my ear. Have I done something wrong? she asked.

I opened my eyes. Sorry, I replied. It's not you.

Are you sure you're okay?

I looked up at her. I couldn't remember her name. You're beautiful, I said.

That's the first five minutes coming to an end, she said, easing herself away from me.

I'd like to pay for another five, I said.

Are you sure?

I nodded.

The blood began to pump through my body and down my legs. I closed my eyes again, my head rolling back into my seat while this girl purred around me, healing me in some way, and I let my thoughts glide towards Peter, remembered the weight of him on top of me, smiled at the memory of it.

When I came out of the booth there was another woman already waiting. She whispered the price of £20 into my ear. We take cash or card, she added. I opened my purse and removed the twenty-pound note Mum had gifted me. There was little thought or hesitation; it was as if I was under some sort of spell. I understood addiction then, the impulse. She handed me a card with the establishment's name and address. A souvenir, she said.

Evelyn and Rebecca were waiting for me by the door. Did someone have a nice time? Evelyn said, tilting her head to inspect me as I approached.

I could feel my cheeks flushing. Did you get what we came for? I asked.

Patience, she said. It's coming.

Back in the car, she directed us through the city streets into the West End, and, suddenly taking a left, we were entering a one-way system and I realised we were near Dad's flat. What would his reaction have been if I'd turned up on his doorstep, unannounced? Would his woman have been there? I carried on, nervous of the streets, drawn further into the one-way system until we turned on to University Avenue.

Pull in wherever you can find a space, Evelyn said. I don't think we're far from the park.

Why? I asked.

She stared at me. Because it'll be nice.

We walked through cast-iron gates and along a path, passing the play park. It was reasonably busy, kids on swings, a little boy shouting out from the tunnel of a play train. Around the periphery sat homeless people, handwritten cardboard signs explaining their individual misfortunes, propped up by bin-bags of possessions, no dogs. We carried on walking until we came to a bench dedicated to someone called Thomas Roberts.

I can't imagine anyone ever dedicating a bench to me, Evelyn said.

To have two places to mourn seems like quite the luxury, I replied.

She cleared her throat. Do people even visit grave sites any more?

The three of us sat down on the bench and looked out across at a footbridge, a trickle of water running beneath it.

I don't even know what I would want to happen to my body once I'm gone, Evelyn said.

I watched this programme once about bodies emitting toxins when they were burnt, I said. Some researcher wanted to sell mushroom death cloaks, which help you decay in an ecologically friendly way once you're in the ground.

Really? she said. How bizarre.

I shrugged. For some reason, that appeals to me.

What colour are the cloaks?

I've no idea.

A woman and young girl started walking across the pebbles, the noise of their shoes echoing under the bridge. They crouched down, with empty milk cartons, trying to scoop up some of the murky brown water. The child was gaunt and freckled, wearing a vest and pants.

What are they doing? I said. There's still water in the taps.

Evelyn paused. Maybe they're just nervous, she said, turning to look at me. Hoarding it for later.

And I wondered if she knew, then – knew about Mum's supplies somehow.

Don't they care that children in other parts of the world are dying from drinking dirty water? I said.

Children have always been dying from drinking dirty water, she replied. You just didn't have to see it in the park.

We drove out of the West End and took the tunnel to Govan, where the shipbuilding used to take place. It was deprived, cheaply valued properties, but with the grandeur of a place that used to be something. Evelyn held the map tight in her hands, this time seeming to really need it, staring down at it while trying to direct me: *the next left, the second right*. We arrived at a residential street of old tenement flats, and I pulled into a space.

Won't be long, Evelyn said, unbuckling her seatbelt.

I did the same.

You're not coming this time, she said. You can stay here and look after Rebecca.

What's here? I asked.

What we need, she replied, before closing her door. She walked away with purpose, buzzing the door to a flat a few metres along from where we were parked. I watched her speak into the mouthpiece on the wall and almost immediately someone buzzed her in, the door quickly closing behind her.

I settled back into my seat, gazing out through the wind-screen. A mattress was lying out on the street, covered in blotches of what I assumed must be someone's bodily fluids. I cast my gaze upwards. I'd always liked being able to see into tenement windows. It felt as though people's lives were openly on display: what they watched on television, what pieces of art they hung on their walls; even their furniture interested me. What would people have thought if they could have seen into our cottage? I noticed then as I looked around that some of the windows had blue and pink baby garments hanging from inside, strung up like a washing line – a display of sorts.

I turned to see Rebecca also gazing up towards the windows, her body upright, tense.

Are you okay? I said. Do you feel unwell?

She looked at me, really met my eye. Her eyes narrowed and for the briefest of moments I thought she was going to try to say something. The moment passed and she turned her face, staring back up towards the washing lines of baby clothes.

The two of us could just run off, I said, smirking. Leave everything and everyone behind, see where the road takes us . . . I laughed. Don't pretend you haven't thought about it. I faced forward again, my hands on the steering wheel. Although, to be honest, I say. I'd have no idea what to do with a baby . . .

I checked my phone. There was this amazing TikTok video of Sebastian Stan which I watched a few times. Then I stupidly checked Twitter, wanting to know if there were any updates on the desalination plants that they'd been banging on about in the news. But it was mostly horrendous images of people fleeing their homes, of children crying. A great fire destroying London. Someone else had written a thread about rape victims struggling to get hold of emergency contraception and that was enough for me to come off. I glanced over again at Rebecca, but she was paying me little attention. And before I knew it I was dialling Dad's number, listening to it ring out.

Finally, he picked up. Hello . . .

You'll never guess where I am?

So you made it here in one piece? he said, with real warmth to his voice. How are you doing, darling?

I'm okay. You?

We took in a stray cat. Did I tell you that already?

I shook my head, didn't think to say *no* aloud. Are you worried yet, about the water?

He paused. I'm always worried.

I thought you said it was wetter here, so there was less reason to worry.

They stopped our mains a few days ago. They've got us going to designated municipal water pumps so they can ration what we're using.

How's that working out?

Well, they're still holding up. We're allowed up to thirty litres per day, per person.

Oh, okay, not bad, then.

He tried to laugh. I suppose not.

Dad, you sound sad again . . . Like you used to.

He was quiet for a moment. I guess, just some days, it all feels like a little too much.

Come back with me, I said. Bring the cat even.

He laughed.

I'm serious, I said.

Don't spend your time worrying about me. I've made my bed, I deserve to lie in it.

Bring your woman too, I said. Mum won't care. She'll only want you to be safe.

Aida . . . is anywhere safe now?

You told me the farm was the safest place in the world. You used to say that if the world was going to end, it would be the farm where you'd want to be.

Yes, but I didn't actually think it was going to happen.

Please come, I said, begging now. I could come and pick you up right now . . .

Darling, I'm not leaving, but please, come round and see me.

Why? We never have nice conversations . . .

I like seeing you, even when you're not saying very nice things.

Afterwards, when the line went dead, I threw my phone on to the dashboard, causing Rebecca to flinch in my rear-view mirror. I reached down the side of the door and found a blue stress ball – no idea where it had come from. Its smell and texture was so artificial that I briefly brought it to my lips, resisting the urge to take a bite and test its composition between my molars. I knew it would be disgusting, but still. I began pulsing it in the palm of my hand, staring at the washing lines of blue and pink garments, tearing little chunks of rubber, fragments landing on my lap.

Evelyn came out of the front door then and made straight for the passenger seat. Her face looked tense, her lips tight, fraught even. She was clutching a brown paper bag and she handed it to me. Inside, there were several bottles of the tablets Mum had requested for Rebecca, and beside them, to my amazement, were boxes of both my long-acting and short-acting insulin, cold in my hands.

Evelyn . . . I said, shaking my head in disbelief. How did you manage this?

What is that? she said, looking down at the shredded stress ball across my lap.

Nothing, I said, brushing it away. I peered back into the bag. Thank you. I considered hugging her, but it didn't seem right.

She placed her hand over mine. I understand, she said.

I glanced up again at the windows with the washing lines of baby clothes. What does it mean? I asked.

What?

The windows, I said, pointing.

She laughed, but it was more of a cough, a noise internalised. Maybe they're for sale.

What, like a knitting shop?

She shrugged, straightening in her seat. I'm finished now, she said. Is there anyone you would like to see before we go back?

No, I said. No one.

She reached into the medicine bag and retrieved Rebecca's tablets. She unscrewed one of the bottles and removed a small white pill. Turning to Rebecca, she offered her the tablet and Rebecca took it, resting it in the palm of her hand.

Take it, Evelyn said, nodding her along. Now.

Slowly, Rebecca brought the tablet up to her lips and put it inside her mouth. Evelyn offered her one of the water bottles and Rebecca began to gulp the contents down, barely leaving a drop.

Evelyn straightened, running her hands across the fabric of her trousers, cupping her knees. I would love to eat some meat, she said, laughing. Maybe your talk about being a vegetarian has prompted me. It's the first time in so long that I've really desired it. Craved it. Before, I was eating because I had to, but now I *want* to eat.

As I drove back, my eyes shifted from the bag of medicine that sat between us to the red glow of the fuel light. Neither of us mentioned the fact that we hadn't stopped for fuel before leaving. It was so stiflingly hot, beads of sweat gathering on my forehead. Evelyn extended her arm out of the passenger window, fingers flexing through the air. She smiled at me, and I smiled back. There was something liberating, that feeling of having the whole world to yourself. We even managed to pick a few tunes up on Smooth Radio and in a way I believed they helped carry us back, that the good vibes were enough to ensure the car didn't give up on us.

And then, when we were less than two miles away, the Corsa started to choke, like a convulsion of sorts. We jolted forward a few metres and then, slowly, the thing came to an abrupt stop, rolling towards the side of the road.

Evelyn and I looked at each other.

You didn't get fuel, she said, a judgemental tone to her voice.

I forgot.

She turned to look at Rebecca, who was sitting looking straight ahead between our two front seats.

You will need to phone one of them and tell them to come and pick us up.

I already had my phone in my hand. There's no signal, I said.

Her eyes widened. How could you be so stupid?

I stared at her. I'm sorry . . .

She ran her hands through her hair, visibly frustrated. Can we walk? she said.

I shrugged. It's a couple of miles, mostly uphill.

For fuck's sake, she shouted, unclipping her seatbelt. Did you hear that, Rebecca? She climbed out and started pulling the seat forward, waiting for Rebecca to get out. She linked her arm with Rebecca's, and they started walking, not bothering to look back at me.

I grabbed the medicine bag, my phone and my near empty bottle of water. Aside from that, there was nothing else to take. I started walking, keeping a few paces behind them, sensing I wasn't welcome. It was the first time I'd seen Evelyn flip like that, and it was unsettling – to be so calm and content one second and furious the next. I took a sip of water and decided I needed to focus on something else as the sun beat down. I started thinking about all those kids I'd looked after as a camp counsellor in America the summer before – wondered how they were faring through the droughts. They'd all come from so much money; it was hard to contemplate how much. I'd been put down on the schedule to teach them tennis, but they'd all been members of a country club and I had known immediately that I was out of my depth. What would a farm girl know about tennis? It was ludicrous.

Up ahead, Evelyn and Rebecca came to a sudden stop.

What the fuck is this? Evelyn shouted.

I started to run, coming to a stop beside them.

I could see it then. A blurring of sorts – a swarm of black and red – spreading and swaying across a stretch of dying grass on the verge. The noise was strange, not like the buzzing of flies but not silent either. I took a step closer, curiosity getting the better of me.

Ladybirds, I said.

It was thousands of ladybirds. Everywhere.

It's like a plague, Evelyn said.

And I just stood watching them. They moved en masse, the shape of their collective changing constantly, shifting ever closer to where we stood.

Keep walking, Evelyn said, gripping Rebecca.

I was still standing, watching. I didn't know ladybirds travelled in swarms, I said.

It's not natural, Evelyn replied. Things are off-kilter.

I started moving away, distancing myself from their mass. But I kept glancing back. I should have been shocked, or disgusted. But it felt as if I was witnessing something important, even if I didn't understand it. I didn't like insects, but I liked ladybirds.

11

Peter and I stood in one of the sheds, watching Bobby struggle to turn a calf inside the heifer's stomach. It took everything out of him, the force of his attempt, the size of the calf, and in the end he couldn't manage it. He staggered back, nearly falling to the ground.

Do you want me to try? Peter asked.

Bobby attempted a laugh. No offence, laddie, but it's not just about holding a heavy load. You've no idea how to turn a calf in the womb.

So, what do we do? Peter said. Should we wake Miriam?

God, no, let the woman sleep after the night she's had with the calving, he said. Aida, will you call Gemma? I think we've gone as far on our own as we can with this one.

I nodded, already making my way out of the shed. I crossed the yard with purpose, straight through the kitchen for the phone in the hall. It was one of the few numbers I knew off by heart and Gemma agreed to come straight over.

As I crossed back into the yard, I thought I saw the curtains move in a window of the campervan – was convinced that Rebecca was staring at me. I'd seen very little of her since we'd returned from our trip to Glasgow. The medication appeared to be working but she had been dehydrated by the time we'd managed to get back on foot and had been ordered to rest by Mum. Mum was so relieved to see the labetalol taking its effect that I never told her we didn't go to the hospital – what did it matter, if we got what we went for? Mum never thought to ask me, either, where all the insulin had come from as I restocked the fridge. Maybe she didn't want to know; maybe that's why she didn't ask for her money back when it became abundantly clearly that it hadn't been used to buy fuel.

I assumed the Corsa was still sitting where we'd left it, the windows rolled down. Perhaps the ladybirds had moved in and made it their new home. The possibility of us getting our hands on petrol now was pretty much zero, and I had to accept that the Corsa's reincarnated life had come to a quick and abrupt end. I still thought about the look on Peter's face when he'd realised that all his hard work had been in vain – that there was nothing wrong with his mechanical skills, only my ability to care for the vehicle properly. We should never have let him fix the car, Mum had said. You got his hopes up, and for what? She was quick to treat it as another example of my recklessness, reminding me that even as a child I'd never been able to look after anything that had been gifted to me. The guinea pig was the example that came to mind. The gift that I'd grown swiftly bored with – neglecting to clean its cage, struggling to remember to feed and water it, no instinct to remember – the creature was just not on my radar. I'd accidentally left the cage door open one day and Rusty's predecessor, Haggis, had got hold of the wee thing, killing it in an instant with a fierce shake of his mouth. It was the first time I'd really understood what they meant when they said Jack Russells were bred for ratting.

Perhaps I was overthinking it, but it felt as though everyone was avoiding me. Peter certainly went out of his way not to see me, and when he did it was only under farm-working conditions. Something had certainly changed in him after we returned without the Corsa – it was as if whatever hope he seemed to hold for his future was extinguished. Maybe he thought of it as his car, and I supposed in a way it might as well have been.

I was certain there was movement again from behind the curtain of the campervan. I came to a stop in front of it and hesitated before trying the handle, but it was locked. I rattled it and waited but still there was nothing. I moved to another door, tried that handle too.

What are you doing? Peter asked, startling me.

I . . . sorry, I just thought Rebecca might need something . . .

She doesn't need anything.

Oh, okay, I'm sorry.

And as I stood, trying to find the words to properly apologise for what had happened, Gemma's car came swinging into view.

Who is that? Peter said cautiously. She was the first stranger to arrive since they'd got here.

That's Gemma, the vet, I said. You'll like her. She's very pragmatic.

Gemma pulled into the yard and got out of her car – a fancy electric Volvo. People talked about the fact that she had her own charging point, that as long as the power stayed on, Gemma would always be able to get out and about to see the animals, regardless of the fuel crisis. And I envied her foresight.

Thanks for coming down so quickly, I said.

It's fine, she said. Does she need a bit of help?

I nodded.

She followed me into the shed, Peter behind us. And, inside, Bobby was crouched down beside the heifer, sweating in his overalls and looking sickly grey.

Poor thing, Bobby said, looking from the heifer and up to Gemma. She's been struggling for hours.

I'd better have a feel, she replied, before we commit to a caesarean.

Really? Peter said, as if he'd never contemplated that such a procedure could be carried out on livestock.

Gemma pulled a long plastic sleeve up past her right elbow. We watched her push her hand up the back end of the heifer and I imagined her moving her wrist inside it – a circular motion. The hand came out quicker than I was expecting, mucus and blood sticking to the plastic sleeve.

Yeah, the calf's too big and in the wrong position for her to push, she said. They'll both die unless I cut her open.

Bobby moved quickly, ushering the heifer into a crush; the head was then clamped to stop the animal from struggling. Her tail whipped up on to her back and swatted a few flies away. Her nose was soft, pink and filled with follicles – it bothered me, maybe in the same way the texture of coral and sponges bothered me. Bobby stroked the heifer's skin on the bridge between her eyes.

Have you seen this done before? I asked, looking at Peter.

He shook his head.

Gemma was quick with the razor, revealing a smooth patch of skin, identical to the underside of suede. And a liquid antiseptic was smeared across the heifer's skin. Gemma's hands were gentle and tender, the anaesthetic administered without complication. I watched her make the incisions along the side of the heifer's stomach and she didn't appear to be in any pain. It was like undoing the zip of a backpack or cutting the fold of an envelope – layers of skin and yellow fat flapping open. So many mammals must have looked the same inside, various-sized organs sitting in the same order. How could such a thing be so easily performed on a standing creature?

Gemma began to struggle from the weight of the calf and Bobby came round to help pull the hind legs out. I took a step closer, as did Peter. And suddenly the calf was lying on the floor,

covered in mucus. Bobby immediately crouched beside the creature, trying to unblock its nostrils, rubbing its stomach, willing
breath into its body.

Gemma was already looping industrial-looking surgical
thread on to a large needle. The calf was still not moving. I
crouched down beside Bobby, felt the urge to do something,
except I didn't know what.

How's he looking, Bobby? Gemma said, her attention fully
on the mother.

No, Bobby finally said. We've lost this one. Not a lick of life
in him.

But your cow will be fine, she said. So that's something.

Yes, Bobby replied. It's just . . . it feels like it's happening all
the time.

But she wasn't listening to him.

I brought my face up a little closer to the calf and stared at
one open eye. Had he over-baked? Had his mother been mal-
nourished? Did he just decide that he wasn't going to bother
with the whole ordeal of birth, only to then be slaughtered? I
had this urge to prod him with my finger, press his stomach in
some attempt to inflate it. I glanced around and Gemma was still
stitching the cow – the needle working hard to pierce the thick
layers of skin, zipping it all back together.

We've another orphan from this morning, Bobby said.

We can skin this one then, I replied. At least that's something.

Bobby smiled. I taught you well.

I turned to see Peter staring at the dead calf, a sadness that
was real and fragile.

You've never seen a stillborn, then, Bobby said. Life and
death, it's all under the one roof here, my lad. He tried to get to
his feet, wobbling a little, before placing his hand on my shoulder. I'll show you how to skin your first calf, he added. If we do it

quickly, with a bit of luck this cow will never know the difference and accept the other little fella as her own.

Will that work? Peter asked.

And I looked from mother to calf, wondering if she really wouldn't know the difference. Maybe the world would have been a happier place if we could have done the same for humans. I focused again on the calf's open eye. It would have been too awkward to try to close it. The sockets were too big. The eyes would glaze over soon, milky-coloured.

Move him away from his mother and we can get started, Bobby said to Peter. Aida will wait until Gemma is finished.

Peter hesitated, before reaching down and grasping limbs.

They headed for the shed next door. I'd only seen a skinning once, but it had stayed with me, wasn't something easily forgotten. Bobby would be quick with his knife, starting at the ankles no doubt, inserting his thumb inside, pulling the hide away from the tendons, deft in his movements even now. He'd never let anyone else do it. What were we meant to do without him?

Are you busy these days, Gemma? I asked.

She was still working away on the cow, but the insides were now hidden. Define busy, she said.

What about medical supplies? I asked. Are you finding it hard to get the things you need?

She turned to look at me for a moment before returning her attention to the job. We're just about managing so far, she said. The quotas aren't great for our business, but they certainly help keep our stock levels in check.

Are the quotas enough? Or do you think they'll need to go further?

She paused again, her hand growing still. Let's just hope for rain, Aida.

*

It was cooler now, more bearable. I walked into our kitchen and opened the fridge, removing one of my insulin pens, peering at the tower of boxes I'd acquired before closing the door over. By having these boxes I'd likely taken away from someone else who was also in need, and was it even enough? There must have been over a year's supply. I reasoned that surely rain would come before then, that surely we'd have adapted to our circumstances better, that goods would be exchanged more easily by some new means we would become accustomed to. Regardless, it was enough to push the fear further down the road, enough to force it to the recesses of my mind. Maybe being an insulin-dependent diabetic had helped me prepare for the drought – I was used to the threat of something being taken away, had grown comfortable with the planning and preparation.

I walked into my bedroom and lay down on my bed, reaching for my glucose meter, the eye of that dead calf still on my mind. Something on the floor caught my attention then, something stuck to one of my discarded socks that had been lying on the floor for days. I reached out for it, taking it in my hand. And stuck to it was a squashed ladybird, flat like a pancake, and for some reason, after everything, it was the ladybird that made me cry. It was the saddest sight in the world.

I wasn't sure how long I just lay there, staring at that ladybird, but at some point I became aware of Mum standing over the threshold of my door, peering in at me.

What? I mumbled, wiping my eyes.

I heard about the calf . . .

I sat up. Did the mother take to the rejected one? I asked. Does she think he's hers?

Mum nodded. She's licking every inch of his little coat.

I smiled, nodding. That's good, I said. I'm glad.

Will you do something for me? she said.

What?

Evelyn was telling me she'd love to see the old ruined cottages that Bobby told her about.

And you want me to take her?

Peter too.

Why?

She hesitated. I want some time alone with Rebecca. I think she's more likely to interact with me when her mother isn't around.

I thought you weren't worried any more.

Will you just do this for me?

You know I don't like it down there, I said.

The heat of the day has passed, she said. It's the best time to go. I just think . . . She paused, really appearing to weigh her words. I just want to be able to assess her, consider the care she's been getting, without her mother's dominating presence.

I don't think Evelyn's my biggest fan at the moment, I said. I don't think Peter is either.

Well, this is your opportunity to turn that around.

I led them along the narrow footpath, past a row of fields, and then the incline came upon us. Peter stayed close, while Evelyn lagged behind a little, seeming to take in everything that she passed.

In the distance I caught sight of one of the lambs they'd sent up on to the hills and I stopped abruptly, causing Peter to stumble at my heels.

If we carry on a little further, I said, we'll start to come down the hill to the bottom of the valley, and that's where the old cottages are.

Do the cottages belong to the farm? Evelyn asked.

Yeah, not that they're of any use to anyone now, I said. My forehead was damp with sweat, and I tried to wipe it away, glancing out across in the other direction to where the wind turbines stood stationary. I tried to feel for the mildest breeze but there was none.

Do you own those? Evelyn asked, pointing to the wind turbines.

I shook my head. That's the next farm over.

It still pained me to think of the lost opportunity. I had wanted them, but it was the Watt family who were responsible for bringing the turbines to the landscape, and even now, after several years, I admired them. I liked the days when they were rotating, when I could marvel at the concept of them capturing energy. It seemed so simple, yet so out of reach for me to comprehend. How did it work? I remembered them arriving on lorries in pieces, eventually forming one structure, standing tall, drilled and embedded into the land. The points of the blades were piercing, slicing birds into pieces if they weren't careful. We'd been offered money, base-rent to have the turbines on our farm too. But there had been a shitload of protests from locals and Bobby had decided he didn't need the hassle. I remembered the posters in people's windows – amateur in their appearance – I'd even stuck one to the fridge, taking the piss, but Mum had taken it down. So what? I'd said. Let them protest. They'd take the money if they were offered it; it's nothing to do with the landscape or it being an eyesore. But Bobby had only shaken his head firmly, his mind made up.

I shielded my eyes to take in their vast expanse. The land where they would have sat was mostly barren anyway, and barely accessible, so why shouldn't it have been made more profitable? Why hadn't we taken the money? Why did some people let pride be their downfall? I stared at the turbines across the valley, liked to think that the sprawling hectares were less lonely with those white beacons blowing in the wind. The tragedy being that the Watts didn't really need to worry about their dairy farm any more – the turbines gave them enough financial stability to weather any storm. Watt himself had boasted to Bobby in the pub once that he'd already begun to cut back on the dairy business, didn't see it as profitable any more, a hobby now more than anything.

It took about thirty minutes to reach the ruins. There wasn't a great deal to see – two dilapidated cottages in a row, condemned and abandoned for years. I sat down on a row of stones that had previously been part of an outside wall, while Evelyn and Peter shuffled around, taking in the space as if it were an excavation site.

Who lived here? Evelyn asked, tapping a crumbling external wall with her foot.

Bobby said an old couple used to rent both cottages, I said. But that must have been when he was a boy. My whole life, it's always just been ruins.

What about squatters? Peter said, peering through a still standing section of wall with a weather-beaten window frame.

They're not exactly habitable, I replied. And I think the old road that led to the cottages was washed away years ago. Flooded when they built the reservoir.

Why do you think the old couple rented *both* cottages? Evelyn asked.

The story that Bobby tells is that they liked their privacy. That, and that the woman used to beat her husband.

Really? Evelyn said, her interest piqued.

I'm sure he said they grew most of their own food – kept a goat, too. Bobby often talks about the goat for some reason.

Self-sufficient before it was fashionable, she said, laughing. Before it was necessary.

Supposedly, they dressed and behaved like tinkers, but they had come from money, I said. Bobby remembers them arranging for a taxi to take them to the city where it was said they'd stay in a lavish hotel, eat expensive food and go to the opera. Then they'd return all clean and shiny to resume their life back in the squalor. I shrugged. I don't know if any of that is true, but I like the story.

I don't understand why anyone would choose to live like that, Peter said.

Evelyn perched herself down beside me, suddenly resting her head lightly on my shoulder before lifting it again. I don't know, she said. I kind of understand why you might want to reject a normal way of living. Perhaps it offers more happiness . . .

It didn't sound like they were happy, Peter replied, sadness still in his voice.

Well, at least they were trying something different, she said.

She got to her feet then and made her way to the second house, which still had a roof partly covering its interior. Patches of wallpaper could still be seen, a sink too. Peter stood beside her, peering in through the windows, before attempting to climb inside.

I wouldn't go in there, I said. It's not safe.

He paused, before retreating and walking around the side of the cottage instead. I followed, instinctively, tracing a line around the foundations.

There was an eeriness about the cottages that made me uncomfortable. The ruins felt sinister, as if they were capable of physically draining something from me. I didn't believe in ghosts, but a sourness clung to these cottages and their patchwork history. Maybe because I believed the story about the woman beating her husband

– that misery had taken place within these walls. There had been a fire at some point too, contained, with no fatalities. Now, a fire wouldn't be containable, the land so dry. All it would take would be a piece of glass glinting in the sun and acres of space would be gone. I imagined wildfires surrounding us on all sides, like the images I saw online. What a horrible way to die. There had been a fire in a residential building next to my university halls and I could still see the way the flames had torn through the place, remembered watching someone's painting hanging on a wall melt to nothing, seeing pieces of timber previously supporting the roof falling to the ground. The building had been made from stone, just like our cottages. I knew stone couldn't burn, but I hadn't appreciated the temperatures a fire could reach, melting whatever and whoever was inside. I only hoped that the fumes of a fire killed people before anything else did.

How did they get their water? Evelyn asked, interrupting my thoughts.

I think maybe from a spring or bore hole.

Evelyn looked at me. But it doesn't exist any more?

I shook my head. I think maybe it was unreliable and dried up.

Peter began throwing a few stones back into the footprint of the first cottage, one landing near the still standing fireplace with no chimneystack above it. *Stop*, I wanted to say. *Stop it*. But I didn't. I just stared at the stones and the dust he'd disturbed.

I used to come down here to camp, I said. When I was in high school, me and a few friends would come here and have a party. It's weird at night, even when people are with you. Like you really are at the end of the world.

No one would ever know if you were here, Evelyn said. I could live here quite happily.

Evelyn . . . I'm sorry about what happened with the car. I have this knack for disappointing people. But I didn't mean to put Rebecca in harm's way.

She looked at me. Were you jealous of your mother's attention to other children when you were young?

I stared at her, confused. I would never do anything to hurt . . .

It's remarkable, she said, interrupting me. Your mother behaves with such love and attentiveness to Rebecca that you would think she were caring for her own daughter.

Well, I said, slowly, maybe Rebecca would make a better daughter than me.

Would she like to be a grandmother at some point?

Sometimes I think more than anything else in the world, I said. Maybe more so because she knows that it isn't going to happen.

And you're sure of that?

I nodded.

Such a big decision to have already made.

Look around, I said. Why would I choose to bring a child into this world if I didn't have to?

She stared at me with an expression that felt unfamiliar. And it seemed as if anything could happen; as if she could snap again, just as she had done when we ran out of fuel. And then suddenly she was on her feet. I could sense the change from the way she shifted her gaze in the direction from which we'd come, in the way she strode with purpose – in the way Peter stopped throwing stones, and in the way he stared out after her.

12

In the service station, no one had come to replenish the dough-nut stand, while only the burger bar, the noodle station and our shop remained open. Outside, the fuel station was already boarded up.

Aaron leaned against a display stand, looking up at the empty space where the television had previously been.

What happened? I asked, pointing at the frame.

He shrugged.

How are we going to get through the night now? I said, already, like a reflex, removing my phone from my pocket.

They closed the outlet shops, Aaron said. My mum and sister got no warning about it. Just turned up on Tuesday and the place was empty.

Shit, Aaron, I'm sorry. I hadn't realised.

I'm not sure what we'll do . . . There's no way we'll survive on my wage alone.

I reached out to touch him, my hand on his arm. Will you leave town?

I've an uncle up on the west coast, he said. It doesn't seem as bad for them. But an invite's never been extended, so . . . make of that what you will. He paused. People are saying it's only a matter of time until the mains water is turned off. Do you believe that?

I don't know . . . I heard it's already happening in the cities.

I keep filling up any container I can find, he said. Knowing that that's just making it worse, but I can't stop.

Do you think you have enough? For you and your family . . .

How much is enough? And for how long? He tilted his head to one side. My mum's been stockpiling all sorts of liquids. She's always been a bit doomsday like that.

I can relate, I said.

What about you? Will you guys have enough to keep you going? Or are you planning on jumping ship?

I don't see us leaving the farm now.

I pulled a price tag that was hanging loose from its plastic holder. When I ran my finger across its sharp edge it cut me. The blood pooled into a tiny bright red droplet on my fingertip, and I stared, somewhat affronted that the pooling of blood hadn't happened on my terms. It was a beautiful shade of red and I wondered if it was a brighter colour than that of the livestock. Maybe I just needed something to affirm my belief that humans were indeed a superior species. Maybe because I didn't quite believe it.

I started pacing the narrow aisles of the shop floor, backwards and forwards. I'd be surprised if a single customer comes in, I said.

Aaron started scrolling through his phone before replying. It's a wonder we haven't all killed ourselves yet. The fact that everything's gone to shit. And we're stuck with it now. Even if things improve – the life of before is gone, isn't it?

I think so . . .

I watched some documentary about Cape Town from years ago . . . he said. Talking then about their problems with water shortages. And it occurred to me, that I just hadn't cared. It was a problem that didn't affect me and therefore I didn't care . . .

Aaron, stop. Please.

So much of the world will be uninhabitable now, he said. And I really didn't want to be alive for this part. Couldn't the climate have waited a couple more hundred years?

There's not much we can do now, I said.

He laughed. Stop being so fucking pragmatic.

I'm angry too.

Sometimes I get angry just looking at my mum, as if somehow she's responsible for all of this. The dismissiveness of it all. That this never used to be something she had to even consider. Older people – they got fucking everything.

Do you think this is the one to get us? I asked.

What do you mean?

There's always been some threat or fear for each generation. Like in the sixties, didn't everyone think there was going to be nuclear war? And then in the eighties . . .

I guess . . .

So, are the droughts what will finally get us? Are they going to wipe us out, like the asteroid did with the dinosaurs? Is this our asteroid? Is this the start of the end of our civilisation?

I don't know, Aida. Quite possibly. Or maybe these desalination plants everyone's talking about will be our salvation. Smarter people than us must be trying to solve these problems – that's the hope, right? We can adapt.

Places like California have been working on desalination plants for years and it hasn't appeared to make things any better, I said. It's the acceleration of the droughts that we can't keep up with.

So what should we do?

I shrugged. Maybe we'll just keep digging holes in the earth until something springs up.

I started scrolling through my own phone, finding a video I'd seen before and loved. It was of this great big dog caught stealing food off the counter and just trying to shimmy away on his two back legs, eyes shifting guiltily, acting as though there was nothing to see. It still made me laugh. But then it ended, like a gentle reprieve, like an advert you wished would last forever, and before I knew it I was watching a video of a famous tennis star crying outside her home as wildfires ravaged the landscape, heading towards her. Then there was something about people south of the border – officials struggling to get a real handle on the death toll from the extreme temperatures – clips of violent fights breaking out over basic rations, the National Health Service having fully collapsed.

A message from Mia at the Premier Inn popped up on my phone then, interrupting my doomsday scrolling, asking if I was working tonight. I ignored it.

Reluctantly, I got up and went for a piss, closing the door to the first cubicle, sliding the lock into place. Even though I hadn't been desperate, now that a toilet was in sight I could barely hold it in, struggling to undo my trousers. And then, when I sat, there was hardly anything, and I strained, a burning pain of sorts, and I wondered if this was the start of a urine infection. I'd never had one before and had never really understood how bad it could be. I was sure I'd seen cranberry juice in the drinks fridge back in our concession, and made a note to pinch one. Afterwards, I investigated the pan, wanting to check for symptoms, but all I could see was the blue of the chemical filtering through the cistern. I stopped at the sinks, once again automatically going for the taps before remembering they'd been sealed off. I diverted my hands to one of the sanitisers, pink and slimy, and squeezed too much out on to my palms, its residue falling into the basin of the sink. I rubbed my hands, and became aware of a woman and girl coming in behind me. The woman caught my eye for a moment, smiling before glancing back down. The girl pressed her hand into another sanitising dispenser, while her backpack threatened to slip down from her shoulder.

Louise . . . the woman said, her name seeming to hang in the air. You're leaking.

What? the girl said.

I realised I was staring at them; I couldn't help it.

The woman took a step closer and lifted a corner of the girl's backpack up from her shoulder. She pressed a hand up against a damp patch. Open the bag, she said. Now.

They seemed oblivious to me hovering there. The girl brought the bag down on to the ground and unzipped it, rummaging until she retrieved a bottle of water, removing it upside down in her hands. The sports cap had come undone, and the mouthpiece was pulled up for sucking on. With the bottle still leaking in her hands, the girl rose to her full height and stared at the woman.

For a moment there was only silence. Then the woman brought her hand up and slapped the girl hard across the cheek. How could you be so fucking careless? she spat. After everything we've talked about.

The girl stood stunned, her palm resting against the slap mark on her cheek. And I was still standing next to them, dumbfounded. Saliva had gathered like a pool in my mouth, and I swallowed it back.

What am I meant to tell your dad? the woman was saying, panic rising through her voice. He'll hang me for this.

Louise's lip quivered. I'm sorry, Mum, she said. It was an accident. I didn't know. Her eyes were wide, scared. I'll tell him. It was me. It's my fault.

I coughed, and this seemed to be enough for them to acknowledge my presence. I can get you another one, I heard myself say. I can replace it for you.

The woman stared at me. She was breathing heavily through her nostrils. I cannot ask you to do that, she said.

It's okay. I work here. Things go missing all the time.

She turned to look at her daughter. Do we have anything in there worth trading? she asked, pointing to the backpack.

The girl was already rummaging through it. A miniature can of deodorant rolled across the floor, then a packet of brightly coloured fine-point pens, some tampons, and headphones. The girl looked up at me blankly, perhaps wondering if I was actually going to make her continue to pull out her possessions.

I don't want anything, I said.

The woman looked at me. But—

Did you just buy it? I asked.

They nodded.

I'll make out that the bottle got damaged when I was taking off the security tag. I paused, waiting for them to say something, but nothing came. Come with me and we'll sort it out. Okay?

Why are you doing this for us? the woman asked.

I just . . . I don't know. I want to help if I can.

I led them out, but as I walked back to my concession they seemed to drag behind. Louise stood by the entrance as if she was keeping watch and the woman came forward, stopping at the till. I went straight to the drinks fridge and picked up an identical bottle of water to the one they had in their bag. Ignoring Aaron's stare, I went behind the counter and fought the security tag off the bottle before handing it over.

The woman clutched the new bottle to her chest and nodded. Thank you, she whispered.

I watched them leave, running my hand under the edge of the counter, my fingers finding an old piece of chewing gum. I dug my nails into the putty texture, scoring line after line across its small surface area.

What was that about? Aaron said, coming to stand beside me. I'd just sold them one.

There was an accident.

Sharon checks the stock levels, especially the water . . .

I doubt Sharon cares at this point, I said.

He laughed a strange, bewildered laugh. You act like it's nothing . . .

They were in a bad way, I said. The bottle she had, it had split in the toilets and was leaking everywhere.

At the sound of footsteps, we turned in the direction of the shop entrance. Lewis, the service station manager, was walking in. He seemed aimless in his approach, bewildered and lost. He came to a stop in front of us and brought his hands up to his face, rubbing the stubble around his mouth.

They've closed the border, he said. That's it.

What? I said.

I just got word from the police that the border is officially closed. They're blocking travel too, around the country – putting in restrictions to try to contain people, stop them overwhelming areas where people think there's more water.

Shit, Aaron said. So, that's it then? No one's going anywhere . . .

Sorry, what do you mean? I asked. We can't even move freely ourselves, within Scotland?

Lewis nodded. That's what I've been told. No movement outside a ten-mile radius, unless you have an exemption from the government.

Who gets the exemptions? I said.

He shrugged. I don't know. They're putting it into law. If they catch you, they'll fine you, or worse. It's included in their emergency powers under the Drought Act.

But my commute to here is more than ten miles . . . Aaron said.

Lewis exhaled. It doesn't matter now anyway. That's the end of this place too. Final nail in the coffin.

Have we been told to close? Aaron asked.

I don't hear anything from anyone, Lewis said, his hands falling by his sides. Look, I just thought you guys would want to know. If you decide to go home early, then I think that's fair enough. I'll try and make sure you get paid for a full shift. But I can't see anyone being asked to come back after tonight.

Head Office hasn't fired us, Aaron said, so I'll keep turning up until I hear otherwise.

The front doors will be locked tomorrow.

Fuck, Aaron said, smacking his hands off some confectionery.

What about Sharon? I said. Surely she needs to inform us . . .

Didn't you hear? Sharon did a runner two days ago – took most of your bottled water in the stock room and the petty cash with her too.

What the fuck? Aaron shouted, now cupping the back of his neck with his hands.

Lewis shrugged again. She was clever about it. She has family in the Highlands, so maybe if she's been fast enough, and has fuel, she'll have made it. He turned to leave. You might as well take whatever you want in here. I doubt it matters now. But I won't have you phoning your friends and family though – can't have them coming round in the middle of the night to loot the place. So, whatever you want, take it quietly. And leave something for me.

Okay, I said. Thank you.

Lewis paused. Is Bobby looking for any workers? For calving?

I shook my head. I don't think so . . . We have someone helping us already.

Okay, he said, and then he was gone.

Aaron went to the fridge and removed a bottle of Fanta from the top shelf. He unscrewed the cap, flipping it across the floor, before bringing the bottle to his mouth. He reminded me of a baby bird trying to feed from its mother, a beak open vertical and wide. The drink was gone in three gulps. He discarded his bottle on to the floor too, before moving to the next aisle and opening a super-sized packet of pretzels.

Aren't you going to pick out what you want to take? he said.

But there was something about the way the confectionery was laid out that made me feel vulgar. It was all at my disposal and I wanted none of it. I eyed the caramel chocolate bars Bobby liked so much, and the boiled rhubarb and custard sweets Sam was partial to sucking on, dark chocolate for myself. Bounty bars for Mum – the only person I ever knew who took the Bounty from the Celebrations box first. And then there were the others – what would they like? It occurred to me that I had no idea. I took a bottle of cranberry juice and began drinking it, disliking the taste. It had never been that bad when mixed with vodka.

My mum will be grateful for anything I bring home, Aaron said. We could fill my car up, what do you say? And then I could drop you off home . . .

He handed me several empty carrier bags and I began to move down the aisles, searching for things I knew we'd eat. I filled one bag with all the chocolate and chewy sweets I could cram into it. In the crisps aisle I filled several bags with various flavours: salt and vinegar, prawn cocktail, cheese and onion. As an afterthought I grabbed some ketchup-flavoured ones too, knowing them to be Sam's guilty pleasure. More bags were filled with bottles of carbonated soft drinks, but I wasn't paying attention to the brands. I gathered all the bottles of water I could find and frantically began removing their security tags.

Mind and leave some for Lewis, Aaron said, throwing a tray of chewing gum into each of our bags.

I rammed bottle after bottle of spring water into the extra-durable carrier bags for us both, finally stopping to leave six under the counter for Lewis.

What else? Aaron said. There must be other things you want . . . Books?

It was a chart of bestsellers – all cookbooks and autobiographies, a few commercial novels. No, I said. I'm laden down with books.

He picked up a book that had a beach scene on the cover and threw it into one of his carrier bags. For my mum, he said. She likes that type of thing. He stopped at the small electronics section. You want any of this?

It was mostly travel adaptors. Why? I said. It's not like we can go anywhere.

Okay, he replied coming to a stop, surveying our destruction of the shelves. Will we go, then?

I hesitated, eyeing up the baby section. Wipes . . . I said, already making my way over and dividing out the packets. I began gathering nappies, checking their sizes.

Aaron touched my elbow. What do you need those for?

I flinched. I . . . does it matter?

He eyed me up, a quizzical expression on his face. Are you . . . ?

No, Aaron, I'm not pregnant.

His face grew red. I'll start taking some of the bags out, he said.

And I followed him, gripping what I could in my hands.

We had to make several trips to get all the bags into his car. And then in the darkness we stood, staring at each other. I became aware of music then, and turned. It was coming from the Premier Inn. I checked my phone again and there was a missed call from Mia.

I began to walk towards the hotel, Aaron following me. There was a path that linked the two buildings, but the slabs were cracked in places, with dead weeds poking through. I often struggled to tell the difference between a flower and a weed. They all grew. And, as I thought about this, I found myself stepping over the cracks like a child hopping from one slab to the next so as not to ruin a game.

Every light seemed to shine bright from the windows of the Premier Inn, music pulsing out of its flimsily built structure. We stood, peering through an empty window into the deserted reception. My finger hovered over the front door's buzzer. I pressed down and there was only static, before a male voice came over the speaker system.

What?

It's Aida. From the service station.

And?

Look, is Mia there? Get Mia.

The buzzer went, long and piercing, and the door was unlocked.

Inside, the reception desk looked as if it had been completely abandoned. A few papers were scattered across the counter; a computer monitor lay on the ground, its screen smashed. Two vending machines hummed with electricity, but they were empty, except for one packet of crisps, caught in the claws of the device, hanging in a permanent state of limbo.

We followed the sign for the restaurant, hearing the chatter of voices and music. The hinges squeaked as I opened the door, causing what felt like the entire room to turn and stare. There was a collective silence and a warmth rose from my neck upwards, spreading to my cheeks. I smiled. I was showing too many teeth.

Mia strode towards us. Are you ignoring me or something?

No . . . I said, glancing around. What's going on?

That's what I've been trying to tell you, she said. They're closing this place down. Some security firm is coming to seal the place up in the morning, so we thought we'd attempt to empty the place out. Have ourselves a wee party! She turned to take in Aaron, a smirk spreading across her face. Don't tell me that is back on . . . she said.

Will you stop behaving like a prick? I said. You know we work together.

It was only then that I really looked around the room, attempted to estimate the size of the party, find faces I might recognise. The space was massive – at least fifty tables spread throughout, behind pillars, down past the counter where they served the food. There were familiar faces, mostly from school, but there were others from the service station concessions, young farmers too, and I acknowledged them with awkward waves and smiles. A group of Aaron's friends ushered him over, and he smiled at me, shrugging, before leaving me to stand on my own. The tallest one of Aaron's friends, Steve, I think, had his arm laced around a girl's body. He was always sleeping with people younger than him.

So, do you know what you want to drink? Mia pressed.

What's open?

She started laughing. We've got the entire bar. There doesn't seem to be any champagne, but I've just opened a bottle of prosecco.

Prosecco's fine, I said.

She handed me a plastic champagne flute filled to the brim. The bubbles fizzed and popped in my mouth, and as I took my first sip I supressed the urge to burp.

Mia leaned in close, nodding towards Aaron. You're not actually going back there, are you? Her words were loud enough still to travel some distance. But if you're done with the last bloke you brought here, I wouldn't mind having a go.

Ignoring her, I said, don't you want to keep some of the booze for yourself, rather than just giving it away?

Why? she said, her tone casual. What's the point? So I can sit on my lonesome arse getting pissed with my mum, while the world goes to shit? If we're going down, don't you think it's better we all go down together?

And I smiled, embracing her.

A woman I recognised, wearing a purple shirt matching Mia's, came over. Do you remember Shona? Mia said. She was the year above us, in Aaron's year.

I nodded. Yeah, hi.

I think I cleaned a room you were in not so long ago, she said, smirking.

Okay . . .

Is it you who's related to Bobby? On the farm? I think my uncle is pals with him.

Yeah, that's me.

Is he still shacked up all queer with the cripple?

I swallowed, my eyes widening. Sorry, what?

She laughed before walking away with a tumbler in her hand. It was filled with a clear liquid, and, as she crossed the floor towards where Aaron and his friends stood, I watched some of it spill on to the carpet, darkening its colour.

Ignore her, Mia said. She's a bitch when she's drunk. She's usually alright. Not sure how I would have survived this job for so long if it hadn't been for her to be honest.

Really? I said, suppressing the urge to walk over and kick her in the shins.

Plus, I think she's always had a thing for Aaron.

What's she drinking? I asked, narrowing my eyes.

Why? You planning on spiking her or something?

Don't be stupid.

It's vodka.

Vodka and what?

Soda.

My mouth curled into a frown. Why would someone choose to drink that?

Honestly, just ignore her . . . She doesn't know what she's saying.

But as I stood watching Shona chat away to Aaron, I found myself imagining all the things I could have said in response. All the things I should have done to defend Bobby and Sam. Shame filled my insides. There was the memory of being at a farmers' ball and sitting at a table, while the men who surrounded me slurred homophobic rhetoric they thought hilarious, and me just sitting there letting it happen, smiling. I suspected they would have had a fair few things to say about me, and Mum too, no doubt.

There was a jukebox in the corner and Aaron and his group of friends migrated towards it, picking tunes. I was terrible with the names of songs. Music held moments in time for me, but the titles didn't seem significant. The sound intensified, a repetitive beat reaching its climax. They were bobbing their heads in time to the beat, knocking back shots of something green, Aaron clinking glasses with Shona, and I watched on, a pang of jealousy surfacing. I didn't want Aaron, but I didn't really want him to be with anyone else either. I wanted to be like one of those animals who marked their territory by leaving a scent. It was the greatest feeling in the world to be wanted – and Aaron had always made me feel wanted.

He threw back another shot and our eyes met. He smiled, hesitating, as if he was thinking of coming over, before seeming to change his mind, returning his attention to Shona.

*

I walked across one of the king-size beds in my bare feet, unable to remember the room number I was in. I had this urge to go and open the door to check, but kept forgetting. There were three other people in the room – a woman called Joanne who used to be in my form class and two guys I vaguely remembered from school – Tom and Graham. Tom could hardly stand, and Joanne was pressing him into the wall, kissing him, his arms dangling over her slender shoulders. I stood, enjoying the softness of the mattress under my feet when a hand reached up and gripped my ankle, pulling me down.

Graham laughed, releasing his grip on me. You were giving me a headache with all that jumping, he said. Chill for a minute, will you?

My head nestled into a pillow, and it felt as if the feathers and fabric were going to envelope me. Do you remember me from school? I said.

You were quiet. Pretty timid, I think.

You were the footballer. I started laughing. Everyone always wanted to kiss you at the school discos.

But not you? he said.

The thought of all those other mouths . . . I said.

He smiled. You think you're special, don't you?

Me? No. I'm nothing.

He sat up, his chin resting on the mattress. I can't quite put my finger on it.

I'm half-Egyptian, I said. Maybe that's it.

I didn't know that.

It wasn't something I wanted known, I said. Don't you remember how racist you all were? And homophobic too. I closed my eyes for a second, acknowledging the buzzing in my head. Probably still are, I added.

Is it your mum who's Egyptian?

I nodded.

My mum's Dutch, he said, offering me his half-drunk bottle of red wine.

I took a swig. It was cheap and harsh, but it didn't matter. I did fancy you, I mumbled.

He straightened, his elbows digging into the mattress. Do you still fancy me?

You're not my type any more.

Really?

I reached forward, vomit beginning to rise up my throat, and made it to the toilet before I threw up in the pan. Some of my vomit landed on the seat, stained red with wine, and I slumped on to my side, wiping my mouth with toilet paper. I tried to flush it all away, but the cistern was half-empty, and in defeat I lay back down on the bathroom floor and stared at a hairline crack on the porcelain sink stand. I let the strangest feeling wash over me – I was thinking that if something were to happen to me and I were to die right here on that bath mat I wouldn't particularly mind. It wasn't that I wanted to die; it was more that I didn't have the energy to fight, and I seemed okay about it. My fears and concerns felt too great to contemplate; how easy it would be, not to have to worry any more. I opened my mouth and spoke to the bathroom: If you were to take me right now, I'd let you. I wouldn't struggle.

There was a banging then on the door to the room, the sound of someone's fist thumping against it. I curled myself up further into a ball and wondered if this was the same room I'd been in with Peter. They were all identical. Someone once told me never to use the kettles, in hotel rooms, that things often found their way inside them. This same person had been on holiday to Majorca and had made a cup of coffee before lifting the lid to refill it, realising there was a dead cockroach inside, boiled alive.

The banging outside wouldn't let up. Slowly, I got to my feet and came out of the bathroom. Everyone else in the room appeared oblivious.

I flung the door open and a man I didn't recognise was facing me. The soda guns, they're all about to run dry, he said.

So?

Everyone's meeting in the bar to see out the last of it. Mia's saying it's important, so fucking move.

Downstairs the music was murmuring on low, and several people were behind the bar, removing bottles from their optics, lining up whatever they could find. Mia was standing on the bar shouting at everyone to be quiet. She held a soda gun in each hand, as if she was armed, ready to shoot. The clock said it was after 4 a.m.

See this? she said, pressing her index fingers down on the buttons. It's gone. That's it. She started to cry, letting the soda guns fall and hit the surface of the bar. That's it, she said. That's it.

People started jeering, thumping their feet off the floor and wolf-whistling. It was too loud. And when I looked back at Mia she was still sobbing, her head cast down towards her feet. Aaron appeared, placing a shot of something clear in my hand, knocking back his own, but I just gripped my glass.

Where's Shona? I asked.

He leaned forward then, stumbling, and tried to kiss me.

Our lips touched for a moment, a lovely familiarity returning, before I pulled away. No, Aaron . . .

He paused, crestfallen. I'm sorry . . . I don't know why . . .

It's okay, I said. It's just, I don't think we should.

He nodded.

Come with me, I said, and we made our way into the restaurant's kitchen and the walk-in fridge, looking to see what was left to eat. There was a frozen loaf of bread, and I began to toast slices, slathering them with cheap runny jam.

We perched ourselves up on opposite counters and ate silently. I could feel a smudge of jam above my top lip and tried to rub it away.

I'm not sure what I did wrong, he said. I thought we had a good thing going . . .

I hesitated, struggled to find the words I wanted to say. Aaron . . . I didn't think you even liked me that much. Like, I thought you were just killing time with me before you left for Bali.

A redness travelled to his cheeks. Yeah, well, maybe I never expressed myself properly.

Maybe I didn't either, I said, it's just . . . I hesitated, the alcohol confusing my thoughts. Look, it's not a big deal, okay, and I wasn't actually going to tell you but . . . last May, just after exams, I realised I was pregnant . . .

What?

So, I dealt with it, and everything is fine now.

He jumped off the counter and came towards me. Why didn't you say anything?

I shrugged. Why burden you with it too?

Because you went through something pretty serious, which I was partly responsible for . . . And you shouldn't have had to do that on your own.

My mum took me, so I wasn't alone.

He rubbed his face. I just . . . I'm sorry, Aida.

I shrugged again, at risk of crying. I couldn't really look at him. We both had our summers planned, I said. I didn't want to ruin anything.

He put his arms around me, embracing me and I didn't want him to let go.

So, what now? I said.

We stop drinking, he said. Wait for morning and go home just like we were meant to.

I'm scared, I said.

Me too.

We walked the corridors until we found an empty room. He watched me inject myself, sitting on the edge of the bed, before pulling the covers back and climbing in. When I lay down next to him, he clasped his hand to mine.

I woke again to someone banging on the door, a heavy thump, and it felt like reliving a dream. I tried to ignore the noise, but it only grew louder. It took a moment to orientate myself – my neck was sore, and I could hardly part my dry lips. The banging outside wouldn't let up. My head was pounding, and I closed my left eye, which seemed to help. Aaron stirred too, sitting up.

A man was shouting from the other side of the door. You do not have the right to be here. Please vacate the premises immediately.

It took all my effort to get to my feet. I could see my hands shaking in front of me. My phone was sitting on the bedside table and when I brought it to life I had twenty-six missed calls from Mum. The time was 9.42 a.m. Fuck, I said, slumping back on to the bed. I felt nauseous again but doubted there was any-thing left to bring up. I had an old familiar feeling. Of all the things to fear in the world, why was it Mum's reaction I feared the most? She'd never hit me; never even smacked me as a kid. It was her temperament though – the sense of unease that would hang over me for weeks, if not months, until the clouds passed and she'd return to her usual self. Or maybe it was just that I'd let her down so many times, lied too often, and now there was nothing left in her to give.

The banging was still going on. Did you hear me in there? the man shouted. Please vacate the premises immediately.

I couldn't find my shoes, but I opened the door anyway, while Aaron dragged himself upright behind me. The man who was waiting filled the frame of the door. He wore some sort of security outfit with a hi-visibility jacket.

I'm sorry, I said. We're leaving now.

What have you guys done? he asked. The place is destroyed.

We were asleep.

He shook his head, stepping aside to let us out.

We walked to the reception. The carpets were ruined, furniture had been dragged into the corridors and broken into pieces. We passed more security guards but I kept my head down, desperate not to be acknowledged. At the entrance, furniture was sitting outside on the dead grass. It looked as if people had been throwing objects from the windows above. Two televisions sat smashed on the pavement. Kettles lay with their lids missing, and an open bible fluttered in the slight breeze. We made our way along the linked path, me still barefoot, and I couldn't bring myself to check my voicemails or phone Mum back.

We stood in the car park of the service station, Aaron's boot filled with our looted goods, the milkshakes having been out of the fridge for hours, the chocolate probably melting. I stared at him, tears suddenly stinging my eyes. He came close and put his arms around me again. His response was so instinctive and sweet that it made me cry even harder.

Calm down, he whispered.

I'm sorry, I replied. Mum came for me . . .

I could feel him nodding through his hug, his chin bobbing above my head.

He patted my back. Where are your shoes?

I don't know.

The tarmac and stones were suddenly painful under my feet, and I hobbled forward, tiptoeing into the passenger seat of his car.

I don't think I can go back to the farm now, I said. I've made a fool of myself too many times.

It'll be okay.

He's dying, I said, the words just coming out as if they were nothing. Bobby. Did I tell you that?

No, you didn't.

I'm sorry. I feel like there's so much I don't tell you, when really it feels like you're the only one I want to tell anything to.

He reached forward and very gently placed a kiss on my forehead.

Aaron, if you get stuck . . . if you, or your mum, or your sister need anything, come to the farm, okay?

We can't do that, he said.

I started shaking my head. Just promise me, if things get too bad, you'll come.

He turned on his engine then and we left, not bothering to look back.

13

From our yard, I stood watching the convoy of vehicles approach from the bottom of the reservoir road. It felt as if everything was turning to dust, the heads of thousands of dandelions blowing through me in the mild breeze. Gemma's Volvo came rattling over the cattle grid first, the other vehicles close behind, and she came to a stop in front of me. I brought my hand up, instinctively gesturing an acknowledgement of hello. Several large agricultural trucks with trailers parked up, Department of Agriculture on the sides of their doors. There wasn't enough room in the yard for them all, and some had to park on the road.

When I walked back into Bobby and Sam's cottage they were waiting, Bobby standing by the fireplace while Rusty the dog sat curled up on Sam's knee, Sam stroking one ear. Mum too was huddled in a chair, arms wrapped around herself, while Evelyn, Peter and Rebecca kept their distance in the campervan.

They're here, I said.

I don't see how we come back from this, Bobby replied. Not again . . . Rusty jumped down from Sam and attempted to paw up at Bobby but was pushed away.

We managed after the foot-and-mouth and we'll manage again, Sam said, ushering Rusty back on to his knee.

Bobby's face broke then and he began to cry, reaching over for Sam's hand as he fell into his armchair. I couldn't recall ever having seen Bobby cry, but then I had been an infant during the last foot-and-mouth outbreak.

I came and crouched down beside Bobby, my hands cupping his knees. Eventually, he wiped his face, clearing his throat. Sorry, my lass, he said, placing his hand on my cheek. It's just . . . what are we without our livestock?

A silence descended upon us, and Bobby struggled out of his seat, walking with me to one of the front windows, peering out. The people outside were huddled together, deep in discussion, documents being exchanged. Bobby took a breath, swallowed. I think they're ready for us, he said.

What now? Mum asked.

Let me do the talking, Bobby said. The less opportunity these people have to ask questions, the better. He turned to face Sam. You ready for this?

Sam nodded.

Bobby gave the smallest flinch of pain as he made to leave, so determined was he not to show anyone he was struggling. Gemma was waiting for us, gravity in her expression as she approached wearing a full-body plastic suit like at the abattoir.

And so it begins, Bobby said, while we all shuffled out behind him.

Another man approached. Mr Sinclair, he said, I'm Dr John McMillan, I'm one of the veterinary officers from . . .

I know who you are, Bobby said.

We regret to inform you that you are within a cull zone under the government's Water Drought Act. I'm sure you're acutely aware of what that means.

Bobby scratched his head. I understand.

The man handed him some documents. This is everything that you need to know.

More people appeared in the yard wearing the same plastic suits. Bobby barely talked about the foot-and-mouth outbreaks, a trauma that still clung to him. Supposedly, he'd never kept whisky in the house until the first outbreak. And now he had a whole cupboard full of the stuff. I was glad to have no memory of it, in the same way that I was glad to miss a funeral, not wanting to face the awkwardness of someone else's grief directly.

Where do you want to start? Bobby said, flicking through the pages he'd been handed.

The cattle, the man said. Approximate numbers and their passports, please. All need to be accounted for.

Sam was already hobbling forward, ledgers of paperwork gripped to his chest. Cattle and sheep, he said, handing them to Bobby, who then handed them to the veterinary officer.

I'm sorry to be here, the man said. But we're living in difficult times. Take comfort if you can in knowing that you're not alone.

Bobby nodded, stoic.

We'll bury them on the premises, somewhere of your choosing. And of course, again, you'll be financially compensated . . . The government will reimburse you for loss of earnings.

Bobby snorted a laugh. It'll barely cover the cost that went into caring for them in the first place.

The team of people split up then, dividing into groups. Peter, who must have been watching, came out from the campervan to greet us.

Is there anything I can do to help? he said.

Bobby nodded. Maybe help organise the pits. The sooner we can have these fuckers off the land, the better.

I'll come too, Mum said. I should be there.

Sam reached out, lightly touching her elbow.

Bobby hesitated, and from his pained expression I could see that he was trying to find a way to save her from the experience, just as he understood her wish not to attend the abattoir. But slowly, he nodded. If you think you're up to it, Miriam, you'd be of great comfort to me.

Sam and I watched them depart, an assumption made that I was not needed, that I would not be of comfort to anyone other than Sam. We retreated inside, sheltering from the relentless sun, the clock on the mantel ticking away, neither of us finding anything to say. Eventually, Sam took himself off to the kitchen area and flicked on the kettle. Are you joining me? he asked.

Okay, I said, Might as well, while we still can . . .

What'd you mean?

While there's still water in the taps.

Don't read too much into things, he said.

I shrugged. Can't be good if they're restricting our travel and killing off our livestock.

Our little Aida, he said. Always so matter of fact.

He made the tea in a teapot before attempting to carry our two cups over on a tray, his knees looking as if they were about to snap under him. I came over, taking the tray, letting him settle back into his seat. When I lifted my cup, it was burning in my hands, and I placed it down on the floor, spilling a few drops on the flagstones. My eyes caught the hearth of the fire, it empty and swept – Sam finally no longer feeling his phantom chills.

He caught me looking and smiled, rubbing at his nostrils. I wish I had the knees to go out with them, he said.

I nodded, lifting the mug up to my lips, it scalding my tongue.

Reaching forward, he took a chocolate caramel bar from the tray and tore open the wrapper. It was one of the bars I'd brought back from my last night at the service station.

When are you and your mother going to start talking again? he said.

Do we have to discuss this right now?

You must understand, Aida. She thought you'd left us . . . Or that something had happened to you. There are horror stories out there about people going missing.

Suddenly, I could feel the tears, threating to leak out and I took another sip of tea if only to distract my central nervous system.

How is the cull carried out? I asked. How will they do it?

It'll be humane. He paused. Stun gun, I suspect. Quick and painless. It'll likely be Gemma who does the majority, and she knew the animals so . . . They'll be treated with respect.

What about the chickens? I said.

What about them?

Do they go too?

He shook his head. They're just considered pets, like Rusty and the sheepdogs. Just for us.

I stayed with Sam for hours, Rusty sleeping on his lap. At some point he attempted to make us lunch, although neither of us had much of an appetite. And as I sat sweating and picking at my food, I wondered if they separated the animals beforehand as they did in the abattoir, or if they just shot them in groups – mothers and siblings watching on. And it made me sick, the ultimate betrayal, when all they'd done wrong was be born.

When there was foot-and-mouth . . . I said.

Uh-huh.

What was it like? Will you tell me?

The plumes of smoke, he said. The smell of flesh. To see everything you've worked for be wiped away . . . It's the hardest thing in the world to contemplate. And you've no control over it. It's happening whether you want it to or not. It's like watching an illness take hold of a person. A grief of its own. He paused, all the while stroking Rusty's coat. We knew men who took their own lives after it happened, you know – it cast a shadow over the whole farming community, he added. But then, really, very little is ever within our control . . . Terrible things are happening to people everywhere. Right this very second someone somewhere will be experiencing something much worse than what we're going through now. Even in happy moments I can feel it, like we're all still connected to one another.

When the front door finally swung open, Bobby looked nearly ready to collapse, Mum bereft, while Peter appeared ravaged and demented. Their hands were thick with dirt, caked into the lines of their palms.

Is it done? I asked.

They're all leaving now, Bobby replied, walking into the open-plan kitchen and opening one of the cupboards. He removed what appeared to be an old bottle of whisky and three crystal tumblers. He began to pour large measures, his hands shaking, pushing the cups forward. Drink, he said, nodding to Mum and Peter. And they did so, without protest, no tremble or shake to their own hands.

Alone, and as dusk descended, I went back into our cottage and ran a shallow bath, enough water to clean myself without feeling too guilty. Crouched on my knees, a bar of soap in my hand, I began to scrub, and only when the water began to cool did I lie down, feeling somewhat better. The water lapped around my torso, my breasts and knees exposed, and I shuffled my weight, causing a mini tsunami to ripple past my toes. Taking a breath, I submerged my head and tried to open my eyes, but the sensation panicked me and the soapy water stung. Weird to think that too much water, as well as too little, had the potential to kill us. I remembered a thread I'd read about people getting rich from long-term water investments on the stock market, people *shorting* stocks, benefiting from the world's collapse. We were composed of more water than anything else, sixty per cent; so much water just walking around. I surfaced then, unable to hold my breath any longer, my lungs weak.

In the kitchen I sat for a while with another cup of tea. I stared out of the window towards the darkness of the yard, a torch shining behind the curtains of the campervan. When had the van last run? Would its battery be dead yet, condemned to a life like my Corsa? My tea turned lukewarm, but I continued sipping it. I couldn't quite bring myself to reheat it in the microwave the way I'd seen both Bobby and Sam do hundreds of times before. I'd never been a fan of microwaves: the image of liquids boiling under electric currents. The one in the service station often had mould up its sides or a puddle of condensation sitting under the plate, germ-riddled. I didn't dare look inside our own microwave for fear of what I would find, although maybe Evelyn had cleaned it without us even noticing.

Mum came in through the back door, seeming a little startled to see me, but she acknowledged me with a nod, which was more than I had been getting.

Are you okay? I said.

She didn't say anything, just closed her eyes for a moment.

Please will you talk to me, I said. I'm sorry, again, for what happened at the service station.

Still, she said nothing. She was capable of cradling her hostility, holding it over us for weeks until she was satisfied by our suffering. Was it some perversion of hers, to want to inflict minor cruelties on those she loved? Maybe it felt like the easiest way to assert herself. Maybe I deserved it.

Please, Mum, I can't take it any more.

She really was unable to look at me.

I had a memory of the hospital then, me waiting on a bed with a bedpan between my legs, expecting at any moment the blood clots to fall, the earliest form of what might have become a baby. There was still no regret, only the image of Mum's disappointment. I think she had expected me not to be able to go through with it.

Do I disgust you? I said.

She took my tea from me and sipped it, wincing at its lukewarm temperature.

Mum, please, do I disgust you?

Of course not.

So why keep punishing me? I've said I'm sorry. I don't know what else I can do . . .

I just feel like I don't even know my own daughter any more. We used to be close.

Did we?

A wounded expression settled on her face and immediately I regretted my words. She stared at me, really taking me in. You've always just behaved as though there are no consequences for anything, that others will pick up the pieces. And even now, after I've just witnessed a mass culling of animals I helped rear, you're still just behaving as if everything is all about you.

I see the way you look at Rebecca, I said. Constantly checking her blood pressure even though it's been fine since she started on those tablets. You're obsessed with her.

You're being ridiculous, she said.

I think that you wish she were your daughter, that the baby growing inside her were your grandchild.

She exhaled. Has Evelyn put this stupid idea in your head?

I stared at her; I wanted to scream. As a kid I had taken issue with her behaving like a mother to others, especially when I thought she could have been more of a mother to me. And yes, rationally I knew that Rebecca needed her attention, even her love and affection more than I did, but still, the five year old in me wanted to pull her way, claim her as my own, tell her that I still needed her.

You've no idea how hard it is to be your daughter, I said. To live under the weight of your expectations.

Mum snorted a laugh. Do you know what I think? I'm so grateful you never had to grow up in Cairo because, in all honesty, I think you would have failed. You don't have the attention span to stick at things the way you'd need to, to come out on top – compete with the millions of other children all vying for the same opportunities and education. Can you even contemplate being taught your school subjects in another language from the age of six? My English is perfect. I was formulating my thoughts in English long before I even moved here. How is your Arabic? She paused. So, yes, I will be forever grateful for the abundance of opportunities you have been given here, even if you don't appreciate them.

What opportunities? I shouted. The world's fucked!

She let out a scream then, one of real frustration, something that came from deep inside. Do you have *any idea* what I've just witnessed today? Can you possibly even begin to imagine?

Suddenly I was on my feet, pulling on a pair of trainers by the back door.

Where are you going *now*? she demanded.

I was already slamming the door.

I found Peter hovering outside the campervan, and I stopped in front of him. Where are the pits? I asked.

He pointed in their direction. About half a mile up past the sheds, he said. On the flat stretch of land that Bobby suggested.

I nodded, already walking away.

His footsteps were behind me, catching up. Why do you want to see it?

I want to know how much space they took up.

You are so strange, he said.

We walked in silence until finally we were there. The land looked as though someone was harvesting crops, that perhaps in months to come something good would grow and prosper. There was a faint noise coming from somewhere in the distance and I glanced around, pulling my phone from my pocket, turning on the touch and flashing it from left to right. What was that? I said.

It'll just be a badger or something, he said.

All the badgers died off, I said. Didn't you know? Supposedly they could be extinct. I directed my torch back to the shallow field. You'd never know it was a mass grave, I said.

I don't know what you were expecting . . .

Maybe I thought it would help me mourn.

He looked at me, my phone-torch illuminating his face. Do you mind not shining that thing in my eyes?

I turned it off.

They're only animals, he said, a vacantness to his voice. I don't see how you can be so attached when they were ultimately always going to end up this way.

When I returned, Mum was in the kitchen on the phone to Dad, telling him the livestock were gone. I sat down at the table beside her and closed my eyes, imagined them both standing there together, debating, contemplating what to do next. She was asking him if he was managing on the new water limit of twenty-five litres, asking whether the municipal pumps in his area were holding up okay. I had this great urge to be hugged by them both, us all together, locked in a tight little circle.

I went into the living room and turned on the television. The news was on, BBC Scotland, and I stood back to take it in for a moment, wanting to know if there'd be any information about these travel restrictions they'd implemented, how long they were likely to last. There was a segment about thousands of fish dying, birds too, all from botulism as disease built up in stagnant, de-oxygenated and nutrient-deficient water. I hadn't even realised botulism was still a thing. The anchor was pleading with us not to eat any dead animals if found. And then attention turned to our current water situation – we were to be assured that municipal water pumps across the country were keeping up with the demand, that there were government plans in place for mass redistribution, that if they had to drain and treat the water in thousands of Scotland's lochs then that was what they would do. The desalination plants were going to redefine our relationship to the sea, acidic or not. We would be reunited with each other soon – the government had reason for optimism.

And then, as the anchor was signing off for the night, the screen froze, the transmission cutting out. I held the remote in my hand, began turning the channels, but it was all the same – just static.

I ran back into the kitchen. Mum, I said, desperately needing her reassurance. There's no more TV . . .

She was gripping the cream slimline phone, the receiver away from her ear. He's gone, she said.

Is it a power cut?

She looked up at the brightness of the kitchen light and slowly shook her head.

When they don't know what to do, they restrict our movements and cut off communication, she said.

No, I replied, refusing to accept what she was saying. I took the phone from her and brought the receiver to my ear, jabbing Dad's number frantically.

Aida, there's no dial tone, she said, but I didn't let that stop me. I supposed I thought that if I just kept pressing the buttons, if I did it really fast, then it wouldn't matter – that I'd get through to him.

Mum prised the phone from my hand, placing the receiver back down on the cradle. She gripped my shoulders, wrapping her arms around me. It's okay, my *habibi*.

I pressed my weight into her. What now?

We should fill up the baths and the sinks, she said. Before they turn the water off for the night. Just to be on the safe side.

Mum ran out towards Bobby and Sam's cottage to plug their bath, while I headed into our bathroom and plugged both the sink and bath, turning on the cold taps as far as they would go. The tub began to fill but the pressure of the water was down – it had dwindled significantly since my shallow bath earlier in the evening. And was the water cloudier than usual? Was I imagining it? I thought about Mum's water-purifying tablets balancing above the doorframe in her storage cupboard, visualised them fizzing away like a bath bomb. The pressure continued to wane as it filled to nearly three-quarters full. And then I heard a rattling, like something being forced up through the pipes.

I just stood there, shaking my head, refusing to accept what I was seeing, except that it was true. We had been waiting for it. Day Zero.

The water drew to nothing more than a trickle, tapering off to droplets. I must have stood there for a long time, just staring at the water before finally reaching over and turning the tap off.

When I straightened, Mum was standing behind me. Is this happening? I said. I'm not imagining this?

We'll check again in the morning, Mum said. It might not be as bad as we think. It might be okay in the morning.

14

Mum and I sat in Bobby and Sam's in silence, none of us knowing what to say about anything. The livestock culling had been almost too much to bear, and now the water. We kept checking the taps. Every hour since 7 a.m. But there was nothing in them – a trickle at best, the reservoir completely bone-dry.

Bobby was sporting this ghostly complexion, paler than I'd ever seen him before. He kept his gaze eerily fixed on his worn hands, clasped together and resting on his knees, while Rusty lay at his feet. Eventually, he said, It's so quiet, isn't it?

Sam's eyes were read and bloodshot as if he'd been crying. I found stacks of paper plates and cups, he said. Must have kept them after we had that community picnic a few years ago . . . I suppose we should start using them so there's less to wash.

Should we tell our guests about the water? Mum said, nodding her head out towards where the campervan was parked. It's not like it'll be any different for them. They're used to being handed rations.

It's not exactly a secret, Bobby said. And they'll find out soon enough, one way or another.

We should figure out exactly how much we have, she said. We've got close to a bathful, and so have you. And there's the tank hidden in the cattle shed. We need to settle on how much we should be using each day – what's to be divided out for drinking and cooking with, what's needed for the vegetable plot and the chickens . . .

Is it enough? I said.

Bobby was quiet for a moment. There is water on this land, he said, a quiet hopefulness entering his voice. It's been here for thousands of years. We just need to find it again.

Mum let a silent laugh escape through her nostrils. No offence, Bobby, but that really doesn't help us right now.

Sam got up and struggled over to the kitchen area. Would anyone mind if I made some tea? Just a small cup . . .

Bobby smacked his fist off his knee. Sam, make a bloody cup of tea. We're not animals.

Maybe someone should go into the village, I said. See if everyone else's water has gone off. Find out about the nearest municipal water point . . .

Sam nodded. That's a good idea.

Take the boy, Bobby said. He could do with the distraction after what he had to witness yesterday with the livestock.

I don't think things like that bother him, I said.

I don't think you're in a position to say that, he replied.

Outside, there appeared to be little movement behind the curtains of the campervan. I knocked on the door. It took a moment before someone opened it. Peter stood there, dishevelled, his clothes filthy, staring down at me from his elevated position.

That's the water finally stopped, I said.

Maybe I was hoping for fear to be present in his eyes, for anxiety to be flickering across his face, but there was nothing. I suppose it was time, he said, nodding, stepping down from the campervan towards me, closing the door behind him. Nothing lasts for ever, he added.

I suppose so. I turned around to look behind me, acknowledging the sheepdogs whimpering, waiting in their outhouse with no real purpose. I'm going to go into the village to see if I can get any information . . . Do you want to come?

Peter drove; it wasn't even a discussion. He rested his elbow on the frame of the open window, an odour lingering, and we hurtled pass the empty reservoir.

To get to the village, we had to pass the Corsa I'd abandoned on the road. Peter came to a sudden stop behind it, the unexpectedness jolting me forward in my seat. We both got out of the vehicle and circled the Corsa. The thing had been ravaged, not that I thought there'd been much to take in the first place. Inside, the seats had been slashed as if people were expecting to find something within them; the bonnet was open, the battery removed, among other things. Peter just stared at it, and it was so incredibly depressing. I could barely take the sadness in his posture.

When we got back on the road, Peter thrashed the Defender around, taking sharp corners in third gear, and I thought if there had been any other vehicles coming in our direction we would have collided with them – could visualise it all happening in slow motion.

We parked in the little Co-op car park, but the place was closed. The main street through the village was deserted too. There was a kids' play park, dilapidated, and I could remember playing in it as a child after school, the days when we didn't have to rush back to the farm.

We walked along the main road and came to a stop outside a seventies-looking roughcast building that had been the police station. It was boarded up, all signs and lettering removed.

We carried on. I'm pretty sure the postman lives in one of these cottages along here, I said. If anyone knows something, it'll be him.

Postmen don't know everything, Peter said.

The cottage was easy to find because the postal van was still sitting outside on the main road, its tyres slashed. I hesitated, hating the idea of disturbing someone, but Peter reached past me and lifted the knocker, dropping it heavily on the worn wooden door.

Nothing.

Maybe he's not in, I said.

Peter was now peering through one of the front windows. There's someone hiding, he said. I can see them . . . He knocked again, and then again, and again, until I thought the brass knocker might come away in his hand.

Finally, the door opened a crack, and there was the village postie, Donald, peering out. He was maybe in his fifties, a crooked, demanding nose, a bachelor all his days despite several women trying to set up blind dates.

What do you want? he spat.

Sorry, I'm Aida, Bobby's . . .

I know who you are, he said, his eyes shifting suspiciously to Peter.

Look, I just . . . The water went off at the farm and I wanted to check if it was the same for everyone . . . And find out where the municipal water pump is . . .

He was silent for a moment. There is none.

What do you mean?

He cast his hands out before us. Do you see one? I don't. I think they only have them in the cities.

So, what are people meant to do? I said.

Nothing, I suspect. There is no help coming. Not now they've blocked the roads.

They wouldn't just abandon everyone, would they? I said.

No one looks out for each other any more, he whispered, his eyes now fixing on the ground. That's what probably got us in this mess in the first place. There is no community, just each person, trying to keep themselves afloat. He brought his eyes up then. I even heard some people were going down to the old flooded lead mines and taking water. Can you imagine? Desperate enough to consider drinking lead water?

Are you alone? I said.

Why do you want to know?

We just want to make sure you're okay, Peter replied.

Did you hear about Sally and her bairn?

Who? I said.

She used to work down at the wee hair salon next to the chemist in town . . . Well, she's dead, he said. The bairn too.

How did it happen?

They're saying it's an *accident*. She used to have that wee lassie on the swings every day.

When I looked up at him, I could see his eyes were stinging with tears.

Okay, thanks for your time, I said.

We walked back along the road, but as we approached the entrance to the play park Peter stopped, staring at the slide and swings for a moment, before entering through the gate, the hinges squeaking.

What are you doing? I hissed, but he was already making big strides towards the slide, climbing the ladder, two steps at a time. At the top, he forced his frame into the narrow seating position.

I came and stood at the bottom. Please will you come down from there, I said.

He stared at me, an excited tone to his voice. I just want to know what it's like.

What are you talking about?

What it's like to play in a play park.

You've never been to a play park . . . ?

He came flying down then, the cotton of his joggers appearing to accelerate him. He planted his feet on the ground, beaming. That's better than I expected, he said. He lay flat, legs extended out, eyes closed, basking in the sun. His posture was so startling to me, so *no fucks*, that I stood there for a while just taking him in.

What's wrong with you? I said.

What do you mean?

How can you say you've never played in a play park before?

Well, maybe I have, but I can't remember.

We should get going, I said.

He was already climbing up the slide, the wrong way, and I irrationally wanted to tell him to use the ladder.

You should have a shot, he said.

No.

I got my phone out from my back pocket and tried to find some internet signal but there was nothing, only buffering. Peter came shooting down the slide again, planting his feet next to me, his knees capable of clamping me to the spot. I'm not leaving until you've been down this slide, he said.

Why?

He shrugged. Don't you think it's worth having a nice moment occasionally?

I rolled my eyes. Are you serious?

He nodded.

I ascended the steps, secretly pleased to be copying him. But I was wearing shorts and my bare legs caused nothing but friction. I had to shuffle down the last section, much to Peter's amusement.

I finally got to my feet, aware of curtains twitching from some of the cottage windows directly across from us. Can we go back now? I said.

He turned and walked away, leaving me sitting on the bottom of the slide.

By the time I reached him he'd already turned the engine of the Defender on. And as I attempted to get in he moved the vehicle forward, only a few inches but enough to make me think that he could leave me behind.

We arrived back in the yard to find Mum sitting on the wooden bench in front of Bobby and Sam's cottage. Her posture was straight, unnatural, and she was staring at the campervan. On the other side of her I could see knitting needles, yellow wool, knotted in a ball.

What's that? I said, pointing to the knitting.

She glanced down at the wool, almost embarrassed. I'm making an umbilical cord hat for the baby, she said. It's silly.

It's not silly, I replied.

All has been very quiet, she said, directing her words to Peter rather than me.

Are you stalking us? he said, trying to inject an unfamiliar humour into his tone.

Is the baby coming? she asked.

Peter didn't say anything.

You're not helping anyone by not saying, she said. That girl hasn't been in the best of health, and she may well suffer if assistance isn't offered to her.

Peter hesitated, looking from the campervan to Mum and back again.

Tell Evelyn I'm coming now, she said. And I'm bringing Aida with me.

I turned to look at her, horrified, wanting no part of this, but Peter was already walking towards the campervan, opening the door and disappearing. I imagined him locking the doors from the inside, refusing to let us come near Rebecca.

Why do I have to come? I said, my voice pleading.

We may need all the help we can get.

Peter opened the back cabin door of the campervan, standing aside to let us in. The place was immaculately clean, the small kitchen counters free of clutter, utensils hanging from hooks, everything designed to have its place. Yet a corrosive stench still hit me as I stepped further into the living quarters. Glancing up above the driver's cabin I could see a stained-looking duvet hanging down from the bunk and imagined Peter sleeping in the space, contorting his limbs to fit. There was a closed door, which I assumed led to the toilet they were often trying to empty, and where the corrosive smell seemed to be radiating from. Finally, towards the back of the campervan there was a table with padded seating surrounding three sides, Rebecca squeezed into one, struggling but silent.

Mum went straight to her. How long has she been like this?

The baby has been trying to come for some time, Evelyn replied with an even tone. Her waters broke yesterday evening. But she only began having contractions earlier today.

Why didn't you tell me? Mum demanded.

I had it under control. Had hoped the baby would have made its appearance by now.

I must check her, Mum said. Please, can I check her?

Evelyn hesitated before nodding.

I need antiseptic wipes to clean my hands, Mum said.

We've some in the toilet, Evelyn replied.

And I was the one standing closest to the door so it was assumed that it should be me that retrieved them.

I opened the door and was hit by this putrid, acidic smell. I gagged and clamped my mouth shut, grabbing the wipes that sat on a little shelf above the toilet/shower, closing the door quickly behind me.

I'm sorry, Evelyn said. I know it's bad.

Mum wiped her hands and wrists frantically, swabbing around her fingernails and the grains of dirt encrusted underneath. Aida, she shouted, as if I were standing outside and not directly behind her. Get some water. A basinful if you can. Get towels too. Whatever you can grab. Now.

I ran, stumbling out of the campervan, across the gravel of the yard and into our kitchen. I grabbed the empty washing up bowl sitting next to the sink and continued on into Mum's bedroom, throwing open one of her cupboards, gathering old, bleach-stained towels, stacks of them toppling in my arms. In the bathroom I stood at a distance from the tub as if I was fearful of what I'd find and peered in; a few stray hairs floated in the water, captivating in their movements. I dunked the washing up bowl into the water, then brought it up, careful not to spill anything, the weight heavy in my hands.

I hurried back to the campervan, balancing the bowl with towels tucked under my arms, that caustic smell hitting me again once inside.

I offered Mum the towels, while Peter placed the bowl down by her feet.

I allowed myself to look at Rebecca properly for the first time. Evelyn was brushing her matted hair back from her face. There was no protest from Rebecca but there was little warmth either. Rebecca's eyes were closed, and Evelyn began to sway her in her seat, rocking her the way you would a newborn.

Why is the baby not coming? Evelyn demanded.

It's footling breech, Mum said. The baby . . . it's coming the wrong way.

Are you sure?

I have delivered enough babies to know when one is in the wrong position, Mum said. The soles of two little feet are coming first.

I felt nauseous, at the image of it, the acid rising in my throat.

Rebecca's eyes were still closed, pain shaking through her body, and Evelyn positioned herself now so that Rebecca's head rested across her lap. I stared at the markings on Rebecca's legs: perfectly formed circles and wondered what had caused them. Cigarettes? It was then I noticed she was missing the top of her middle toe, just a small stump, long-standing scarring where a toenail should have been. She remained silent while her body fought against what was happening to her. She didn't make a sound, nothing more than a whispered gasp – everything she did, she did in silence.

Rebecca, I need you to shuffle forward if you can, Mum said. I want your pelvis to be in line with the end of this seat. Can you do that for me?

Evelyn began trying to shuffle her, asking Peter to help manoeuvre her legs, which he did without hesitation.

I should go, I said.

Wait in the front cabin, Mum ordered. If we need help, we'll need it fast.

I nodded, horrified but obedient, taking myself to the passenger seat in the front cabin, the fabric ripped, wadding trying to escape from the seams. Peter forced himself down into the driver's seat, the large steering wheel in his hands like he was ready to take us for a drive. He turned to look at me, opened his mouth to say something, before deciding against it.

We shouldn't touch her, Mum was saying. It needs to be hands off. We're hoping for a spontaneous vaginal breech delivery; we don't want to introduce too much interference at this stage.

What does that mean? Evelyn shouted. We can't just leave her like this.

I kept my focus straight ahead; couldn't bear to look round.

We have her in the right position, Mum said. If I touch the baby while it's trying to come I could slow down the process and cause the baby distress. Mum's voice was different, a serious, professional tone. Do you understand? Once the umbilical cord emerges, I will be able to intervene.

Through the windscreen, another beautiful afternoon sky spread out before us. There was a digital clock, but it was set to the wrong time – saying it was 6:21p.m. when it couldn't have been past 3 p.m. Pieces of paper and junk were crammed into every space imaginable and I tried to focus on each individual item, anything to drown out the noise of Mum and Evelyn – anything to stop me from thinking about the water too.

I can see it's a boy, Mum was saying. Hold him gently for support while I try and guide the head out.

Peter gripped the steering wheel tightly. Around the rear-view mirror hung an old Alpine air freshener, like a dried cotton swab now. I had this urge to lick it, imagined it feeling like a dehydrated tongue. I clenched my bottom, my thighs pushed tightly together. I couldn't really comprehend the idea of what was happening to Rebecca's body. What was taking place behind me didn't seem anything like the most natural thing in the world.

And then there was this baby, screaming, really exercising his lungs, and I spun around in shock. Mum was wiping mucus away from around his nose and mouth, the way she would with a lamb. And only then did I realise that I hadn't expected the baby to survive. Like an omen, I'd subconsciously assumed that the fate of this child was to have been the same as that stillborn calf Bobby had shown Peter how to skin. And it was overwhelming, the noise of this baby causing me to cup my ears.

223

Do you have a blanket? Mum said.

Evelyn began rummaging in cupboards, pulling clothes out sporadically. She threw an old jumper at Mum. This is cosy, she said. It always kept me warm.

And Mum began to swaddle the baby in the bobbled sweater, wrapping and tucking the sleeves in around him.

Evelyn took the baby from Mum, cradling him into her. I was aware of Rebecca trying to pull herself up into a sitting position. Wait, Mum said, trying to press her back down. We need to clamp and cut the cord. She opened one of the drawers and found a bread knife. Do you have twine or something I can knot the cord with?

Evelyn nodded towards the cupboard above Mum's head, her gaze still locked on the baby. Mum found a roll of ribbon, like what you'd wrap around a parcel, and cut off a length before tying a tight knot around the umbilical cord.

Rebecca buried her cheek into the cushion of the seat and looked out of the back window, to the view of our empty fields. She made no move to engage with her child, no gesture of holding her hands out to take him from Evelyn. And I understood, believed that not everyone had a maternal instinct. That sometimes maybe love didn't conquer all.

I carried on staring at Rebecca, who was still gazing out of the window, lifeless and vacant. There was blood and bodily fluids everywhere.

Does Rebecca want to hold him? Mum asked, directing her question to Evelyn.

The baby began to whimper, building himself up into a cry, and Evelyn began to pace around the cramped space, gently rocking him. But within seconds she had lost all control of his emotions, her shushing having little effect.

I think he wants his mother's milk, Mum said.

Rebecca stared out blankly.

Evelyn began to shake her head, as though she was waking from a dream, confused by her surroundings. She shuffled herself around the frame of the table then, along the sofas until she was next to Rebecca. She began pulling at the string that was tied in a knot across the top of Rebecca's kaftan. I watched Evelyn remove Rebecca's breasts, small and flat like pancakes. She forced the baby into her arms and began trying to align a breast to the baby's mouth. The baby fussed and cried, his face turning left and right, his mouth open like a little beak, waiting to be fed.

Evelyn was flustered. I've never done this before, she said. I never breastfed.

I can help, if you'd let me . . . Mum replied.

The crying escalated into a piercing wail, while Rebecca turned away from Evelyn, forcing her to retreat. Mum extended her arms out and reluctantly Evelyn offered the baby up to her. Slowly, Mum shuffled in around the table until she was next to Rebecca. Mum stroked some hair away from her face, her touch gentle and tender. Rebecca looked down, taking her baby in for the first time, her hands slowly coming up to touch him, and Mum settled him in her arms, aligning the baby to her chest, nose to nipple. Rebecca closed her eyes. And finally, her baby managed to find what he was looking for, a calmness descending upon the campervan as he began to feed.

15

We were filthy, Mum allowing everyone only two baby wipes a day for our general hygiene, the toilets off limits except during the night, the land now used for relieving ourselves, a spade and a few sheets of toilet paper for anything more than a piss. I felt mostly for Rebecca – the idea of not being able to shower or wash yourself properly after childbirth, after all the blood and mucus – she looked emotionally and physically destroyed. Sheep and cows had perfected the talent of licking themselves clean; perhaps that was what we'd end up resorting to.

Since the baby's arrival, Mum had also relaxed her rule about not letting our guests get too familiar. There had been no request either for them to push on, not there was anywhere for them to go with the travel restrictions still in place. And despite it feeling like the world was ending, it was nice; I remembered being grateful for the shift in dynamics.

Evelyn sat on Bobby and Sam's sofa, cradling the baby in her arms, a flustered quality to her approach, while Rebecca sat silently next to her. By no means did Evelyn come across as a natural grandmother, but I kind of got it. I didn't think I was the type of person capable of holding a baby properly. Some people, like Mum, just seemed to be drawn to babies, pulled in by their energy, but that had never been me.

The baby began to cry and Mum hustled in, scooping him up from Evelyn, bringing him upright, his head cradling in next to her neck. He's an upright baby, she said. Loves being upright, so he does.

I wondered what it was that Mum couldn't get enough of – perhaps it was his innocence, enough to stir some form of hope in her pessimistic heart. We were obsessed with ensuring no harm came to a child, that their innocence wasn't taken too soon. Bobby and Sam must have felt the same, because they were so serene around him, almost euphoric.

Does the wee fella have a name yet? Bobby said, peering down towards him, a warm expression settling across his face.

Noah . . . ? Evelyn said. But we're in no rush to confirm. It could easily change.

Are you hungry? Mum asked Rebecca, crouching down in front of her, the baby safely in her arms.

Rebecca didn't respond, only lowered her head further.

She's so tired, Evelyn said. I want her to rest as much as possible. Not have to worry about the baby . . .

Mum nodded, her face trying to remain diplomatic. A baby needs to know his mother's smell, though, she said. It's good bonding for them to spend lots of time together.

Rebecca just sat there, indifferent, as if none of this was anything to do with her. Maybe Evelyn wanted to be seen as *the* mother instead. Weren't there stories of underage and unmarried girls having babies, and the grandparents raising them as their own? A girl having to feign delight at the arrival of a new sibling . . .

How is his feeding getting on? Mum pressed.

Evelyn shrugged. So-so . . . He feeds a lot.

Mum smiled. They tend to do that at the beginning. She reached forward and waved in Rebecca's face, suddenly and unnaturally needing to obtain her attention. Rebecca looked up and stared at her, the smallest hint of a smile perhaps trying to surface. I thought we could try some baby massage, Mum said. Evelyn mentioned that he's been very unsettled during the night.

You can show me how to do it . . . Evelyn said.

Mum held up a hand. I think it would be good for Rebecca to learn, she said, if that's okay with you.

Evelyn hesitated before nodding.

Mum pulled a blanket off from the arm of Sam's chair. Okay if I use this? she asked, looking up at him, already spreading the fabric out across the floor.

Yes, he replied. Of course.

It's really good for bonding, Mum said, settling Noah on the blanket, smiling down at him and rubbing his belly. He was wearing a little yellow duck babygro Mum had found from up the loft, most likely an outfit I myself had worn as a newborn.

So, Mum said, addressing Rebecca with her hands. Do you want to come down here?

Rebecca didn't initially move, and Evelyn had to nudge her.

Mum shuffled out of the way, allowing Rebecca to kneel on the floor, Noah's little feet centred in front of her. Mum then began undoing the poppers of his babygro until his bare legs were exposed, a nappy from my service station supply wrapped around his torso. This should be nice for him, she said. He'll enjoy it.

Mum removed a small bottle of oil from a pocket in her redundant overalls, squeezing some on to her hands, rubbing them together. Okay, she said. You watch me and then you have a go. She began thumbing Noah's little toes, running her fingers under the sole of his right foot, lightly applying pressure. She then began to rub his leg, up past his thigh until she arrived at his nappy line. As she began massaging back down his leg he stared at her, content. Your turn, Mum said to Rebecca, offering her the oil.

Slowly, Rebecca offered the palms of her hands up to Mum, and she squeezed oil on to them, was encouraged to rub them together. And then, nodding her on, we watched Rebecca copy Mum's movements with Noah's left leg, her touch reluctant, as if she was likely to break him.

With any luck this will help settle his stomach, Mum said.

Will it stop him from waking so often in the night? Evelyn asked.

I suspect he has a touch of gastric reflux, Mum replied. So, until his stomach matures, I imagine he'll continue to be unsettled when lying horizontal for prolonged periods of time. She paused. But yes, hopefully, this will help.

When I looked down Rebecca and her baby were staring at each other, eyes locked, as she carried on rubbing his skin, stroking his downy hair. She was smiling.

I'm not sure how long we all spent sitting there, watching her rub her child's skin, but there was something mesmerising about it. It was the first time my mind had taken a break from thinking about the water. There was an agitation in everything I did, this sickening dread that had taken root in my stomach and stopped me from sleeping.

Afterwards, as I made to leave, I was aware of Bobby close behind me, following me over the threshold and out into the yard. He gripped an old carrier bag, folded over like a parcel in his hand, and with a glint in his eye he brought his mouth close to my ear. Do you have something pressing you need to do? he asked.

Is that a joke?

He ushered me further into the yard, all secretive and cautious, glancing behind to check if anyone was following us. I want you to come with me across the land, he whispered.

Why?

To find the water.

I stared at him. No way, I said. Mum and Sam won't go for it. You're in no fit state to be going anywhere.

He took me by my arm, half-guiding me, half-leaning on me as we headed towards my kitchen. Inside, he closed the door behind us, suddenly inspecting the counters.

We don't have long, he said. Do you have some biscuits?

Yeah . . .

Okay, well, bring some, just a few.

I was shaking my head, but I still opened a cupboard, removing a few digestive biscuits, accepting that Bobby always got his way.

I grabbed an empty water bottle too, the mouthpiece practically chewed to pieces. In the bathroom I dunked it under the remaining bathwater, particles of dust and a few more stray hairs floating on the surface.

We set off, passing the section of barren land that we now used as our own mini landfill, continuing on past several fields, the sheepdogs in tow, everyone else apparently unaware of our disappearance. As we hit a steadier incline the sheepdogs looped themselves around in excitement, so deprived of purpose, while Bobby began to slow, struggling to keep up with what I thought was a modest pace.

There is no need for you to be trekking up here, I said, turning to inspect him. I can't exactly drag you back down by the ankles. And if anything happens to you, Sam will never forgive me.

Oh, would you wheesht, he choked. I'm still more than capable of accessing any point on this land.

It's too hot for this, I replied. We should have more water with us. Maybe we should turn back.

It's water we're going for, he said. He was wearing his tweed cap, hiding the wispy strands of grey he refused to cut off, and

231

when he rubbed his sweaty forehead he forced the cap to sit squint, pointing at an awkward angle. He held a shepherd's crook, which he thumped into the baked ground, steadying his balance. Taking a moment to catch his breath, he looked out as if he was truly trying to survey the land. It's still a beautiful place, he said. Don't you think, despite everything?

I nodded.

The dogs were panting, their tongues hanging loose, pink and dry. I reached down with my water bottle and squirted some into one mouth and then the next. I felt sorry for them in the sweltering heat. It was unfair that they couldn't sweat through their coats.

If anyone sees you doing that they'll lynch us, Bobby said.

When I glanced at him, his head was turned away and his eyes were closed, as though he was meditating, eerily calm and at peace.

What's going to happen to this place, Bobby?

He smiled, rubbing his nose. Somehow, they've convinced us all that we're each other's enemy, he said, that one another is to blame for this mess. But this drought, whatever this is – we as individual people didn't cause it. Our little livestock farm isn't to blame for all of this. We just didn't have the big fancy lobbyists fighting our corner.

The whole system's flawed, isn't it? I said. None of us were ever going to manage reversing anything. It was inevitable. We didn't have it in us.

It all just used to make so much more sense, Bobby said. I never felt guilty about how we conducted ourselves. Never felt guilty about our livestock business. We had employees who enjoyed working here. We cared for the animals we reared.

Do you remember a few years ago when we went ten-pin bowling across the border for our Christmas party? I said, smiling.

He laughed, although it seemed to cause him discomfort. You're a terrible bowler, aren't you? Refused to even put your fingers in the holes.

No wonder, I replied. Have you any idea how many other people's fingers have been inside those things. It's an absolute breeding ground. Even the idea gives me the boak . . .

He paused then. Go on ahead, he said. I need to take a leak and I could be some time.

I watched him huddle behind a dying gorse bush before I turned and continued a little further, coming to a stop and sitting on a rock, waiting, worried that he might never return.

He approached me slowly, wiping his hands off his trousers, attempting another laugh. Nice to think that in one particular spot at least the ground will be somewhat nourished, he said. A small contribution on my part, wouldn't you say? I just wish it weren't so damn painful.

I tried to stop a swelling in my throat, nervous about the tears that might fall. I had to turn away; couldn't look at him. I knew he hated acknowledging any part of his failing body.

People do that, you know, he said, tapping his crook once again into the baked ground. Drink their own urine to survive hostile and harsh environments. Did you know that? He paused. Of course you did. You can learn anything on the internet these days.

I've never drunk my own piss, I said.

But if you had to . . .

I guess, if I had to.

I'm obsessed with urine now. Who knew . . . ? Was in the toilet since 4 a.m. inspecting it, he said. The pain seems to intensify through the night. It's easier if I sit on the toilet seat rather than stand. He shrugged. The fresh blood that stains the pan, it always startles me even when I know it will be there.

How do you manage? I asked. To hide your pain so well.

I've suffered a lot of pain in my life. You adjust. Anyway, it could be worse. As Sam likes to remind me, someone always has it worse. He stopped then, struggling to catch his breath, his body bent over his crook. I offered him my bottle of water and he took a sip. I cannot stomach the water in other places, he said. Maybe that's why I've never really left.

Water is water, I replied. I think at this stage we just need to worry about having enough.

Ahead, we spotted a few rogue sheep on the hills, and Bobby raised his hand to silence me. Look at them, he whispered. Gorgeous.

Do you think there's enough up here for them to survive on?

At least they get a chance, he said, continuing to stare at them, transfixed.

They appeared unfazed by the dwindling brown landscape that surrounded them, and I thought they were lucky – not to think too far ahead about where things were coming from. I wondered if they'd start to fight with one another, vie for the little nourishment they had, or would they all accept defeat together?

Maybe we should check them over? I said.

I was expecting him to round the dogs on the sheep and bring them in for closer inspection but instead he kept walking, overtaking me. Let them be, he said. I'd rather not know if there's a problem with foot rot or maggots.

We descended to lower ground and finally to the old well where his grandfather had supposedly divined a spring from the very spot in which we stood. The rusting parts of the well that remained were antiquated, the growth of dying weeds and moss dominating. A steel sheet was covering the ground where the well must have been underneath. How deep would it have been? I wondered. Did some holes just continue on into the centre of the earth?

Okay, so what now? I said.

He ignored me, opening up the crumpled carrier bag he'd been carrying this entire time in the same hand as his crook. Carefully he removed two metal rods, bent at the ends like handles.

What are you doing?

These were my grandfather's, he replied. He was the best water diviner in the land, and he could make water flow from the same spot others had tried before him. It was these same rods that found him this well. And this well used to be our main source of water before we connected to the mains.

With cautious steps he began to move forward, the rods moving from left to right and back again in his hands. He paused, assessing the ground under his feet before turning to me. You're meant to offer the land something, he said. A peace offering of sorts . . .

Like what?

The biscuits, he said. Crumple them up and begin spreading them around the land. Spread them as far as you can.

Bobby . . .

Please, he said, with urgency, a pleading tone to his voice I wasn't used to hearing. Just humour me.

Reluctantly, I began breaking up the digestives, scattering crumbs here and there, slowly, some of it catching in the mild breeze, and I wondered if this was what it was like to scatter someone's ashes.

Do you think this will help? I said.

Well, it doesn't hurt to keep on the right side of nature, does it?

I snorted a laugh.

There's a wee trowel in that carrier bag over there, he said. Will you grab it? I want to be ready to dig if we see any signs.

I stared at him, sceptical, before nodding.

If we can find another source we can get the pump back in action, he said.

That pump? I asked, pointing to the corroded heap of metal, I'm not sure that'll be useable.

Why don't you try it? he said, without looking at me, his attention still focused on the rods he held steady in his hands.

Bending down and with the hand trowel tucked in under my arm, I began to pump the handle, the mouth of the tap green from corrosion. Slowly, copper-coloured droplets began to fall on to my fingers, and I had to stop myself from wiping them away in disgust.

Give it a few more pumps, he said.

And I did. But there was no miracle, no sudden flow of clear spring water as Bobby had so desperately wanted. Had I believed it too? Perhaps I had been indulging myself. The dirty droplets eventually ceased to fall. A real sadness came over me then as I got to my feet. Maybe somewhere out there in the distance there was land with its own unhindered spring, but it wasn't ours.

I'm not going mad, you know, Bobby said. The water that once flowed here had nothing to do with the reservoir. I need you to believe that. We *did* have our own spring. I swear to you. I carried buckets of water as a boy across the fields and back to the cottages.

I believe you, I said.

I still have the paperwork from when that pump was installed. It'll be folded up in my bureau somewhere. It worked, he said. I thought it would last for ever.

Maybe it's for the best, I said. Can't these types of things get easily contaminated? E-coli, or whatever.

We never had any problems before. The environmentalists were always running tests in the area. There's always been some lead in the water compared to other parts of the country. But it's never been high enough to be dangerous. Never caused us a bother in our whole lives. The best water I've ever tasted.

Let's keep looking, I said.

I stayed very close to him, the sun beating down on our backs. And with whatever energy Bobby had left, he used it to cover as many square metres as he could with those rods tight in his hands, pausing unsteadily for a moment with hope before moving on. The sweat poured off him, and at one point I thought he was going to be sick. I offered him the last of the water in my bottle. He shook his head, but I insisted. You're not going to die on me out here, like this.

Reluctantly, he held his divining rods in one hand and took the bottle from me; it shook as he brought it to his lips.

What happens if we don't find water? I said.

His bottom lip was fleshy, and droplets of water rested there, before he licked them away. What are you expecting me to say?

I threw his little trowel to the ground then, and it clattered on the dry earth. And I realised I was crying, because the reality of it all was startling. There was no more water. The taps and land had nothing to offer us. There was no back-up.

Bobby slumped slowly to the ground and lifted his cap off his head, wiping his forehead with it. I'm sorry, Aida, he said. He inhaled through his nostrils and let out a breath all the while holding his diaphragm. I really thought it was going to work.

I went to where he was and curled in next to him, resting my head on his shoulder. Should we try the sticks one more time? I said.

He placed a kiss on my forehead, his lips still damp with water. No, lass. It's enough now.

*

As evening approached, I could see Peter sitting on an old stool, his back pressed up against the body of the campervan, a blade in his hand, shavings at his feet. It looked as though he was whittling a piece of wood into what was perhaps a spoon. He nodded to me in acknowledgment before focusing once again on the blade and wood.

I need you to take me somewhere, I said.

He stopped carving, looked up. I'm not going back to the pits, he said.

Not there.

Then where?

I need to know how bad things are likely to get . . .

We climbed into the Defender, him driving, picking up speed, the bank of the empty reservoir hurtling past us in a blur. He kept his eyes on the road, turning, the force of his manoeuvre causing me to slide in my seat. Eventually, we joined the motorway, a straight stretch ahead of us, passing only a handful of cars, until about two miles from the border we were met with roadblocks and Peter brought the Defender to a stop.

Maybe this is as far as we can go, I said, realising that part of me was glad, relieved.

He peered forward before putting the Defender into gear, pressing down on the accelerator and swerving round the roadblocks, up on to the hard shoulder, gravel terrain underneath.

The area was completely deserted, and we continued on until we were confronted by another set of roadblocks, this time positioned along the embankment, causing Peter to brake suddenly. I stared out of the windscreen, the headlights illuminating a path in front.

I guess it's on foot from here, he said.

I didn't say anything, just unclipped my seatbelt and opened my door, while he turned off the engine. I realised I was biting the skin around one of my fingernails. We ventured under an overpass, our footsteps echoing, and I thought about people committing suicide by jumping in front of cars as they travelled at speed. It would have been an instant death. But what about the drivers? Would trauma like that scar you for life, or could you compartmentalise it and force it to the recesses of your mind?

I was trailing behind, glancing repeatedly over my shoulder as if I was expecting a car to come racing towards us. Maybe this wasn't a good idea, I said.

Peter turned to look at me. I've seen the worst of the farm; maybe it's time you saw the worst of the world.

He quickened his pace, and I had this urge to reach out and grab his jacket, rein him back towards me. We carried on until we saw more lights, the noise of life even. Within minutes we were approaching armed soldiers and police. It was all bulletproof vests, helmets, rifles and steel-toed boots. One of the soldiers, seeing us, halted our approach, and for a brief moment I held this irrational fear that he would assume we were on the wrong side of the border and cast us across. I felt his gaze, his gun strung limp across his shoulder, but he didn't seem especially surprised to see us.

You've taken a wrong turn, he said. Take my advice and turn back before you see things you can't unsee.

A few people were walking back past us. Mostly, they looked like parents – distraught and angry, looking for their children. And none of them seemed to have found who they were searching for.

Please, I said. I just need to understand.

The soldier stared at me, shinning a torch in my face. You live on one of the farms, he said. Bobby's place . . .

I nodded.

Good lambs where you come from.

There used to be, I said. Before they were culled.

Well, how about a deal, then – some frozen lamb chops, a few shanks too, and you can sniff around here as much as you like.

We haven't come to cause trouble.

Just a few cuts from your freezer is all I'm asking for. I doubt you'd even notice them gone.

I hesitated, looking from the soldier to Peter and back again before nodding.

Good, he said, reaching into his pocket and removing a reel of blue stickers. He pulled one off and pressed it firmly on to my chest. It said VISITOR. And then he did the same to Peter. I'm not sure what it is you're hoping to see, to be honest, he said, but knock yourselves out.

A wall had been erected as far as the eye could see – concrete pillars, barbed wire and Perspex marking it out, creating a physical barrier between two countries that previously only had an invisible line. And the sign that used to say *Welcome to Scotland* was no longer there. There were queues of vehicles, lanes of traffic with doors open and people passing from one to the other. As the soldier ushered us closer, I could see that the cars at the front of the queue were laden with possessions. The soldier accompanied us along the borderline. On the other side thousands of tents covered the land, multicoloured, interspersed with portable toilets. Even from where I stood the stench was overwhelming and I tried to swallow it back, instinctively bringing the collar of my T-shirt up towards my nose. The chemical toilet in the campervan was nothing compared to this.

A few people on the other side noticed our arrival and came up to the divide, shouting, trying to squeeze limbs out through the gaps where they could find them. It was too much. I adjusted my eyes, tried to take in less of the picture.

So, this is what it's like when ten times our population try to enter the country, I said.

A teenage boy was standing close to a section of Perspex, and he tapped his finger against it although the sound was inaudible. He was staring straight at us, thin and grey, eyes swollen. I took a step back, creating distance from the boy who couldn't touch me.

Do they have food? I said.

The soldier shrugged. Whatever they brought with them. We have no resources to send over. We have very little ourselves now.

Surely anywhere is better than staying here . . . I said.

It's hope that brings them here, the soldier replied. The idea that things could be better across the line. They've no fucking idea.

I turned to look at Peter, but he wouldn't meet my eye, had turned his back on the border wall.

What's the death toll? I asked.

No idea, the soldier said. But disease must be rife. Our job is only to maintain order on this side of the border. We've no control over there. It's essentially lawless. He shrugged. Don't get too close or they'll try to pull you forward. A woman nearly suffocated not so long ago because they gripped her through the gaps. We had to use our guns to set her free.

Some of the vehicles looked abandoned and I wondered what had become of their families. A line had to be drawn somewhere, but to watch the car in front of you make it past the border and then be told you would go no further must have been too much to bear. At least the people miles back in the queues had been able to adjust their expectations. They'd have known they were never going to make it across.

The crowd bulged and swelled; a trampling of bodies to see two people who were free of their situation. Perhaps they thought we were a figment of their imagination. If the concrete barriers were to give way, I thought, there would be nothing left of us.

I took a step back, trying to take Peter with me, but the crowd sensed my retreat. *I'll do anything you want*, someone's voice echoed out. *Anything*. And the way it was articulated was so sad and sinister, and it made the darkest of notions float to the forefront of my mind. Was I capable of forcing someone into anything? We were probably all capable, I thought. But to be in a position of such power . . . I couldn't decide if that would agree with me or not.

A commotion broke out perhaps only ten, fifteen metres away from where we stood. Two soldiers were dragging a man by the arms, his legs trailing across the tarmac. His clothes were filthy, his body fragile and weak. They came to a stop and pinned his face to the ground, elbows pressing into his cheek. He began to wail. And, behind him, two more soldiers dragged a woman and child by their arms to where he was held, their force unwavering. The swell of people behind the border started shouting and chanting – a primal, destructive noise.

What's happening? I shouted as we were instructed to move back.

He tried to get across, the soldier said, somewhat flippantly. Now he will be executed. He spoke like it was nothing, shrugging his shoulders indifferently.

Is that necessary? I said with disbelief in my voice.

It stops others from attempting it, the soldier replied. It's our most effective means. He exhaled. When enough time has passed, and memories begin to fade, we do get more attempting to cross though. It's like clockwork.

Has anyone managed it? Peter asked.

The soldier shrugged again. If they have and we haven't caught them, then best of luck to them. We can only execute the ones we catch.

The soldier walked towards the man pinned to the ground. He began instructing other soldiers to bring him upright, cuffing him to a long, exposed steel rod set into a concrete frame. I watched four soldiers form a perfect horizontal line facing the chained man. He was begging them, a stain on his crotch spreading, urine on the tarmac. Our soldier gave a command that was indecipherable, and the soldiers raised their guns in unison. He gave a final order, and they fired their rifles at the man chained like an animal. For a moment nothing happened but then he toppled forward, his forehead nearly touching his shoes, while his cuffed hand dangled limp in the air, his fingers fanning out as if he was conducting music.

I was screaming, my voice hoarse, but Peter remained perfectly silent. The thousands gathered behind the wall had also grown momentarily silent. I turned to look at them and they reminded me of a painting. Their collective noise instantly returned, the uproar and fear of a wolf pack, the inhumanity of it all.

The lifeless body was unshackled, and the soldiers immediately turned their attention to the woman and child, who together had crumpled to the ground. And it was all so unnecessary – all this death, like dying of cancer when you knew there'd likely be a cure in a few years time.

I watched the young boy be prised from the woman, his wailing so painful and piercing that I wanted to cup my ears. The woman appeared resigned to her fate, silent, letting the soldiers take her without a fight. But as they attempted to shackle her to the makeshift frame I found myself sprinting forward, pulling away from Peter's grip.

Please don't do this, I said to the soldier. Don't kill her and the boy. I'll . . .

You'll do what? he said.

The child broke free of his restraint and dashed to his mother, his bare legs wrapping around her body. What age was he? It was difficult to tell. To my untrained eye perhaps five but he could easily have been older. I had no real idea.

It's time for you to leave, the soldier said. That's enough for one evening. With his gun he pointed us back in the direction in which we'd come. I'll be in touch about the lamb, he shouted.

And, as we began to walk with pace, Peter's grip tight around my wrist, we heard the gunshots echo out behind us.

16

There was a change in Bobby after we'd gone looking for water – a physical exhaustion but also something deeper. Maybe it was his hope that had been extinguished. Or maybe it was the fact that he was still a dying man. Mum was furious at me for letting him walk across those fields in the heat of the day, divining as if there was no tomorrow. But after seeing those people at the border I tried to find the words to explain that none of it really mattered any more. Our water was depleting, quicker than any of us wanted to confess.

With the television losing transmission we'd settled into a routine of watching the most random assortment of DVDs. We must have been the only home to still be watching DVDs after the streaming services had come into play. I supposed it was to our benefit now. Mum had found the *Frasier* DVD box set in one of Bobby and Sam's cupboards and we'd been working our way through them, discs playing on loop for hours, a background noise drowning out the silence – nothing to interrupt our day except for them. The episode that came on next was when the whole family went to a ski chalet up in the mountains – much misunderstanding and confusion, resulting in a lot of hilarious bed-hopping. There was a real nineties feel to the show: the décor, the clothes, the way everything appeared to be so simple. It looked like a lovely time to have been an adult and I was jealous, really jealous. Had *climate change* even been a phrase then?

It was just me and Peter who were watching it, and I was laughing a lot, at the innocent nature of the comedy – of two wealthy men, who were somehow so likeable and endearing. And it was towards the end of this episode, when Frasier realised that no one in the chaos had been lusting after him, that the power cut out. The television's life was sucked from it, like something being physically drained from within. Peter sat up from his slumped position and we looked at one another. I got to my feet and attempted to switch the light on, but nothing happened. I walked into the kitchen area and looked at the cooker, its digital clock having disappeared. I opened the fridge. The light inside was off.

Fuck, I said.

Does this happen a lot? Peter said.

I ran out the front door, past Bobby and Sam sitting out on the bench, across the yard and into our cottage, but the light in our fridge was off too.

Mum, I shouted.

What? her voice called out from her bedroom.

The power has gone off.

She padded through, coming to a stop in front of me. It tends to happen occasionally, she said, attempting a calming and assured tone. Give it an hour.

Do you think it will come back on?

She shrugged. Honestly, I don't know anything any more

We waited for hours, all the while worrying about all the food that would be defrosting in the chest freezer out in the shed. By evening Bobby deemed it concerning enough to merit turning on the outside diesel generator, which was linked to their cottage. It was left to me and Mum to consider how best to deal with all the defrosting food, having forced as much of it as we could into Bobby and Sam's indoor American-style fridge-freezer. My insulin was transported over too, dominating one whole shelf of their fridge. There was too much of everything, cuts of meat that wouldn't have fitted, and we had no choice but to let them thaw out. Mum divided up food that needed consuming first. And we devised a plan to keep one of each insulin pen in a lunch bag with an ice pack in it, so that I could keep some insulin in our cottage, without consciously needing to be in Bobby and Sam's. The only thing I really had to remember, aside from the obvious, was to swap the ice packs over.

We existed in this further state of limbo for the first three days after the power went out, still assuming that it might come back on. It was like this weird paradox, feeling like we had more food than we knew what to do with, but also silently acknowledging that there would be no more once it was all gone. I found myself setting timer goals – waiting a few hours before going back into our cottage and letting my finger hover over the light switch before closing my eyes and flicking it. Slowly, I'd open one eye to see that there was still no power. At night, everything would be plunged into darkness, except for Bobby and Sam's cottage. Our own cottage was not really any different from the campervan now.

By day four, we'd once again settled into an altered routine of acceptance – so adaptable had we become. We spent our days fussing over the baby, less so over Rebecca, taking it in turns to water the vegetable plot with a sports bottle of bathwater, checking on the chickens who were still miraculously laying eggs. Evelyn and Rebecca spent more time in their campervan, Peter less so. And we returned to watching Frasier.

The spa episode was on, the one when Niles and Frasier were desperate to attain the most exclusive membership, never satisfied with what they had. And when the credits began to roll, Bobby turned abruptly, asking Mum to *take care of the dogs*.

What do you mean? she said, straightening.

He shrugged, unwilling to meet her eye. They need to go.

I paused the start of a new episode, Niles's face freeze-framed. The sheepdogs? I said.

Bobby closed his eyes. Do Rusty last, he said. Don't let him know what's happening. I'd do it myself, but . . .

Mum was quiet for a moment. Bobby . . . Surely that's not necessary?

Sam had been sitting silently beside Bobby, but he rose from his seat then and walked into the back hall, slamming their bedroom door shut.

There are too many mouths to feed and water, Bobby replied. They have to go.

But . . . Mum said. Things might get better. Let's not act in haste.

Do you think they will? he said. Because I don't think the taps are coming back on, and I don't the power is coming back on either. And let me tell you this, the diesel for the generator won't last forever . . . He faltered then, swaying slightly like a sail in the breeze before keeling over.

Mum tried to grip him, but it was like he was falling through her arms, his cheek hitting the side of a table. A noise escaped from his lips, like air slowly being released from a balloon.

Suddenly, we were all trying to lift him up between us, me, Mum and Peter, heaving his crumpled body into a standing position. He needs to lie down, Mum said, as we shuffled back across the flagstone flooring to one of the sofas, easing him down gently.

His eyes seemed to roll inwards and he lay lifeless. Bobby! I shouted.

It's okay, Aida, Mum said, trying to reassure me.

What's wrong with him? Peter asked.

No one spoke for a moment.

He's dying, Mum finally said. He has cancer.

I wondered . . . Peter said.

Mum placed a hand on Bobby's chest and her fingers rose and fell in rhythm with his breathing. He just needs more rest, she added. He's been doing too much lately, she added, casting a look at me. Slowly, he stirred, and she lifted his head, placing a cushion behind. You're okay, she said. Everything's okay.

He looked so frail, a tiny man with disproportionate hands. Why did he still insist on wearing checked farming shirts all the time? They hung from him, flaps of fabric. I knew with certainty then that the expensive brogues he'd worn to the hospital wouldn't be getting another outing.

What happened? he asked. And there was a bruise already forming on his face.

You've just had a fall, but you're okay.

I'm sorry, he was saying, his voice breaking.

I walked out into the yard, Peter following me. Aida, he called. Had he ever actually called me by my name before? It felt foreign. I stopped and he faced me, his eyes drawn to the ground. I'm sorry, he said. I thought he hadn't been looking well, but . . .

It's not something he wanted people to know.

Has he long left?

I don't know . . .

I realised Mum was standing behind us, shielding her eyes from the sun as she peered out. Peter . . . she said, a cowardly, sheepish tone to her voice. You're good with a shotgun, is that true?

I've got a reasonable aim.

She paused. Can you help me with the sheepdogs? And then I'll come back and do Rusty last.

I had to get away, couldn't listen to the words coming from Mum's mouth. I walked towards the gateposts, balanced myself across the cattle grid and just kept going. Mum was calling my name, but I didn't bother replying. I was aware then of the door to the campervan being slammed shut, of someone running to catch me, an unfamiliar buoyancy to their steps. A hand brushed up against my skin, Evelyn's long, beautiful fingers.

Where are you going? she asked, in a tone that made it sound as if I amused her.

I don't know . . .

Have you walked across the reservoir yet?

I shook my head.

Well, let's do it.

Doesn't Rebecca need you? The baby . . .

They're sleeping, she said. I think you need me right now.

We carried on down the road, keeping in step with one another, until we got to the gates of the water works. There was an opening in the metal fence, as if someone had taken clippers and cut through it, forming a perfect square. Evelyn gestured with her hand for me to slip through first, which I managed with ease. She followed behind me, placing her hand on my shoulder as we began to walk again.

I love coming down here, she said.

Why?

In the same why I liked seeing those ruined cottages, she said. I like to inhabit places that are no longer loved. She paused, smiling at me. There was an old hospital near where I used to live when I was growing up. It was a castle in a forest that at some point they'd turned into a hospital for mental people.

I don't think that's what you're meant to call it, I said.

She rolled her eyes. We don't need to be politically correct any more. No one cares. She carried on walking. Anyway, after the fifties, or maybe the sixties, it was closed down and the place deserted. They put a big wire fence around its parameter, and it was kind of just left to the elements, the only people really passing it being dog-walkers, and youngsters looking to get away from their parents. People started having parties in it. I lost my virginity there, in one of the old wards, sitting upright in a filthy armchair if you can believe that.

I tried to laugh. Is this the story of how Peter was conceived?

She smirked. No, it is not.

So why are you telling me all this?

She paused. I don't know . . . I guess I just wanted to tell someone the story. I'm not sure I've ever told anyone the truth about that before. I cut my leg open on a piece of broken glass. And I was so scared someone would find out what I'd been up to that I said nothing. It got infected in the end and I ended up in hospital on intravenous antibiotics. They said I was lucky not to have lost my leg. She paused. I still think about that old condemned hospital all the time. It had these metal staircases that got built on the outside of the building and they corroded and threatened to come down into the vegetation that grew around it. I wonder what it all looks like now.

We came to a stop at the edge of the bank.

Why don't we walk across the riverbed? she said.

Why?

She laughed. Have you always been like this? Does nothing interest you?

We came down past one of the sides and stepped across the stones and pebbles until we were standing on a flatter stretch, right in the middle of the reservoir.

Isn't it odd to walk across something that we shouldn't be able to? Evelyn said.

I looked around, the old washing-line poles in my sight, like a shipwreck brought to the surface. I don't think I like it, I said. It's weird. Like forbidden land.

She laughed, tucking a strand of hair behind her ear, and it was then that I saw the black mark on her neck. I was so used to searching my own body for those black little beads, obsessed with the fear of catching Lyme disease.

You have a tick on your neck, I said.

She looked confused. What?

I lifted the seam of my T-shirt and began pulling on a thread, ripping it off in my hands. I was so close to her now that I could feel her breath, and I brought my hands up towards the tick, tying the beginning of a knot before expertly lassoing it around the body, tightening my knot. It was relatively large in size, had been nestled in there for a few days, I suspected. Don't move, I said, my own breath now on her neck.

Okay, she whispered.

I yanked the thread, the tick coming away beautifully, fully intact in my hand. I threw it on to the stones and stood on it as best I could.

Thank you, she said.

I shrugged. You'd do the same for me.

Evelyn cleared her throat. I'm not sure I could have done that . . . She reached out to take my hand, squeezing it. Sometimes I still think about those ladybirds, she said. Did you ever tell your mother about them?

I shook my head again.

You really don't give much away. She paused then, looking down to where I'd stood on the tick, rubbing her fingers on her neck where it had been latched. Your mother is a natural with Noah, isn't she? Just like you said she would be. I envy her so.

Well, she gets to hand the baby back, I said, trying to laugh. It's you and Rebecca who are doing all the heavy lifting. It must be difficult.

She nodded, her focus now off in the distance. What are the odds of success if we were to attempt another trip to Glasgow in the Defender? she said.

I spluttered a laugh. Probably zero, I replied. What with the travel restrictions, not to mention what happened last time.

Perhaps these are just challenges we need to overcome, physically and mentally.

There's no way, I said.

Don't you worry about your father? Isn't it at least worth trying?

I paused. Why do you want to go?

For Rebecca and Noah. For my money. There is money owed to me and it's in Glasgow.

Is money even relevant any more? I said.

Money is always relevant.

I kicked at a stone under my feet.

All I'm asking is that you think about it, okay? You don't need to decide yet, but just think about it. Our little secret.

I cleared my throat. Peter took me to the border, I said.

And what did you think?

That if I were on the other side I would probably have done anything in the world to get across.

She nodded. You and I, we're similar. We're not those people who sacrifice ourselves for others. We're not the firemen who go into a building as it burns. We're the people who make sure we get out first.

Maybe you're right, I said.

Can I ask you something? she said.

Sure.

I saw Bobby filling the generator with diesel . . .

Yeah?

Had you anticipated this happening? All the prepping . . .

Bobby just likes to be organised. We've had power out-
ages before. Living on a farm in the middle of nowhere isn't
exactly reliable.

It's just, he made out when we first arrived that he didn't have
any diesel to spare for the campervan. Yet you could probably
run that generator for months with the stockpiles he has.

I hesitated. What he does with his diesel is his prerogative, is
it not?

If he had known us, would he have given us some?

Would you have left us if he had? I said.

I returned to Bobby and Sam's cottage to find the open-plan
empty. I made my way through to the back hall and found Bobby's bedroom door ajar, him on the mattress, his body heaped
with blankets despite the heat of the day, and I knew only Sam
would have been capable of this care.

How are you feeling? I asked.

I'm still in the bad books, he whispered, closing his eyes.

Where's Sam? I asked.

I think he needed some fresh air. He's so angry at me,
for everything . . . But also, because I've stopped taking my
tablets.

Why?

He exhaled through his nostrils. They don't make me feel
good, he said. I'm groggy and woozy, and I don't want to feel
like that any more.

The cancer plagued his face, cast a shadow over his cheeks. I tried to imagine his chest beating like a drum, pumping blood across veins and arteries, his heart the size of a foot pump.

Are you scared, Bobby?

He opened his eyes, a sharpness and clarity to them now. I'm scared for everyone I'm leaving behind. I suspect I'll be gone before I know things are getting better for you all.

Do you believe in another place? I asked.

He was quiet for a moment. Yes, but I don't know where it is. Or if I'm going there.

You're the best person I know, I said, my throat sore, having to bite down on my lip to stop myself from crying.

Look, don't be worrying about me, lass, he said. I've lived the life I wanted. You and your mum, having to deal with me, and Sam . . . it's not been fair on either of you.

Don't say that.

I was excited for you when you left for Edinburgh, he whispered. Really I was. Knew it was something you wanted. Knew you didn't want to be here.

We heard the front door to the cottage opening then, Sam's pained steps across the flagstone flooring. I wiped my face, really struggling.

Do you know what I'd love? he said, his voice a mere whisper.

What? I managed to say.

To have the house filled with laughter and music. Just once. Just one last time. Wouldn't that be lovely?

Is that something you're up to? I said.

I want to see him smile again, he said, nodding his head out in the direction towards the open living space and to where Sam would be.

I nodded. Okay, let's do it.

Tomorrow night, he said. I want this place to be filled with laughter.

Are you hungry? Can I get you anything?

I just don't think I can stomach much.

There's bacon, I said.

Bacon? Well, I mean, I could probably manage a rasher of bacon or two – there's hardly anything to them anyway.

Brown sauce?

Of course.

I'll see what I can do, I said, gently bending to kiss his forehead.

In the open-plan Rusty was sitting on Sam's knee.

Without a word I opened their fridge and removed rashers of bacon in clingfilm.

What are you doing? Sam asked.

Bobby wants some bacon . . .

I can make him bacon, he said, but he made no move to come forward and take over.

I let the oil sizzle before placing two rashers in the pan. Do you want some? I asked, but he didn't reply.

I watched the bacon turn from a fleshy red to a leathery pink, tough in texture. I was turning the rashers over with tongs, the fat a golden brown, when I heard Peter and Mum return in the Defender, knowing the job with the sheepdogs would be complete. Sam knew it too, his hold on Rusty tight. I put the two crispy rashers on a small paper plate and took them through to Bobby, but he was sleeping again.

I heard Mum coming in and went back to see her. She was rubbing her face, tired already. Okay, she said, looking at Sam.

But his eyes were focused on Rusty, his hand rubbing the dog's belly. Don't take him, Miriam, please . . . And he began to cry, deep, sobbing tears that couldn't be contained. Everything that I love is being taken away from me, he said.

Rusty rolled on to his front and jumped down, padding over to lap water from his bowl. Sam called him back, panicked, his hand whacking his knee in desperation, demanding the dog return to him.

We love you, Sam. But there's no water . . . For Rusty or for any of us . . .

Rusty returned to his master's feet. Sam brought the dog up beside him, clinging to his small body as you would a hot water bottle.

I took a step towards them, the plate of bacon still in my hand.

Please don't do it, he whispered. I know Bobby asked you to, but please don't . . . I'm begging you.

I've no choice, Mum said. And it should be one of us to see it through.

Sam was quiet for a moment. How will you do it?

Quickly, painlessly, she replied. He won't even know what's happening.

Sam brought Rusty up to his neck and cuddled into him, letting the tears continue to fall. You've been a great wee guy, he said. We couldn't have asked for better. And you've had a good run. He held him out then, inspecting him for a moment before finally handing him over.

I stepped forward, taking Rusty under my arm because I doubted he'd go to Mum. He peered out, tail wagging, oblivious to his fate.

I'll need his lead, Mum said. And some snacks that he loves.

I offered her the plate with the bacon on it, and she stared at it for a moment before taking both rashers in her hand. And then we were leaving the cottage, the dog still nuzzled comfortably under my arm.

Outside, Peter was waiting. Do you want me to come?

Mum faltered. No, I'll do this one myself.

I'll come with you, I said.

No, Aida. You won't.

He won't go with you, I said. He trusts me.

In the Defender, Rusty stood proudly on my knee, front paws on the dashboard, a different class of traveller from the sheepdogs. He pressed his nose up against the window and his tail wagged while Mum tried to focus on the road ahead, the spade and shotgun sitting in the compartment behind us. When was the last time she'd used the gun? There had been the foxes attacking some sheep the year before. One had ripped the face off a ewe and she had put the poor thing out of its misery.

As she drove, I tried the dial on the radio but there was only static. Mum pulled up off the dirt road and sat for a moment, the land sprawling and vast. One of the turbines was in view, standing stationary. I looked at Rusty and Rusty stared back.

Why here? I asked.

Why not here? It's far enough away . . .

We just sat there for a while, staring out at the harsh landscape. There was a hill ahead of us, and I knew that on the top of it sat a sundial.

We used to climb that hill so often with your dad when you were younger, do you remember? Mum said. I don't know when we stopped . . .

I always used to think it was massive, I replied, stroking Rusty's coat. But actually it's quite feeble. I turned to look at her, realised I was reaching for her hand.

When I was a little girl, she said, two stray cats tried to make a home for themselves in our garden. I'd taken a shine to them and given them names – Tut and Khamun, or something ridiculous – anyway, I was quite taken with these cats but Baba, seeing them, was convinced they were riddled with disease. Everything had rabies then. He brought a man in off the street and the man, right there and then, drowned them in a bucket of water, pressing another bucket down on top of them while I watched. And as she spoke there wasn't really any sadness in her voice, more like she was merely telling an anecdote.

I wish you hadn't told me that, I said.

When will it all end? she asked. When will there be a glimmer of hope?

I just started shaking my head; once again I couldn't find any words to offer her comfort, not when she was about to shoot the family pet.

Do you think about Cairo much? I asked.

Mostly I think about my brother.

What was he like?

She smiled, her eyes cast off in the distance. He was a good boy, she said. It was Ahmus who found me the money to study over here. I never got the chance to pay him back. She paused. I know Egypt has had no water for a long time; I don't need to read articles online to understand this. It makes me think how odd that I am here – that this is now my home, this land. And I wonder what Ahmus would have made of it all. Would he have laughed that buildings here were not designed with reinforced concrete columns in the anticipation of more floors being added?

I'm sorry I never got to meet him, I said.

She stared at Rusty settled on my knee.

The wind turbines began to spin slowly in the distance, and I wished we could have exchanged their energy for water, offered it up to the gods – shown them that we were at least trying to make amends for all the damage and abuse on our part – for the assumption that what we needed would always be there. Poorer countries were used to making deals with higher powers, accepting sacrifices and loss, but here we were so used to getting our way – outraged at even the notion of having to struggle.

We got out of the Defender and Rusty followed. I contemplated just telling him to run free, hoping he would leave, and his fate be left unknown, like the sheep up on the hills, but I knew he was too loyal, that he'd always find a way back home.

I'm sorry, Mum said, speaking to Rusty now.

He sat watching us, his tongue hanging out.

I know we've not always seen eye to eye but honestly, she said, I'd rather do anything other than this.

What's the best way to do it? I asked.

I'd planned to put him on his lead and tie him to a tree where he couldn't escape, she said. But that act seems cruel now.

Rusty wasn't paying any attention; he was off sniffing the base of an exposed tree root, and I watched Mum tear off the rashers of bacon, scattering them on the ground, wanting him to enjoy his last supper. He was within shooting distance, his muscular rear facing us, the tail wagging, licking the ground where the bacon had been only moments before.

Mum loaded the shotgun, clicked the barrel closed and raised it up, taking aim as she removed the safety latch. I couldn't watch, drew my head down towards the ground, waited for the shot, a sickness inside me at the memory of that little boy at the border running to his mother. A sickness for what we'd all become: nothing but thirsty animals, so easily capable of harming one another.

The shot went off, loud and echoing through the sky, no birds left to startle, perhaps having migrated to a more prosperous land, if one existed. When I dared to look, I could see Rusty pottering around in front of us, completely uninterested in the noise of the gun, so familiar was he with it.

Did you miss?

Mum exhaled. Have you ever known me to miss a shot?

I just stared at her.

Perhaps I'm not as pragmatic as I've led myself to believe, she said, slumping backwards against the bonnet of the Defender.

I called out to Rusty, and he came to me, no idea of how close he'd come, and we climbed back into the Defender then, Rusty on my knee.

He can share some of my water, Mum said. He won't take from anyone else.

He can have his own little share of water, I said. No one will ever know.

She turned on the engine. I remember when Rusty ate my bar of eighty per cent cocoa chocolate, she said. It cost Bobby £75 to get his stomach pumped. He was indestructible then and he's indestructible now.

Maybe he'll be the last one standing, I said.

17

I shaved my legs, running a wet wipe over my skin, the blade slicing through thick dark hair, a spot of blood on my knee-cap. I wiped the blood away with my index finger and sucked on it, ferrous and rich. Afterwards, I changed into a dress I hadn't worn since leaving Edinburgh and, staring at myself in the mirror, I decided that I looked nice, like someone I used to be.

Mum swung her head round the door, giving me the once-over. It doesn't leave much to the imagination, she said.

I smirked. It's a warm evening.

She came to a stop behind me. Sometimes I can't believe that I made you, she said.

I leaned into her. Are we capable of having a nice time, do you think? Will we be able to pretend for one night?

She nodded. Bobby has asked for a party, she said, and that is what we shall give him.

I followed her into the hall to find big dusty black bin bags sitting there, blocking our path, the plastic stretched to an almost grey-white in places. What's all this shit? I said, looking down at the bags.

It's the things I kept from when you were little. I thought it might be of use to Rebecca and Noah.

Why did you keep so much?

She shrugged, a sadness momentarily lingering. I suppose I thought I'd have more . . .

I hesitated, considered her words. I'm sorry it was only me.

I worried about you too much, she said. Maybe it was my body's way of saying that it wouldn't have been good for me to worry more. That there wouldn't be enough *worry* to go around. She came closer then, squeezed my elbow. Can you help me take some of it over?

I nodded, lifting one bag in each hand, careful not to let the dust brush against my dress.

On entering Bobby and Sam's cottage, I stopped to take in the sight before me. The open-plan was dripping with Mexican themed decorations, colours of the rainbow – leftovers from a party that Bobby had thrown for Sam's sixty-fifth birthday. Music was pumping out of the speaker, attached to their record player, while Sam wore a sombrero, seasoning a giant cut of beef ribs at the counter. He caught me staring and said, Don't you worry, little one. I've sorted you out with something too.

What, a sombrero or the food?

H smiled. A nut roast and all the veg. And some cauliflower cheese.

I reached forward and kissed his cheek, the smell of him familiar. Drought or no drought, he would have smelled the same, a musty, shoe-polish scent mixed in with Dettol.

In the corner of the room Rusty lay in his bed, asleep and oblivious. I looked around again. I didn't know it was going to be themed, I said.

Well, I just thought it would be fun, Bobby said, nestled into his armchair with a blanket over his knees, a false bushy cowboy moustache stuck to his face. We might never get a chance to use it all again, so . . . He held my eye for a moment, before turning away. And your mum's been my little helper, which is always a joy! He winked. Anyway, I thought Rebecca might like it. Something nice after everything she's been through.

I came and crouched down to kiss him on the cheek. Do I get a moustache too? I said, pointing to the packet, and he nodded, taking his time to pick one out for me.

Can you open the champagne? Sam said, pointing to the bottle already in an ice bucket as he watched me stick my moustache on. I found some chunks of ice in the freezer that needed defrosting, so I chipped some off, he added, smirking. Thought I was being quite clever there. I wouldn't fancy drinking old, defrosted water, would you?

I removed the bottle from the ice, cold droplets dripping on to the table as I began to pull the foil from around the cork. I didn't know we were the type of house to keep champagne . . . I said.

You're ruining my beautiful table, Sam said with affection. Move the bottle away from the tablecloth when you're pouring. He'd made a real effort, bringing out the best china plates and crystal glasses, the fancy fabric napkins, and the elaborate centrepiece of candlesticks in holders.

The pop was loud as I forced the cork from the bottle, startling everyone. Bobby was slow on his feet, but he made his way over and pointed to the crystal saucers sitting out separately. Fill us up, he said. Let's have a moment before the chaos truly kicks in. And on his instruction I filled four champagne glasses to the brim and we clinked the crystal together as a family, sipping the bubbles, and in that moment I wanted everything to stop. I so desperately wanted the evening to be just us, to really give Bobby the party he deserved. But then there was the knock on the door, and they were filing in, one after the other, they too having brought their few shareable possessions: Peter with a dirty-looking bottle of vodka in his hands, Rebecca gripping a tin of something that no longer had a label, while Evelyn walked in, an irritated Noah upright in her arms.

Can I take him? Mum said, already reaching for his little body.

There was the briefest hesitation from Evelyn before she handed him over.

Mum began to bounce Noah to a rhythm in her arms that was soothing, while Bobby peered down affectionately at him. Aida, Mum called, nodding towards the bin bags we'd brought in. Why don't you show Rebecca what we've got for her?

Obediently, and with everyone's eyes on me, I began to unknot the bags, like a funny little Santa bearing gifts.

Mum smiled at Rebecca. We've managed to find some more baby things for you to look at . . .

That's too kind, Evelyn said. Honestly . . .

And then Mum was trying to show Rebecca, one-handed, all the things she'd amassed: the baby carrier, some toys, a book with black and white pictures because he wouldn't be able to see in colour yet. A little mirror so he could peer at himself, a silky, floating scarf for texture. She had everything.

Peter nudged my shoulder, nodding towards the decorations. What is this . . . ?

Bobby laughed, it paining him. Well, I know, lad, but . . . we thought it would be nice for the lass. For all of you, he said, handing Peter his own fake moustache. A wee bit of fun, sure.

Evelyn took a step further into the open-plan space and smiled this beam of a smile, her teeth exposed. Quite the atmosphere you've managed to create here.

It was mostly Miriam's efforts, Bobby said.

Mum smiled at the mention of her name. Well, it's not much really . . .

I began pouring drinks for everyone else and there was the immediate buzz of noise and chatter. Sam's cheeks were a real ruddy red and he pushed his sombrero a little further up off his forehead, wiping sweat away with his palm.

What can I do, Sam? I said. What else needs doing?

He glanced around the busy counters, perhaps trying to formulate order in his mind. Can you start putting oatcakes on everyone's plate? I've defrosted my home-made salmon pâté but it needs cut up and there's a portion of mushroom pâté for you.

I nodded, already directing myself to the cupboards, crouching for the packets of thick oatcakes they were partial to in this house. If it had been me I'd have gone for the thinner cuts, rather than those big triangular slabs. I'd have to slather mine in pâté as not to choke.

In the living space I was aware of Evelyn cackling at something Bobby was telling her, settling into a seat beside him, and Bobby was holding Noah, cradling him in his arms. Oh, would you look at those wee fingers, he said.

Okay? Sam said, startling me.

I nodded, ripping open a packet of oatcakes.

I watched Peter move around the room, inspecting the decorations, stopping at a sign pinned to the mantle that read: *Nacho Average Party*! I thought about the party the props had initially been bought for, what a roaring success it had been. And it was strange to think of happy memories stuck in time, reflecting now on the realities that had taken place since – we'd had no idea what was to come. Dad had overseen the drinks, the perfect host, and to the unwitting eye the perfect husband too.

I needed another drink. Decided the evening would be a success if I could keep old memories at bay, if I didn't think too far ahead, if I just carried on drinking. I checked my bloods then, lifting my skirt up enough so that my thigh was exposed. Setting the dial on my pen, I pierced my skin with the needle and injected myself. When I looked up, Peter was staring at me.

Sam called us to the table, and we took our seats, Rebecca settling herself into a seat between Mum and Evelyn, Noah being handed to her as he began to fuss for his milk. Mum draped a tea towel over Rebecca's shoulder in a bid to offer her some privacy, and we all averted our gaze as the noise of Noah's feeding became audible.

When we'd finished our starters, I rose to clear away the china plates. I stacked them on the counter, not a scrap or crumb to be seen, much to Rusty's disappointment. I wasn't sure what we were meant to do with these plates now – we'd been using baby wipes to wipe down our cutlery and utensils, the paper plates and cups being disposed of, but it didn't seem right to use a wet wipe on china.

Sam had brought the joint of meat out from the oven before we had our starters, and the smell filled the room as it rested. He took the vegetables out of the oven as well as my nut roast and cauliflower cheese, and I hovered around him, asking what else there was for me to do. The bigger bone-china plates were sitting waiting to be used – they were the type of thing I imagined someone asking for on their wedding list – items they were likely to keep for a lifetime, along with newly engraved cutlery. I couldn't imagine getting married; felt more certain than ever now that marriage wouldn't be part of my future.

Sam oversaw my distribution of the vegetables on to each plate, budging me out of the way so he could take care of the sauce reducing over the hob, check that the frozen corn cobs weren't turning funny from being boiled too long in their pot. As I made to turn, he gave me this huge beaming smile and planted a kiss on my cheek. It was so rare and so beautiful that it caught me off guard – to see him truly happy in that moment.

We moved on to red wine for our main, all except for Rebecca who had a tall glass of Coke, which she reached for silently, taking a sip. No one thought to ask her if she'd like a glass of wine like every other adult around the table; maybe they worried about the booze passing into her milk. And then there was that familiar buzz of chatter again, appreciative noises for how lovely the food was, everyone cutting into their strips of pink beef, my nut roast, the wine delicious, and it was all so lovely, everyone just grateful.

At some point in the evening we realised that the music had finished, and Bobby struggled up on to his feet, taking each step slowly until he was picking a new record for us to listen to. The alcohol continued to flow, and I kept thinking that I should slow down, pace myself, alternate with a soft drink, but then I remembered that none of it mattered. Dessert was a cheesecake, the last of the unopened cream cheese mixed in with cocoa powder and sugar, chocolate buttons placed on top. It was rich and delicious, and I had to massively top up my bolus insulin. I'd talked about making the leap to veganism many times, delayed it again and again, dairy always my downfall. But as I licked the last of the cheesecake off my spoon I realised there was nothing else standing in my way now. Cheese was going. It would be cartons of tofu and all the different types of beans I could eat out of a tin now anyway.

I watched Bobby take a couple of small mouthfuls of cheesecake before pushing the bowl away, having barely touched any of his main, the meat cut into the tiniest of chunks, while Sam forced everything into his mouth, quickly, as if it was something to be tackled rather than enjoyed. I couldn't imagine either of them giving up meat, tried to visualise them working their way down to the last steak, the last lamb chop, wondering what they'd feed themselves, aside from the tatties in the vegetable plot. Did we even have enough water now to keep the potatoes alive? And as I continued to stare, these thoughts circulating in my head, I realised, very clearly then, that Bobby wouldn't be here to see the last of the meat be consumed. He would himself be feeding the soil.

As the plates got cleared away, Evelyn began ushering Rebecca on to her feet and towards the door. Rebecca's eyes flickered, hesitant in her stare, and I interrupted this as a plea to stay. Confident now with the alcohol running through me, I said, Wait. You're not going, are you?

She's tired, Evelyn replied.

No, stay, I said, instinctively reaching for Rebecca's arm. I think you should stay with us . . . All these things, I said, nodding towards the bin bags, these used to belong to me . . .

She really is tired, Evelyn pressed.

No, I shouted. She wants to stay. And I turned then, frantically removing things from the bags once again. The baby carrier was in my grip, and I pulled at the straps, straightening the thing out. Let's practise again. This will make things so much easier. I held the straps up, gesturing to Rebecca to slide her arms through, the fabric pressing up against her front, while I clipped every-thing into place behind her back. Okay, I said, animated, excited, taking the liberty of removing Noah from Evelyn's embrace. So how do you do it again, Mum? You just slide him in at the front and then tighten the straps? Make sure his wee legs are dangling down like this? I took a step back, inspecting my handiwork, oblivious to everyone else. He'll love it, I said. Won't he, Mum?

There was silence.

I was aware of a reddening to my face, a wooziness coming across me. I wish I could be carried about like this, I said.

Evelyn looked at me as if I had assaulted her. Never take Noah like that, she said. You have no idea how to hold a baby.

I . . .

Bobby cleared his throat. Aida's just had a little too much to drink, but she only wants to help . . .

Evelyn looked at Noah strapped to Rebecca. Her face was expressionless, while Rebecca looked down at her child, appearing a little distressed, as if he was a package she'd never asked for.

I didn't hurt him, I said, foolish and embarrassed.

I'm sorry, Evelyn said. I didn't mean to snap. She pointed to the bags as if she was trying to appease me. Thank you. And then she was escorting Rebecca out of the door with Noah still strapped to her chest.

It was after 2 a.m. I'd carried on drinking, everyone else too, except for Rebecca, who was back in the campervan for the night. Evelyn and Mum both cupped in their hands some concoction mixed up by Peter, sipping it slowly, Noah sleeping between them. Another song had just started, its volume low – a man asking his woman not to leave him. Bobby stood, gripping Sam's arms. Facing each other, they began to sway slowly from side to side. When the song finished, Bobby, unsteadily, came and sat next to me, resting his head on my shoulder. My Aida, he said, a boozy smile settling on his face. You cannot take things with you to the grave, can you? So, this is just lovely, enjoying ourselves while we still can. He paused, trying to keep his bearings. And when we drink, we laugh. And we've not laughed properly in so long.

I nodded, barely able to focus on him.

He tried to get to his feet again, attempting to sway across the room, until Peter was helping him into Sam's lap.

Suddenly I was on my feet. I couldn't decide if I needed to be sick or if I needed to lie down in a dark room. I opened the door without anyone really acknowledging me doing so. Our cottage, powerless, was in complete darkness and I stumbled across the yard, guided only by the moon and the glow of lights coming from Bobby and Sam's. I paused, staring at the campervan, before staggering towards it, trying the handle of the back cabin. It was open and I found myself climbing inside, the familiar stench of the place forcing vomit up towards my mouth. I could see the silhouette of Rebecca's frame in the corner of the seating area. She was sitting up, her back pressed up against one of the cushions around the little table. Images of her giving birth filtered into my mind, and I blinked, thinking that would help push them away. I suspected there were still stains on the cushions if I looked closely.

I crept towards her, and she flinched.

What happened to you? I whispered.

Rebecca didn't answer me.

I took another step forward, my feet unsteady, thinking I could buckle and fall at any moment. You're the saddest person I've ever met in my entire life, I said, slurring my words. I wish you'd let me know . . .

And then there was someone behind me, taking me by the arm and leading me away. When I looked up it was Peter, but there was no force to his grip. Come on, he said, let's get you into bed.

As he guided me towards my kitchen I reached up and kissed him. His didn't pull away but I was aware of it being me that held our lips together. He was passive, and as he ushered me along the yard there was something gentle about his approach that infuriated me. From Bobby's cottage I could hear the thrum of music on low – country music still – maybe Dolly Parton but I wasn't sure. Peter ushered me along until we were in my bedroom, appearing familiar with the layout. He guided me down on to my bed and took off my shoes.

Join me, I said, a laugh surfacing from deep down.

Do you need your insulin? he said.

I shrugged.

He handed me my meter and test strips, practically pricking my finger for me. When the reading came up, he showed me the screen, and I squinted, before shaking my head.

You need to sleep, he said, pulling the duvet across my body.

No, I said, shaking my head again. Stay with me.

He lingered there for a moment.

I dropped my arm to the floor and felt under my bed for the condom packet, its foil cool between my fingers.

Quietly, so quietly that I could have missed it, he said, I wish we'd never come here.

And then he was gone.

The room began to spin, saliva gathering at the back of my mouth, an endless supply surfacing from behind my molars that I couldn't swallow down quickly enough. I made it to the bathroom before I was sick in the toilet. My aim was off, and chunks of my undigested food lay on either side of the pan. I realised then that I should have gone outside. I shrugged at the mess, focused on one little sweetcorn kernel and thought how odd it was that corn could work its way through your entire digestive system and come out completely intact – the journey it had been on, and yet the acid in my stomach, the pressure of my digestive system, wasn't enough to destroy it. It was amazing. Eventually I pulled myself up and got back into bed, still wearing the dress I'd been so careful to pick out earlier in the evening. The smell of vomit was still strong but, regardless, I fell into a drunken stupor, oblivious to the world around me, uncaring in that moment that Peter hadn't stayed, uncaring that Rebecca was by herself, uncaring that everything would have to be faced in the morning.

*

When I woke, I could barely lift my head off the pillow. There was a strange noise coming from somewhere inside the house and I couldn't decipher what it was. I stumbled on to my feet, feeling filthy in my clothes and wanting nothing more than to strip down to the bone and shower. Would Mum allow me a half-basin and cloth? What about my vomit in the bathroom? The kitchen was empty, but a few glasses and bottles had been brought through and were scattered across the table. There was the noise again, a groan of sorts, like someone in pain, and I assumed it to be Bobby before realising that he wouldn't be in our cottage.

I pushed Mum's bedroom door open but even in the darkness, with her curtains drawn, I could tell the room was empty. I tiptoed down the hall, following the muffled sounds until I was outside the living room. I stepped closer to the door and tried to rest my ear up against the wood. Mum was whispering something, her tone soothing and gentle.

I placed my fingers on the door and pushed it open, the catch of the door having never worked properly. I could see two bodies huddled together on the sofa, the bobbled blanket I often napped under covering them. It was Mum and Peter. They had their bare arms wrapped around one another, their feet entwined, pointing towards the window, and I realised they must have been waiting for the sun to come up.

I had an overwhelming sense that I was intruding, that perhaps they should be allowed to have this moment in private. Peter was holding Mum close, and she turned and kissed him on the lips. When they pulled apart, I saw him smile at her – a look I didn't recognise – maybe a tenderness I didn't realise he possessed. Then they became aware of me, Mum's arms and feet frantic, trying to burrow her naked body further under the blanket. In contrast, Peter appeared unflustered by my presence.

My breath fogged out of me; gulps expelled through great effort.

What are you doing? I said.

No one said anything for a moment. Mum remained completely still, practically a statue.

I shook my head. Felt sick all over again.

Did you come to see the sunrise? Peter said, a calmness to his tone that was infuriating. He kept his hand on Mum, as though he wanted to keep her close for as long as possible. I think he knew that once he let go, that would be it.

What are you doing? I repeated, my voice tight.

Mum gripped the blanket round her, trying her hardest to tuck it in under her arms as she would a towel. Aida . . .

How could you?

We thought you were asleep, she whispered, hiding her eyes behind the palms of her hands.

Peter sat up, naked and exposed. It's not a big deal, he said.

I stared at him. Are you fucking serious? I shouted.

Mum closed her eyes for a moment. I'm sorry . . . Can you give us a minute to put on our clothes?

I snapped. I couldn't stand the sight of them together, couldn't stand his touch being on her. I went to where he sat, too casual in his posture, bent towards him and smacked him across the face. And it felt good, cathartic. I made to do it again. I was screaming – it was a noise I didn't know I could make. Raw and animalistic.

Calm down, Mum shouted.

No! I screamed back, crying now, tears streaming down. What the fuck?

I ran, slamming the living room door behind me, but it bounced back in my wake, leaving the door ajar as I stormed into the kitchen. I was still screaming but there was no consistency to my words. There was fury, a sense of injustice, pulsing out of me. I hated fucking everyone and everything. Nothing was mine. Nothing had ever been mine.

I grew still, weak and faint, gripping the sink counter, my head painful. I had no idea what my blood sugar was. Stumbling, I rummaged through cupboards desperately looking for test strips. And my meter, where was it?

Mum was now behind me, talking to me, helping me look for it without me telling her what I needed. It was Peter who fetched the meter, remembering it was on my bedside table. Mum lowered me into a seat, was quick with her actions, pricking my finger and inserting the strip into the end of the meter. Suddenly, she was lowering herself to my level, telling Peter to leave us alone.

Is she okay? he said.

Just leave us, please, she said.

I was all over the place, shaking my head frantically.

She cupped my face in her hands. You're having a hypo, she said, forcing some dextrose tablets into my mouth, as I continued to shake with anger and sickness and confusion. Chew on them, darling. Please, Aida. Keep chewing. That's it. Well done.

And finally I began to feel the effects of my dextrose tablets. I covered my face with my hands and began to sob. I'm fine, I said. I'm okay.

Mum tried to place her arms around me, but I pushed her away. I'm sorry . . . she said.

I swallowed.

So, he never told you we slept together? I whispered.

What?

Peter fucked me. After we went to the abattoir. I tried to smile, a sinister expression that stopped me from crying.

Mum was quiet for a moment. I didn't know, Aida. Obviously, I didn't know.

18

I lay in bed until early afternoon, the hangover and image of Mum and Peter enough to stop any sleep from arriving. I thought back to being at the border, of those people begging and promising me anything just for a grain of hope. If it had been me on the other side of the border, would I have been able to offer the same? Would I be willing to do anything to survive? I honestly didn't know.

I had no idea where we all stood. Would being with the same man make Mum and I see each other differently? Were we repulsive to one another now? At some point I moved to the living room. I stared at the sofa where I'd found them, taking the blanket that had wrapped them in my hands, bringing it to my nose and inhaling. There was no scent; it smelled the same as everything else in the room. As the sun shone in, I could see dust particles landing across the table and windowsills. I tried the handle on Mum's storage cupboard, rattling it a few times against the lock.

In the bathroom, very little water was left in the tub, a bug floating dead, grime around the edges. With paper towels, I did my best to gather up and clean the vomit I'd left from the previous night. My mouth was so dry, a fuzziness on my tongue, but I couldn't bring myself to scoop up some of the remaining water. In the kitchen, I found an old carton of pineapple juice in a cupboard above the disused fridge. It was out of date but made from fruit concentrate, so I reasoned it would be fine. I injected myself with insulin and then poured some of the juice into a paper cup and gulped it down, the sugar almost too overpowering. I refilled the cup and carried it through to Mum's room. She was curled up, her back to the window, and I placed the cup down on her bedside table.

She turned to look at me, her fingers brushing against me, trying to take hold of me, but I retreated.

I took the carton out into the yard. Maybe I thought I needed to make something of a peace offering to Peter after slapping him. For no logical reason, I was less angry at him than I was at Mum. Why were we always less angry at the men?

I knocked on the door and took a step back. Peter opened it, wearing shorts and a ripped T-shirt. His eyes were bloodshot, and it looked as if he hadn't slept.

Hi, I said.

Hi.

I held up the carton of pineapple juice. Do you have some cups?

He nodded, rubbing his head before retreating and then returning with some of his own disposable paper cups that looked as if they'd already been used for something else. He held three between his hands while I filled them up. When I'd finished there was still a quarter of the carton left and I shook it in my hand.

Things got out of hand last night, he said, his tone gentle and boyish, embarrassed even. Too much alcohol . . .

Yeah, I said. Definitely too much alcohol.

I knocked on Bobby's door but they're not answering, he said. Thought I should try and help tidy up or whatever. Make myself useful somehow after the mess I got myself into. Apologise to them . . .

Apologise to them for what?

He shrugged. Just . . . Everything.

There was a breeze on my back, and I paused for a moment to acknowledge it, wondered if I could be teased into thinking that a change of weather was in the air. I let the warm wind ripple over my top, my skin tingling underneath.

There was no one to be seen in Bobby and Sam's cottage, the place a disaster zone: dirty dishes and cups covering all the surfaces, decorations and sombreros littering the floor, empty glass bottles, the smell of food that had been left out and was now inedible. How disgustingly frivolously we behaved when drunk. I thought about the plastic beer cups at music festivals, at the memory of a little girl collecting stacks of them, taller in height than she herself, reclaiming ten pence for every cup she picked up off the ground, making a profit when all of us were too busy getting wasted. And I just stood there like that for a while, trying to settle myself, the congealed texture of the scraps left on plates turning my fragile stomach.

It occurred to me then that it wasn't like Bobby and Sam not to be up yet – both incapable of lying in. I stepped back, cautious, making my way into the back hall.

Bobby? I called out. Sam?

All the doors off the hall were closed and Rusty lay on the flagstones, whimpering, his nose brushing up against the door to their bedroom. I bent down and gave him a pat. By the back door there was a little puddle of dog piss.

Hello? I shouted, but still there was only silence. I turned the handle on the door, and it creaked open, Rusty running in. Over the threshold, I stared at Bobby and Sam huddled together on the cast-iron bedframe. They looked as though they were sleeping, but as I crept forward I could see the paleness of their faces, the limpness of their hands. By the bedside table sat packets of tablets, most of the blister pockets popped empty.

Saliva once again gathered in my mouth. I ran back into the kitchen, making it to the sink before I vomited for the second time in less than twelve hours, all over the dishes stacked up inside it.

Afterwards, I sat down in one of the armchairs by the fireplace and wiped my mouth. Bobby's glass was still on the coffee table, his grease-stained fingerprints all over it. Rusty was whimpering in the other room, couldn't understand why neither of them were inviting him up on to the bed beside them. My breathing was heavy, and I brought a hand to my chest, trying to soothe my broken heart. I thought about a passenger sitting on a plane, during which time a loved one would die, but for those precious hours while everyone else lived in trauma they would enjoy a blissful kind of ignorance. What a privilege it would have been to have had those hours. And I wanted to rewind the clock, go back to pouring pineapple juice, oblivious to what awaited me. No matter how much I willed it, I could not change the situation. Snippets of conversation from the night before ran through my mind. Had they been cryptic in their words of affection? I agonised over the things I could have said, like a speech I wanted to prepare, thinking somehow it would make a difference. When was the last time I'd told them that I loved them?

I wasn't sure for how long I sat there, ignoring Rusty's cries. Eventually, I returned to the back hall, my feet creaking over the tread of the entrance to their bathroom. And right in front of me, inside the porcelain of the toilet, was a trail of Bobby's blood. I stared at it for a moment, squinting to get a better look. I took the toilet brush and wiped the blood away, mixing it in with day-old urine, likely a mix of both Bobby and Sam.

I'd left the bedroom door ajar, and as I inched closer I stared at their sock-clad feet resting at the bottom of the bed. I came to Bobby's side first and placed a hand on his knee, patting it gently, before picking up an empty strip of tablets. I wondered if it had been a pleasant death. They didn't look as if they'd been in discomfort; they looked calm and peaceful together. Whose lungs had deflated first? Whose heart slowed last to its final beat? Did one of them watch the other go? Sam had his arm around Bobby's shoulder and Bobby's head was nuzzled into Sam's collarbone. I envied their love – envied that they were together until the end. What would that have felt like? I placed a kiss on Bobby's forehead before walking around to the other side and doing the same to Sam.

I sat on the edge of the bed then and I couldn't hold it in any more. I sobbed, letting the tears flow, running down my face. I kept cupping my hand over my mouth, trying to contain the noise despite there being no one to hear me. I could have stayed there for hours. Maybe I did.

I heard the front door opening and Mum walking through. I knew her even by the way she walked into a room. Hello . . . she said. Where is everyone?

Mum, I called out, trying to wipe my face. Wait. I'll come to you.

What's wrong? she said, worry already in her voice.

Just wait, I said, now on my feet, closing the bedroom door behind me.

When I entered the kitchen, she was standing by one of the armchairs. She looked up at me, her mouth already frowning, anticipating bad news. I gestured with my hand for her to sit.

What is it? she said.

I rubbed at my cheeks; I couldn't seem to find the words.

Aida . . . what's wrong? You're scaring me.

And I started to cry again. They're gone, I said. They went together. An overdose.

She was silent for a moment. No, she said, shaking her head. No.

I rubbed my face, shrugging at the surreal experience of it all. They just look like they're sleeping, I said.

Mum clasped her hands over her head, her eyes hidden behind palms. She began to shake her head wildly from side to side, tears escaping and silently running down her cheeks. No, it cannot be.

Mum . . .

She went to open her mouth but only a stunted breath escaped.

And we sat there together in silence, a fly or bluebottle buzzing and landing on the dirty plates on the kitchen counter.

Eventually Mum said, I should see them.

I led her through the hall, and, gripping Rusty in my arms, reached for the handle.

She stopped me before I'd fully opened the door. You said they look like they're sleeping. That's right, isn't it?

I nodded, pushing the door open further.

Mum stared at them. Do you think they've been gone for long? she asked, moving forward to delicately place an index finger on the top of Sam's big, sock-clad toe.

They're not warm any more . . . I said.

What do you call it . . . she said, *Rigor mortis*? They'll be stuck like this. We'll have to pry them apart.

Do we report this to someone? I said.

I don't know how we'll get them out of here, Mum said, and she just stared at them, shaking her head slightly in confusion, as if she could only allow pragmatic thoughts to filter through her mind.

Mum . . . Does someone need to certify their deaths?

She looked at me then, holding my eye. No, we're on our own. We've always been on our own.

Can we go back into the kitchen? I said. I can't be in here any more.

Mum led the way until we were both sitting in armchairs again.

We need to bury them somewhere they'd like to be, I said.

Mum was still shaking her head. How could they expect us to do this for them? she said, with little emotion in her voice, as if she were reporting something she'd simply overheard. She got to her feet and walked to the kitchen, stopping to inspect my latest vomit that covered some of the dirty dishes. We should try and tidy this place up, she said. They'd hate to see the place like this . . . Mum faltered then. What are we meant to do without them?

We need to pick a nice spot and lay them to rest, I said. Promise me we'll do that. Now. While we still can.

We'll need some help, she said, nodding her head towards the campervan.

By the bedroom door Peter stood over the threshold looking in. So, how do we go about this? he asked. Someone take Sam's shoulders and someone else pull Bobby away . . . ?

I stared at him, horrified by his casualness.

I'm sorry, he said. I've never done this before.

I think we try and then wrap them up in their duvet and sheets, Mum said.

I like the idea of them being buried with something that smells familiar, I replied.

Can you reverse the Defender to the door? Peter asked, turning to me. We can make a start here and then we'll place them into the back.

I nodded, hesitant to move.

Aida . . . Mum said. It's okay. We can do this.

Outside, I was slow to get into the driver's seat, and for a moment I just sat there looking out across the cluttered dashboard. I could feel my breathing getting tighter. In the cabin behind me there was enough space in among the folded seats and farming equipment to lie down. I climbed over and reached for an old checked blanket, spreading it across my body, a pair of waterproof trousers rolled up behind my head as a pillow. I lay out flat, my eyes cast up to the ceiling. Tears began to slide down my cheeks. Everything around me was silent and I tried to keep my lips clamped shut but it was impossible. I let out a small, contained howl before I closed my eyes. When I opened them again it took me a moment to remember why I had come out into the Defender in the first place.

I clambered back into the front seat, turned on the ignition and reversed the Defender across the yard without stalling it, lining it up with the door of the cottage. In the back window of the campervan I could see Evelyn and Rebecca staring out.

Mum and Peter had managed to manoeuvre both bodies in their crooked postures out towards the door, having wrapped the duvet around one and the bedsheets around the other, their faces covered. But despite not being able to see them, I still knew which was Bobby and which was Sam.

If you open the back door . . . Peter said.

I nodded, doing as he asked. Just be careful with them, please.

Of course, he said, as he climbed into the back, instructing Mum to help him as he dragged Bobby's body first through the open door. He was struggling as he did so, clearly trying to take most of the weight himself, Mum too giving it everything she had, physically stronger than I'd ever given her credit for.

Peter drove us along the dirt track, me sitting up front with him, while Mum stayed in the back with Bobby and Sam.

Are we near? I said, pointing out ahead. Is this the place you were talking about?

A little further along, Mum replied, looking past our shoulders to see out the windscreen.

What's so important about being up here? I said. What's the significance?

There's a little stretch by the forest I know they used to like. They'd drive up there when they wanted some time to themselves, by the conifers.

I didn't know that . . .

Peter manoeuvred the Defender over a ditch and the track levelled out. When we stopped, we were looking at a small stretch of land that was cupped by the dying brown forest. Peter pulled on the handbrake and I jumped out, landing on a patch of dead grass, suddenly needing to shield my eyes from the sun.

Where should we put them? Peter said, taking a spade in his hand.

Over by the trees but not too close to the roots, Mum said. They'll get in the way, and we'll not be able to dig deep enough.

As Peter made his way over, I sat down on the baked earth and began pulling strands of brown grass from their roots. I reached down for more but Mum placed her hand over mine, stopping me. Don't do that, she said.

It's dead anyway.

Just let it be.

I can't believe they left us, I said. I keep thinking a trick is being played on me.

They'll be happy here, Mum said.

I should help him dig, I said, nodding to where Peter was breaking ground.

No, it should be me, Mum replied, not moving.

And as I sat watching, I suddenly felt so overwhelmingly tired, as if I'd inherited some of the weight Bobby and Sam had left behind. There was only peace for them now; they didn't need to endure any of this any more. Did souls ever look down and observe their corpses? It occurred to me then that I'd never really considered the idea of a soul being a real thing until now. Maybe it was my way of needing an afterlife, of clinging to the concept that *this* was not it.

When I go, Mum said to me, if things get better . . . if we get rain and get to live a civil life once again . . . will you promise to cremate me?

I turned to stare at her. Why?

She shrugged. I've always preferred the idea of cremation. Of being burnt to nothing. I find the notion of a coffin claustrophobic.

Maybe I'll donate my body to a university, I finally said. It might be nice, like I've cheated the system somehow. I paused. Do you think we'd still have universities? Will that be a thing? Will cadavers still be something people want?

I'm not sure, to be honest, Mum said, rising to her feet as she spoke, heading to the Defender. She removed another spade from the passenger seat but, when she approached, Peter was quick to dismiss her.

I'll work better on my own, he said.

How far down do you need to dig? I asked, getting to my feet too, coming closer.

I don't know, Mum said. As deep as the holes they dig at funerals.

I've never been to a funeral, Peter replied.

Mum paused. Maybe this wide? she said, extending her arms out from her sides. And then just the length of their bodies and down.

And suddenly I began laughing, a cackle rising from the back of my throat.

What's so funny? she asked.

I was still laughing; I couldn't seem to stop. It's not funny, I said. It's just the weirdest conversation I think we've ever had.

Are you sure you're okay to do this? Mum said, addressing Peter.

I stopped laughing then. What choice does he have?

No one spoke.

The earth was so hard and compact underfoot, desperate for moisture, but Peter didn't stop digging. He just kept forcing his spade into the ground, periodically wiping sweat from his forehead.

Do you think life will grow on top of them? I asked.

What?

Nature – grass and weeds? Daisies maybe?

I don't know, Mum said.

I just don't like the idea of nothing growing above them.

I think you're overthinking it.

In cemetery plots, though, they put turf down, don't they? So that grass is forced to grow and cover the hole in the ground.

Mum reached for my arm, gripping me. Aida, stop this, she said.

What?

She paused. Do you think maybe we should talk about what happened last night?

No. Absolutely not.

I'm embarrassed by my behaviour.

Please, Mum . . . I said.

Loneliness is good for no one, she whispered, so gently that she sounded like a child. I guess it was just nice to feel like I was wanted.

Fine. Let's stop now.

She shifted. I really should take a turn at digging . . .

I smiled then. Don't bother with the empty gestures, Miriam.

But I should do something, she reasoned. Get supplies for us. Food. Water.

I was quick to move. No, I want to go, I said. Leave you two alone . . .

Aida, don't . . .

Just let me go, okay?

Mum took a step closer towards me. You don't have access to the supplies, she whispered.

Has it come to that now? I said. The supply cupboard . . .

For some fresh water at least.

Give me the key, then, I said.

She stared at me, hesitant, turning then to look at Peter who was digging away, oblivious.

You can't be the only gatekeeper, I said. I live there too.

Mum blinked a few times, biting on her bottom lip. Fine, she whispered, feeling for the key tucked into her T-shirt, slowly removing it from around her neck. She made such a pantomime of trying to be as inconspicuous as possible that it really wasn't inconspicuous at all. I exhaled as she watched me place the key around my own neck. He's seen you naked, Mum. He's seen the fucking key.

I took the Defender down to the cottages, leaving Mum and Peter behind. For a moment I fantasised about grabbing my insulin, some supplies from the cupboard and just driving off. Surely the fantasy version was better than sticking around here. And then I caught sight of Bobby and Sam in the rear-view mirror. I'd momentarily forgotten that they were still with me.

I parked in the yard and hurried into our cottage. I kept my head low, sensing Evelyn peering at me through the campervan window. I locked the back door and made a beeline for the living room, closing the curtains to ensure no one could see in. The lock on the cupboard door was surprisingly tough and I contemplated the idea of Mum having given me the wrong key. But with the force of both hands the lock finally turned.

It had been a while since I'd seen inside the cupboard, and I had to admit that it was quite impressive. I reached for one of the water containers on the ground, breaking open the plastic seal. It was heavy, five litres' worth, and I struggled to decant it into a water bottle, a little patch of damp resting on the linoleum-lined floor of the cupboard. I glanced around as if I were expecting someone to be there before bending further, my nose practically touching the floor as I extended my tongue, lapping the water up like an animal. Afterwards, I brought the container to my lips and took several gulps, flooding my stomach, my lungs expanding, my body seeming to come to life in a way that no longer felt recognisable.

Picking up a packet of gingersnap biscuits, I made my way back out into the yard, realising that the door to Bobby and Sam's cottage was open. A bin bag was sitting outside, Evelyn cleaning the cottage, muttering to herself. Maybe this was her way of helping, her contribution, doing what she did best when there was nothing else to do.

I made the journey back, glancing once again in the rear-view mirror to take in the sight of Bobby and Sam wrapped up in their bedding. I caught a glimpse of Sam's hair poking out from the sheets. I brought the Defender to a sudden stop on the track and stared at Sam's hair, almost expecting the strands to move, perhaps for Sam then to poke his head out and ask what the hell was going on. But of course there was nothing. How could they have done this to us? And suddenly I was screaming in my seat, thumping my hands on the steering wheel. Everything in my body seemed to hurt again but I kept thrashing out, my fist hitting the dashboard, the fans shifting from downward to upward slats. I thumped my knees until I was sure that I'd left bruises. Afterwards, I let myself cry again, but only for a few minutes, enough to release the pressure that had been building up inside.

When I returned to the row of conifers, Mum was sitting on the ground, watching Peter, a tension there that felt new. I offered her the full bottle of water, tore the gingersnaps open, but she ushered with her head for Peter to take them.

Peter threw his spade down and gulped the water in front of me, leaving maybe half of it, before taking a tower of ginger-snaps, snapping them and forcing them into his mouth as if he hadn't eaten in weeks, as if he hadn't sat down the night before and demolished a three-course meal.

I was cautious, taking a step back as though I needed to inspect them both.

Do you think it's deep enough yet? Mum asked, nodding in the direction of the grave, her voice sounding very controlled.

Peter began circling the hole he'd dug, his mouth still chewing on gingersnaps.

I walked over to the hole then, a few steps away from Peter, and peered inside. It was narrow and perhaps not quite long enough, but it was deep, probably up past my waist. Maybe . . . I said. It looks pretty deep.

Mum nodded. I don't think we need to dig any more, she said.

Who do we put in first? Peter asked.

Bobby, Mum said. He should be closest to the ground. Plus, he's older.

What does that have to do with anything? I said.

He would have passed away first. Then when it was Sam's time he'd have gone on top.

Peter opened the back compartment and climbed inside to where Bobby and Sam's heads lay, while Mum and I stood out-side, staring at their socked feet.

I think we just go for it, Peter said. I'll lift Bobby from here and you both take the legs. And as he spoke he was already attempting to remove Bobby, the covers coming undone, his pose and posture awkwardly exposed.

Seeing Bobby like this, without Sam's body fitting to him like a jigsaw, was horrific. I jumped back, a shriek escaping from my mouth at the sight of him, the weight of his body pressing up on Mum.

She exhaled a deep, shuddering breath, gripping one leg. It's okay, she panted, trying to offer me reassurance. It's going to be okay. They'll be together.

I nodded, reluctantly taking Bobby's other leg. We took a firm hold and angled Bobby out of the cab, while Peter tried to take most of the weight. He shuffled forward and then we were carrying Bobby across the grass, struggling, and when we finally made it to the grave Bobby was somewhat unceremoniously rolled into it.

Looking at what we'd done, I screamed, hysteria rising within me. He's facing the wrong way, I shouted. He's facing downwards.

I don't think there's anything we can do now, Mum said. But I don't think he'll mind.

Peter was already gripping Sam's shoulders, waiting for us to take the legs. And as we repeated the same actions, Sam a lighter corpse, we managed to get him into the grave facing upwards towards the sun.

Is there anything you want to say to them? Mum asked.

No, I said, shaking my head. I've already said what I wanted to say.

Mum took the spade that was upended in the heaped earth and scooped some dirt on to it, throwing it in on top of them. Bye, boys, she said. Love you more than you'll ever know.

I took the spade from her and began shovelling earth into the hole as quickly as I could. Without my realising it, Peter returned, and he was prising the spade from my grip, and finally I relented, watched as he worked quickly, almost effortlessly while Mum and I settled once again on the grass near by.

I never understood why they felt the need to be so discreet, I finally said as we watched most of the gravel and soil disappear back into the ground.

Don't be so naïve, Mum replied. You know what this community's like. I don't think Bobby ever really came to terms with it himself. Rumours were harmful in such a narrow-minded place. How were these people not suffocating on their own ignorance? *Bachelors*, she said, hearing the falseness and injustice of it in her voice.

I think that's the saddest thing I've ever heard, I said. People only want to be happy. Don't we all deserve that?

The farming world is a complicated one. And Bobby came from a different generation, she replied. Perhaps we would have been asking too much of an old man.

But Sam . . . Wouldn't he have wanted to live his life more openly?

Mum shrugged. I don't know. Maybe all he needed or wanted was Bobby. You're forgetting that being gay was illegal here until 1980.

Fucking madness, I said.

When Peter was finished, he threw his spade to the ground and I got to my feet, coming to pat the grave affectionately. Stepping back, I acknowledged the mound of displaced earth that was proof to me that Bobby and Sam lay here. I thought about making a cross from some sticks but decided they wouldn't have wanted that. It was peaceful and quiet, a pocket of earth somewhat undisturbed. It was the best offering we could have given them.

19

Evelyn was waiting for me, sitting out on Bobby and Sam's bench. It was barely dawn. She patted at the empty space next to her and I sat down. She shuffled a little closer, put her arm around me.

I can't imagine what you must be feeling right now, she said.

I shrugged. Numb.

Are you sleeping?

I shook my head.

They were wonderful people, she said. I'm so sorry.

I closed my eyes, leaning into her. I could have stayed like that all day.

I think we should get out of here, she said. Like we did before.

I sat up then, suddenly alert. You want to try going to Glasgow now?

She turned to look at me, all motherly with concern. You need to get away from here, clear your mind.

I don't think I can, Evelyn. I'm so tired.

I closed my eyes again, shadows fluttering across my eyelids.

I think I can get us water, she said. I opened my eyes. If we can make it back to where we went before, I can get us water.

She pointed then to the parked Defender, Rebecca already sitting up front inside. I walked towards Rebecca, staring in at her, but I couldn't read her expression, it was completely vacant. And in her arms, Noah slept.

Evelyn was beside me. Peter will stay with your mum . . . she said, placing the key to the Defender in my hand.

I struggled to string a sentence together, everything felt like a chore – questioning her felt too hard. It was nice to be told to do something – to be given direction, even just for a short time.

I climbed into the driver's seat, while Evelyn got in beside Rebecca, pushing her a little further towards me.

We should leave a note for Mum, I said.

Peter will tell her. He knows where we're going.

I turned the engine on. I have no money . . .

You won't need any.

Rebecca shifted beside me, her leg resting next to the gearstick. Taking her in, I could see that she was clean – the cleanest I'd seen her in a long time. Evelyn must have given her her ration of baby wipes. And what was she wearing? A clean, flowery kaftan dress. I inhaled, trying to decipher if she smelled nice. I thought she did.

We set off, the Defender juddering a little until I got a handle on the gears. The fuel gauge was near the top, Peter perhaps having topped it up with red diesel. As we drove past, the reservoir looked like a crater to me now, this vast, expansive space that served no purpose. I realised I was cold, in a way I hadn't felt in so long. I turned the fan up but then remembered that it didn't work. I was still wearing the shorts and T-shirt I'd slept in, my bed filthy, the linen not having been changed in so long. I wished I had brought a jumper. I wished I'd brushed my hair. I wanted to brush my teeth; my breath was foul.

Are there back roads we can take? Evelyn said.

There's the old motorway . . .

Let's take that for as long as we can, then.

As I changed gear, my fingers brushed up against Rebecca's leg and there was the smallest reflex, her shifting away momentarily. The roads were completely deserted, cars abandoned along verges, litter fluttering across tarmac. There wasn't really anything stopping us – I wasn't sure what I had been expecting – maybe rows and rows of policemen linking arms, creating human chains across the land. And I began to think we'd make it, that maybe we could reach Dad. He had no way of knowing about Bobby and Sam, and I needed him to know. I needed him to tell me he would come back with us and make everything better.

We had probably clocked up nearly twenty miles, growing more confident in ourselves, before we saw the first roadblocks, positioned across in the middle of the old motorway. On our side, a police car was parked, but it didn't look as if it had moved in a long time.

I brought the Defender to a stop, realising then that the rattle that had been under the frame, which reminded me of Bobby, was no longer there. Peter must have fixed the bushings.

Do you think there's another way . . . Evelyn said.

Two men were stepping out of the police car, wearing casual clothes, no uniform to be seen. One of them raised his hand.

We should turn back, I said, but Evelyn was already rolling down her window.

Let's just see what they say. They might be able to help us get through.

We watched him approach, my hands gripping the steering wheel. If we had to make a quick escape, was I capable of doing so in the Defender? Would I stall it at the very moment we needed to be gaining speed?

I thought I recognised the man but couldn't place him. Maybe he had been at the party the last night in the Premier Inn. He came right up to Evelyn's window and peered in, his hands curling over the glass, while the other man stayed by the roadblock, shifting his head from left to right, as if someone was watching him, as if someone was watching us all.

What are you ladies doing out here? he said.

Evelyn's composure was relaxed, assured. We're trying to reach the baby's father in the city.

Why?

You don't think a child needs their parent?

Why did he leave? the man asked.

For money. Can't you see that we're all dying out here without any resources?

You need to turn around, he replied.

Please, just let us through. What's one car to you?

You are at risk of a fine.

And what? I doubt anyone has the resources to follow up on that. No one cares.

The man cast his gaze in through the window, staring at Rebecca and the baby, before settling on me. From the way he lingered I got the sense that he too recognised me.

Are you all related?

Yes, Evelyn said.

Do you have documents to prove that?

Why do you need that? she said.

We've had a lot of trouble with smuggling across the border. Trafficking. He paused, staring now at Rebecca, whose gaze was fixed ahead, straight on the blocked road. You see, in every crisis there is always an opportunity to be had, he added. So, when I see a woman carrying a baby, and things look shifty – and let me tell you, things are looking shifty – I ask myself a few questions.

Please, Evelyn said, her tone as soft and endearing as it would go. There must be something we can do . . .

Do I know you? he said, pointing to me.

I don't think so, I said.

Isn't there *anything* we can do? she pressed.

He paused, rocking backwards on his heels. I tell you what, he said, returning his attention to Evelyn. How about you leave her here, he said, pointing to me, and I'll let the pair of you carry on.

What? I said, as the blood began to pound through my body, rushing through my head, my ears. Nothing made sense. Was I something to be traded? Or was I being protected? I glanced at my driver's door, eyes hovering over the old lock, wasn't sure if it even worked any more. My mind and body were working at different speeds, and I'd never really felt anything like it. Was this the purest form of fear? Mum didn't even know where I was. I was so fucking stupid. And if something happened to me, what would be left of her?

Evelyn . . . I said. Please, can we just go back?

She raised her hand, gesturing me to stop.

I can't drive, she finally said, speaking to the man. Her words so pragmatic; all of logistics and nothing else.

Was it flight or fight mode they talked about? I remembered us discussing it at school once and had never truly known what it felt like until that moment. Were you meant to stay and fight, or flee? What was the best one?

I kicked the car into reverse and spun it round, no time to think about the difficulty of the gearstick or if I'd find third instead of first. I just drove with the most clarity and necessity of my life. I truly believed that if I didn't drive away at that very moment I'd never be going home. And the suffering I thought I'd endured would be nothing compared to this potential unknown. Evil existed in the world, and I'd touched it, could feel it on me.

I carried on speeding down the old motorway, my foot pressed down on the accelerator. Evelyn was shouting at me, but I wasn't listening to her. My eyes darted from the windscreen to my rear-view mirror, convinced someone would appear at any moment. We were wearing no seatbelts, and I knew that if I crashed it would be the end of us all.

As we approached the village, I finally slowed, acknowledging the play park and the deserted streets before coming to a stop.

When we went to Glasgow that first time . . . I said. What did those blue and pink baby clothes in the windows really mean?

Why are you asking me that?

I need to know what all this was for.

She stared out the window, the swings in her sight.

There are people in the world, she said, who are desperate to be parents but can't. And adoption can be a very traumatic experience. There are very few young babies available. Instead, damaged older children are handed over, with no support, and these new parents are just expected to pick up the pieces. When someone decides to adopt, it's always a gamble. You'll never really know who you've got until you get them home. And it's not like rescuing a pet. It's not as easy to return them if they're too much of a handful.

It took a moment for everything to click into place, perhaps because I didn't want it to be true – couldn't imagine it. What, so that place in Glasgow sells babies?

People pay such good money for newborns. Even toddlers up to a certain age . . . They don't retain the damage and trauma of older children. They're a clean slate.

It was so clear to me then, a clarity that came with fear, thoughts running in their most primal form. Rebecca isn't your daughter, is she . . . ? I whispered.

I took her from a worse situation, she said. You have to remember that. Most of the time the girls are actually happier in their new existence, have better living conditions than before.

Often, they are sold by their own desperate parents. She paused. I take Rebecca away from that – and I take away the burden of a child she doesn't want. A lot of rich people, celebrities even, get their children this way. It is a happy ending for all.

Noah's sleeping head flopped from one side of Rebecca's chest to the other. I reached for Rebecca's free hand and rubbed her fingers but there was no response.

Evelyn caught my eye as I glanced sideways. You're looking at me with real disgust, but really, it's just a business like every other. Just like a livestock farm. Supply and demand.

But how can you . . . How can you bring yourself to do that?

You're mad at me, and I understand, but my role has always been about finding peaceful solutions. If you really want to be mad and disgusted with someone, be mad and disgusted at the men who think their sexual desires and fantasies can always be justified, regardless of consent, regardless of age. Men. It's always been the fucking men.

I felt sick, but not a sickness that I could purge from my system. It was a sickness that would stay with me, cling to my skin and my hair and my guts – remind me of my own flawed contributions to this world we inhabited.

So, you sell Noah to the highest bidder . . . And as I spoke, I was suddenly aware of the absurdity of the conversation. What happens to Rebecca after?

The girls are usually given a job . . . A nail bar or something. They'll get training . . . Well, that was before the drought changed everything, so I'm not sure now. That's not really my area of expertise. Other people deal with that side of things.

But she's still essentially trafficked? I said, the words spluttering out of me.

I wouldn't call it that, Evelyn said.

I started shaking my head.

It's a scary world out there, Aida. But that's the reality of it. Things are not nice, not everyone can be sheltered from the storm.

Please, I said. Leave Rebecca and Noah with us and go. You don't want them, and you can't get rid of them now, so . . .

Go where? she demanded. And with what? We don't have any money and neither do you.

What about a sense of doing the right thing? I said, desperate. Not everything is about money.

Evelyn snorted. Our entire social construct works on the premise that money is more important than life, she said. And whether you want to believe it or not, your family subscribes to those values too. Your whole farming model relied upon it. You like to think that you're better than all of this but you're not. You're no different.

By the time we made it over the cattle grid and into the yard there was only silence between us, nothing left to say. Mum had been waiting, sitting on Bobby and Sam's bench, and she ran towards us, screaming at me for putting her through yet another excruciating experience. But I wasn't listening to her. I was already marching into our front hall, doing the only thing that made sense to me. I flung the cupboard door open and there it was, Bobby's shotgun resting in its usual spot next to the sledge. I grabbed it, the weight familiar in my hands, and searched the cupboard for the box of cartridges, opening the barrel and shoving two cartridges in. It was an odd sensation; difficult to explain. But I felt so furious, so compelled to do what I did. I was sure it was the only way to get them to leave – the only way to purge these people and their rot off our land and out of our lives. And it was freeing too, living momentarily without a conscience.

I took a breath, reasoned there was no going back, and ran out of the front door, rounding the corner into the yard, aiming the shotgun at Evelyn.

Everything happened in slow motion then. Evelyn raised her hands into the air, panic surfacing across her face. Although I wasn't listening to the actual words that she spoke, I knew from her face that she was pleading with me, genuinely fearful, perhaps for the first time in her entire life. And I liked it.

Aida! Mum screamed. Put the gun down.

I ignored her, the gun level with Evelyn's head.

Have you lost your mind? Mum shouted.

I didn't waver. Something had changed in me; a fear and anger pulsing through my body that felt so pure and genuine. They're not what you think, I said to Mum, not taking my eyes off Evelyn. She's not Rebecca's mother. They're fucking people-traffickers.

Peter emerged then from the back cabin door of their campervan. Aida, you don't have to do this, he said, attempting his most reassuring voice. You need to calm down.

I'm perfectly calm, I spat. Can't you tell?

Please . . . he said.

I stumbled a little before bringing the gun closer to Evelyn's face. You don't understand, I said. It's all wrong. It's all so fucking wrong and inhumane.

I flicked the safety off on the shotgun. I remembered the first time I was shown how to shoot, taken by Bobby to clay pigeon shooting, how I'd been nervous initially, at the idea of holding something that had the potential to cause real harm – a stranger handing me a loaded gun, giving me instructions. Then I was taking aim, following this disk of clay through the sky and smashing it to pieces. And I was an excellent shot; a natural, they'd told me, calling me Calamity Jane.

Aida, please . . . Mum begged. This isn't you. Don't do something you'll regret.

Evelyn cleared her throat, some confidence surfacing. This is ludicrous, she said, a laugh snorting through her nostrils.

Fuck you, I spat, taking aim, my finger hovering over the trigger.

Peter shifted and for a moment I thought he was going to stand in front of Evelyn like a shield, but instead he just turned to look at her, staring at her face as though he was inspecting a painting.

Don't think I won't, I said. It'll be no different from killing a fox.

Peter stared at me. If you were going to kill her you would have done it already. You wouldn't have hesitated.

You don't know that, I said. And I realised I was crying, the shotgun shaking in my hands.

Peter approached slowly, offering a gesture of peace before lowering the barrel of the gun down towards the ground, gently removing it from my grip.

I don't know what's happened here, I said. We used to be decent, didn't we? People were good to each other. Weren't they?

A silence filled the yard, only the noise of Noah whimpering in Rebecca's arms.

Peter straightened, as though an invisible line had been drawn between us all. I could see his hands were filthy, dirt ingrained under his fingernails. I remembered him digging into my skin with those same fingers. His touch had been on Mum now too. I wanted to be sick all over again.

Don't begrudge us for wanting the same as you, Evelyn said. We're all just trying to survive. We're all doing what we need to, to survive.

We're all dying, I said.

Noah was wailing now, and Evelyn took him from Rebecca, ushering her to get inside the campervan.

Can I take you in? Peter said, addressing me. I think you need to sit down.

I nodded, defeated, and slowly, very slowly, with him still holding the shotgun, he guided me back into our living room, Mum following suit. He nodded for us to sit, and we did so, Mum and I squeezed close together on the corduroy sofa. Evelyn came in then, patting Noah's back, walking into the centre of the room.

She gazed down at us. It's been a terrible ordeal, she said, shoogling Noah, so composed despite him being upset.

What happens now? I whispered, while Mum just seemed to sit there, the shock of it all too much.

Being stuck here really isn't so bad, she said. All this space and privacy. She smiled. We're going to move into Bobby and Sam's cottage, she added. It will be good for us all to stick together, don't you think?

I was already shaking my head. It's too soon, I said. It's still their home.

It needs to be lived in, Evelyn said.

I was aware of Peter standing behind Evelyn, the barrel of the shotgun now open, hanging over his arm.

Are we being given a choice? Mum asked.

Evelyn leaned against Mum's storage cupboard, tapping a repetitive rhythm on Noah's back. We found some more water. Did we tell you?

I sat up. Where? Down the old well?

No, she replied, shaking her head. We found a tank stashed behind some old junk in one of the empty calving sheds. She paused. Bobby must have been taking precautions . . . So, it got me thinking that if there's one in an old shed then there is likely to be more stashed about, don't you think?

Mum swallowed. Perhaps, she said.

Evelyn brought Noah out in front of her, smiling at his crying little face. I cleaned Bobby and Sam's place from top to bottom and I can't find any more supplies hidden there, she said. And then I began looking in here, and do you know what? I found nothing. Except for this cupboard, she said, tapping it with her finger. And it's got me so curious. I just need to know what you keep in here that's so important it needs to be locked away.

Mum didn't say anything.

I wondered if it was money. Farmers are always trying to stash their money somewhere, aren't they?

We're bankrupt, Mum said.

Evelyn came close and stopped, lowering Noah towards Mum so that their noses were nearly touching. Mum reached out for Noah, but Evelyn pulled him back, laughing. You really are desperate, aren't you?

Mum stared at Noah, trying to offer him a smile. He can sense this tension, she said. It affects children, even from infancy.

Peter tells me there's a key around your neck.

Please, Mum said. Don't harm him.

Harm Noah? Evelyn said. He's my most valuable possession.

Slowly, Mum brought the chain up from inside her T-shirt and showcased the key that I imagined was warm from resting against her breastbone. I had never given too much thought to its appearance but as she held its weight in her hand it occurred to me that it had probably been tugging her down and altering her posture. It was old, long, teeth cut into various-sized rectangles. If I'd believed in such a thing, it was the type of key that might have brought the house good fortune.

Mum held out the key to Evelyn, who placed it inside the lock. It was stubborn, in the same way it had been with me, and Evelyn looked doubtful before it finally clicked. And then she was opening the door, while Peter peered in behind her.

A sigh escaped from Evelyn's lips. Bloody hell, Miriam . . . You've been holding out on us.

I'm sure most people have been doing some form of stock-piling, Mum said.

Evelyn snorted a laugh. Well, only those with means. Not everyone is in such a privileged position. She looked at Peter and they held each other's eye for a moment, something unspoken being communicated between them. If we were ever going to rebel against them and attack, this would have been the moment, when they were still distracted by shock at the sheer scale of Mum's hoarding. But we did nothing, and the moment passed.

Evelyn turned to look at us. Well, this changes everything, she said. Honestly, Miriam, I had no idea you were such a prepper.

We can share it, Mum said.

Evelyn shook her head, still appearing stunned by the contents before her. I think the time for sharing has passed, she said. You were rationing us with half-filled bottles of water from your bathtub, while all this time you had this at your disposal.

It wasn't like that, Mum said. We weren't using this ourselves either.

Evelyn paused, a plan formulating in her mind. Perhaps you should experience what it's like to live like us for a while . . . She nodded, definitive then. Things are going to work a little differently from now on. But change isn't always bad. It's life-affirming. It's just a matter of embracing it. She looked at me and then Mum. Try to relax, okay? People want to experience these extreme ways of life all the time – didn't there used to be celebrities going off to uninhabited islands to see if they could survive, hunt and gut animals, catch fish with spears? This isn't as hard as that.

Why are you doing this? I asked.

Because I'm desperate, she replied. Because I'm an animal. And that's what animals do. We take from the weak to ensure our own survival.

She started instructing Peter to remove the contents from the cupboard, and he nodded silently, already heaving supplies out across the floor in front of us, lifting a five-kilo sack of rice in his arms. We watched him strip the cupboard bare. How long had it taken Mum to acquire those supplies? Months and months, a year maybe. And it was gone from her in less than twenty minutes. They didn't stop there either – they went through our kitchen cupboards too, removing anything that could be consumed. And we let them, everything now out with our control.

Afterwards, Evelyn measured out rations of supplies and placed them on the coffee table for us. We'll give you back your camping stove, she said, winking at Mum.

You haven't given us any water, I said.

She hesitated and then nodded before leaving and returning with one of our old sports cap water bottles, the mouthpiece chewed and jagged, filled just slightly more than halfway up.

My insulin . . . ?

Evelyn scrunched her noise. Don't worry, I'll keep it safe and refrigerated for you in Bobby and Sam's.

I looked at her, my desperation visible.

Don't look so scared, she said. The insulin is of no use to us. Sure, we could get good money for it. There will always be people desperate for insulin, but it doesn't matter now does it, we can't get to the city? Really what I'm trying to say is that we mean you no harm. So, when you need more, let us know and we'll ensure that you get some.

Stop this, Mum said. Please. Things have gone too far. I admit that perhaps we could have been more generous with the water, but you must understand, we hadn't accounted for you.

Well, this will give you the opportunity to think about your actions.

What are you going to do with us? I asked.

I'm not a monster, Evelyn said, as if she was trying to apologise, as if this was completely out of her control. You are not prisoners. Just like us, you are free to leave whenever you want. Maybe you should – if you do decide to go, then do let me know and I can pack up some insulin for you.

Go where? Mum said.

Evelyn shrugged. That's not really my problem.

Alone, in the kitchen with our rations, we stared at one another. We need to remain calm, Mum said. Okay, so what do we have? We have a roof over our head, we have food, water . . . They didn't take your meter and test strips, did they?

I shook my head, holding up the lunch pack.

Okay, well that's something, and they'll not stop you from getting your insulin. She paused. Shelter, food, water, medicine, that's all we need.

I began pacing the floor, my feet sticking to the linoleum. We'll have to boil the pasta and rice in water . . .

We'll cook then drain any water that's left.

Rice-water . . . I said, retrieving my meter. I pricked my finger and squeezed a droplet of blood to the surface, dropping it on the end of the testing strip. The device calibrated and then, as if on autopilot, I removed the test strip and put it in the bin. How many times in my life had a carried out that procedure? I imagined stopping it all, throwing the meter away, succumbing to what I assumed would eventually take me – some heart condition, a stroke maybe, a diabetic coma. It felt as if I had never been destined to lead a long, healthy life. I injected myself with some short-acting insulin, while Mum placed a portion of rice into a pot on the camping stove, covering it with as little water as possible, letting it come to the boil, before turning the temperature down and placing a lid on top.

She was trying to *sell* Rebecca and Noah, I said, my voice nothing more than a whisper. They wouldn't have come back if we'd managed to get past the checkpoint.

Mum wrapped her arms around me, resting her face against my back.

What if they do something to her? I said.

She kissed my head. Couldn't think of anything to say to make things better, and that was her job. Wasn't a mother meant to always offer comfort to her child?

After ten minutes she turned the cooker off and let the rice sit, the water having completely evaporated.

We're like those people who lose their homes in hurricanes and tornadoes, I said. We're completely adrift.

Except we still have all our possessions, she replied. Our own beds and duvets, our lumpy corduroy couches. She started spooning out the rice, looking into the pot. I think I've just made the best rice of my life and I wasn't even trying.

I brought two bowls down from the cupboard and Mum divided the portions up, trying to put more in my bowl, while I shoved some back into hers.

Do you want a sauce or something with it? I said. It'll be pretty bland otherwise.

Chilli sauce? she said. I think they left us an unopened bottle in a cupboard.

I shook my head. It'll only make us thirsty. I took a mouthful and swallowed.

Is it okay? Mum asked.

I nodded. There was a buzzing in my head, my right temple thumping. I'd just become aware of it, and I thought about finding some paracetamol, but the effort seemed too great, and I wouldn't have been able to swallow it without using some of our water.

What do you think their long-term plan is? Mum said.

Maybe they're hoping we'll do what Bobby and Sam did, I replied, and disappear.

Stop that, Mum demanded. Don't say that. They didn't *disappear*.

Sorry, I said, focusing on my bowl, my face practically fitting inside the rim.

Mum cleared her throat, her fork clattering off her bowl. Evelyn knew we wouldn't be able to turn them away, she said. Not with Rebecca. It was always going to be this way.

When did you become so defeatist? I said, my voice louder than I had initially intended.

Please, she pleaded. Let's not fight. That's what they want us to do – to turn on each other.

What if they never leave now? I said.

I don't know, darling . . .

Maybe we *should* leave then, I said. We could leave right now, couldn't we? Surely there are other places we could go where we won't get stopped?

We have nothing to bribe or trade with, Mum said. We'd get nowhere. And anyway, she added, looking down at the floor, this is my home. Why should they be able to force me out? I don't want to leave.

Why not? Because of Bobby and Sam? I don't think they'd mind, I said. Honestly. People migrate for a reason; the ones who stay behind are usually the ones left regretting their actions. I nodded, seeming suddenly very sure of my logic.

But . . .

But what? I pleaded.

Maybe I'm foolish, but I think that Rebecca and Noah are now our responsibility. No one knows about Noah, and that scares me . . . To the rest of the world, he doesn't even exist.

AUTUMN

20

It was pitch black outside, two or three in the morning, and Mum and I each lay across a sofa in the living room, Rusty tucked in beside me. It wasn't as if we'd agreed to sleep there, but neither of us had any desire to be alone. I had always liked those twilight hours before daybreak. In my second year at Edinburgh, I'd started seeing this guy who didn't want anything serious, and despite me also not wanting anything serious, I'd taken his aloofness as a challenge, making it my mission to make him fall in love with me. I'd thought of it as an experiment, him having no idea, until it got out of hand. Initially there was the satisfaction of *winning*, but soon he had become possessive and overbearing. He'd even started talking about us having kids together. It was terrifying, but I was too cowardly to put an end to things, and so in the summer months, when others returned to their families and I chose to stay in the city, citing a summer job, I began hiding out in Aaron's flatshare, while he worked for a fancy architectural firm on placement. It was a place I felt safe; no one, especially this boyfriend, could find me there. And Aaron and I had so much fun, sometimes staying up until the early hours of the morning, just talking. We'd get takeaways and sit in his freezing living room, wrapped in blankets, watching films we'd recommended to each other, while my phone would ring constantly, set on silent, from a boyfriend I didn't know how to dump. Aaron and I always ended up sharing his bed and that was when the sleeping together started. Aaron had had a girlfriend at the time too, who I think he had quite liked. Odd that for the entire time we were in Edinburgh together we'd never claimed to be anything more than friends. And now, as I sank further into the sagging cushions of my own sofa, I couldn't stop thinking of him in his home with his mum and sister. I prayed for him to be okay, for him to be surviving. I just wasn't sure who I was praying to.

I could hear Mum turning, hitting the padding of the sofa underneath her.

Have you slept? I whispered.

No. You?

No.

We hadn't left the farm in what seemed like so long. Perhaps the rest of the world had already forgotten us. Or maybe there was no one left now but us.

Mum shifted, her jaw moving as she yawned. Can I ask you something?

What? I said.

Did you ever tell Aaron?

I paused, suspicious of her ability to read my mind. The night I didn't come home after my last shift at the service station, I said. That was the night I told him.

Why didn't you tell him at the time? she said.

I suppose I was worried he'd talk me into keeping it.

Would it have changed your mind if he had wanted it?

I shook my head. You having me – that was advantageous to *you*. It was an opportunity to change things up, to stay . . . But, for me, it would have tied me to something I didn't want. I paused. Maybe we won't all die of drought or famine. Maybe we'll simply diminish because people like me will refuse to reproduce, even if we're capable of it.

Maybe you'll change your mind . . .

Maybe this is why we're all so uncertain in our twenties – because our elders are constantly questioning our choices.

Mum cleared her throat. You know what happens to livestock that don't reproduce.

I tried to laugh. Maybe men hate the idea of women not reproducing because it makes them feel like they're losing control – no more little boys to grow into men.

Well, spare a thought for Noah, she said.

I do. Every day.

I wish they'd let us see them, she whispered. Even just for a minute.

Do you still think I made a mistake, getting rid of the baby?

She was quiet for a moment. Aida, I was upset that you'd got yourself into that situation, but honestly, perhaps you're right. I'm relieved now at the decision you made.

Her words startled me, a winding of sorts that I hadn't been expecting. Really?

Mum started to cry then, but it seemed almost cathartic – a release.

It's okay, I said.

I'm sorry, she said. I'm not sure why I'm crying.

It's fine, I whispered, my mind already back at the clinic, the paperwork, looking around at some of the other girls and women who had no one there to support them. When my name had been called, I'd walked away from her, and she had waited the entire time; brought a book with her – *The Five People You Meet In Heaven*. And when I finally came out, I had felt lighter, physically lighter.

Anyway, I said. Don't you think people without children are happier? Like a selfish happiness that people with children pretend doesn't exist?

You bring me a different type of happiness, she said. I wouldn't change a thing.

People who use the expression *There's nowhere I'd rather be*, or *I wouldn't change a thing*, are lying. It only serves to mask their regret or longing for something else.

She started to laugh. So, should I confess that some of my happiest memories were in that brief period of life between arriving in Scotland as a student and falling pregnant with you?

I think it's good to be honest, I said.

It was a selfish happiness that was only attainable before your existence – a time when I was the most important person to me, she said. And then we had you and it was hard, but we loved you. There is nothing like the love I have for you, but there is also nothing like the worry you endure as a parent. Sometimes I'm envious that you don't carry that weight. She paused. I suppose you couldn't have been too scary, since we did try to make another one. There were miscarriages . . . But nothing ever stuck.

I didn't know that, I said. About the miscarriages . . .

Well, it is what it is.

For a moment nothing more was said, while Mum shifted once again in the darkness, trying to get comfortable.

You know, she said, at least once a day I replay the memory of your father leaving me, his resolve, knowing he was waiting for you to not live in our home any more. It was all so calculated. I wonder, for how long did he want to leave, how many years had he been waiting? She paused. I got on to my hands and knees, she said, and begged him not to leave. Isn't that just humiliating? I could laugh at the humiliation of it all.

Why did you continue to give him so much of your time?

Because I realised, finally – truly understood what would have happened if he'd stayed.

Oh, please . . . I replied, exasperated.

You still don't see it, she said. You can't accept that someone's mental health is as important as their physical health. Just look at Sam.

Don't talk to me about mental health, I said. Your generation have fucked up my generation's mental health. You didn't have to deal with all this existential threat.

Mum fell quiet. I think your father would have killed himself if he hadn't got away, she said. Genuinely, that's what I believe.

I don't think that, I said.

How do you know? she said. You never stopped to look.

I paused. Really? Did I not?

Mum didn't reply.

Do you think he's okay? I asked.

God, I hope so.

I pulled my knees up to my chest and lay there, tight like a ball.

You should have met someone else after he left, I said. I think you could have been happy if you'd given yourself the chance. It makes me sad.

In the morning, we waited in the kitchen for our rations. It was usually Peter who brought them, leaving them by the door. Sometimes it would be the most basic of things: crackers, a tin of fruit; other times it would be something more interesting: some lamb chops Evelyn had cooked, a can of Sprite. I consumed whatever I was given. They always gave us water – one mug full and Mum put a coaster over the top to stop anything from landing in it, taking a small amount out and leaving it in Rusty's bowl. And in turn I'd learned to adjust my insulin, consuming less of everything. I marvelled at how quickly we could lower our expectations; to merely exist seemed enough.

I sat down at the kitchen table and checked my blood sugar, before reducing my long-acting insulin from fourteen to eleven units. I lifted my T-shirt up and injected myself, my abdomen exposed, bruised from the last site I'd injected from.

Have you other bruising? Mum said, watching me.

I shrugged.

Is it sore?

No, I said. I think I'm just worn down.

She was stroking Rusty affectionately behind the ears, something I rarely, if ever, saw her do. Just be extra-cautious, okay, she said.

I nodded, putting my insulin back in the lunch pack. I'll need some new insulin pens soon . . . I said.

She nodded, her thoughts off in the distance.

What are you thinking? I said.

I'm thinking that despite everything we are actually quite lucky, she said.

Are we?

If we hadn't been living on this farm, she said, we wouldn't have had access to a generator and we wouldn't have been able to continue to survive this way. You wouldn't have been able to refrigerate your insulin at all. She paused. Others will have died already but we are still here. This is something we have to continue to be grateful for.

I came and placed a kiss on her head, because she could have her moments but I did love her. She was all I had, and I was grateful for that. Maybe she was all I was ever going to have.

Peter arrived then, knocking on the kitchen door. I opened it to find the usual tray sitting on the ground, Peter already retreating, aiming for Bobby and Sam's bench in the fresh morning light. I watched as he set to carving more wood in his hand. I wasn't sure how many spoons he'd managed to make so far – maybe he was saving them up for something special, or maybe spoons were all he knew how to make.

Evelyn came out and stood beside him. She called my name.

What? I shouted.

Your hens, she said. They're not laying eggs any more.

Okay . . .

I want to show you.

She began walking around to the hen house, beckoning me to follow. I stopped at the entrance, watching as she lowered her head to get inside. Look, she said, waving her hands about. Each day I've been coming, and nothing . . .

I shrugged. I don't know what you want me to do . . .

She grabbed the closest hen to her, it flapping in her hands. And then in one quick motion she snapped its neck. It was instant, it had not suffered, but the suddenness caused me to retreat, my back bumping up against the mesh frame.

She began to climb out of the coop with the hen still in her hand. I thought we'd have chicken for dinner tonight, she said, throwing the bird to me as she spoke.

What do you want me to do with it?

Pluck it, she said before walking away.

I crouched down and stared at it. I took it by its broken neck, trailing it along the ground across the yard while Peter carried on carving his next spoon.

Mum watched from the door, wincing at our dead poultry.

Have you ever plucked a chicken before? I asked, heaving it on to the table.

She nodded. When I was a girl, with my mama.

Can you show me, please?

She nodded again, sitting down beside me, resolved. And we got to work.

*

As evening set in, I could hear Peter out in the yard, aimless with nothing to do. Sometimes he would sit in the Defender, turn on the engine and rev it, as if he was threatening to leave us all behind, but he never did. I couldn't focus on reading fiction any more, but in the living room I found my old human biology textbook from high school. The edges were curled inwards, half the cover torn away. Inside, my name was scrawled in pencil. My handwriting was childish then, and it still was now. I had assumed it would mature with time, imagined beautiful sprawling lines, but they'd never come. Flicking through the pages, I stopped in the middle at an image of the human body. All the internals were illustrated – the arteries and veins, tendons and bones – intricately drawn, the human body a perfect design. Our bodies would continue on for weeks, if not longer, without the consumption of food, but they would last merely days without water. And I wanted there to be an illustration of what that would look like. Which organs would begin to shut down first? Did some go at the same time? The textbook wouldn't have done any of it justice – I wanted medieval images, like the ones of bodies being hanged, drawn and quartered, or from when doctors used to operate on their patients without anaesthetic – peeling back skin, an audience watching behind. I wanted things to *hurt* more. The numbness was irritating, infuriating.

I walked into the bathroom and stared at the empty tub, murky lines of residue marking the bottom. The water we'd initially drawn was now fully gone, evaporation having taken a share, and I felt cheated, by its disappearing without consent. How much water was left in the country? There was an irrational anger at my lack of control, the same way I'd grow frustrated when a simple task was thwarted – the arm of a jacket being inside out, rummaging for keys in a handbag. Why did everything take so much effort?

I stripped my clothes off and inspected myself. The bruising from where I was injecting my insulin was quite compelling – amazing that your body held the ability to store so many shades of colour. I found some wet wipes in a cupboard and attempted to give myself a good clean. I tried to pretend I was at a music festival, the only means of cleaning myself in my tent, the stench of the tent feeling all too familiar. My hair was greasy and limp, and I found a can of dry shampoo, spraying it across my scalp, but it made little difference. There was gunk in my eyes now, itchy and red, my eyelashes sticking together. I cried then, maybe because I thought it would help as a way of cleaning, but also because I felt as if we were being picked apart, slowly, very slowly. Could I have just stopped taking my insulin? I didn't think I was capable.

Suddenly I heard Peter call out to someone in the yard and a male voice replied from a distance. We hadn't seen anyone else in so long that I could barely contain myself. I grabbed my dirty clothes and flung them on, nearly tripping. I ran into the living room and peered out of the window, and sure enough there was a figure making its way down towards us, nearly at the cattle grid, but I couldn't make out who it was, their steps slow, their feet struggling, a filthy wide-brimmed hat shading their face from the sun. And I ran out, noticing, like a shock to the system, the cooling in temperature, the air not thick and sickly as it had previously been, even just days before.

By the gateposts, Peter stood with Bobby's shotgun, the man now on the ground. Peter came forward and pressed his foot into the back of the man's neck, suppressing a wail from escaping. He was nothing but skin and bone, emaciated, trying to shield himself. And Peter looked hungry and excited, as if he'd been waiting for this all along.

My immediate fear was that it was Aaron, or Dad, unrecognisable. I was cautious in my approach, coming to a stop beside Peter, and in that moment my body relaxed with relief, knowing it was neither of them. But then who was it? Was it the soldier from the border, finally turning up to claim his lamb chops? Peering closer, I realised with shock that it was actually Lewis, the service station manager.

Lewis . . . I said.

He tried to look up at me. They left me, Aida. My wife and kids. They took everything and left.

Peter's foot was still pressing into Lewis's neck, the barrel of Bobby's gun firmly aimed in anticipation. You know this man? he said.

He used to be my boss.

Why's he here? Peter asked, aggressive in his tone.

I used to help Bobby with the lambing sometimes when he was short . . . Lewis managed. I didn't know where else to go.

Mum was behind us now. Get your foot off him, she said.

Evelyn was approaching too, authority seeping in with each of her strides. Who the fuck is this? she said.

Peter nodded towards me. Ask Aida. Says it's her boss.

Evelyn observed us all as if she was watching a play unfold. Is this true? she said. Or are you just trying to be kind to this man?

It's true.

I didn't mean to cause trouble, Lewis said. He looked deathly, as if he hadn't eaten in weeks. Miriam . . . he said, still straining under Peter.

I pulled at Peter, trying to dislodge his foot. And finally Lewis was free, and Mum was the one helping him to his feet.

I turned, twitchy, staring back at Bobby's cottage as if I expected him to come marching out.

We need to get you inside, Mum said, already ushering him towards our kitchen door. You need to eat and drink something.

He turned his head, casting a glance across the yard as he tried to steady himself in Mum's wake. Who are these people? he asked, his words coming out in almost a whisper. Where's Bobby?

He's gone, Evelyn shouted behind us. Dead.

Lewis stared at me, his eyes huge.

Mum nodded. It's true. And as she spoke, her eyes fixed on Evelyn, as if she was waiting for Evelyn to tell her what to do next.

Evelyn tilted her head to one side, gauging Lewis in some way.

You look like you've not slept in days, I said, coming round to help him. We guided him through the kitchen and down the hall into the living room, ushering him into one of the sagging corduroy sofas.

I've never been in your home before, he whispered.

Evelyn came in behind us, standing by the door, a warning smile on her face.

It must have been a difficult journey, Mum said. What's it like out there?

My wife took the car . . . he whispered, his throat raspy and dry. But there was hardly any fuel so I've no idea if they're okay or not . . . I don't even know how far they would have got . . . Terrible things are happening out there. It's lawless.

Mum nodded, a passive expression settling across her face. I envied her ability to adjust her face to what the tone of the room required. What a life skill to have acquired.

So do you want something to eat? Evelyn asked, her tone guarded.

He nodded. Thank you.

Evelyn departed and Lewis looked from me to Mum and back again.

I hugged my knees. The seasons were finally changing – I could see it in the hairs on my arms, the goosebumps I hadn't felt for so long. Rusty, who had been sleeping in his bed by the empty larder cupboard, got up to inspect Lewis, had a sniff around his ankles before returning to his bed, unimpressed, only interested in Bobby and Sam's return, not anyone else's arrival.

Lewis closed his eyes for a moment before opening them. I'm sorry if my turning up has caused you a problem. I wasn't even sure if you'd still be here. I heard this rumour that places up north were getting some rainfall, but there's no way to get there. I just worry about my kids . . . He looked at me with total despair. I just keep thinking, hoping, that if we can wait it out a little longer . . .

Evelyn returned then, carrying a plate with some oatcakes and cheap, artificial cheese paste from Bobby and Sam's fridge. Here, she said, handing it to him.

He took a bite, devouring the first few oatcakes, crumbs falling from his mouth. We could see he was dehydrated but knew better than to ask for water.

Okay? Evelyn said.

He nodded.

Good. She paused then. Look, I'm sorry to be the bearer of bad news, but you can't stay, she said.

Sorry?

There's nothing here. So, you can't stay.

I've nowhere else to go, he said, pleading.

I'm sorry, that's just the harsh reality of where things stand. When you're finished eating, Peter will see you off the farm.

I looked from her to Mum. Mum's eyes were focused on the ground, too cowardly to look up. But then I wasn't raising my voice either. Everything Evelyn had said was true.

We watched him finish his plate, ravenous, yet knowing there was nothing to be gained by finishing too quickly.

They forced him back out into the yard and we were expected to watch. He was begging Peter to let him stay even just one night but Peter kept shaking his head. The shotgun wasn't in sight any more but after several unsuccessful attempts to usher Lewis over the cattle grid, Peter lost his temper completely and we watched in silence as he began to beat him, a horror that seemed to play out in slow motion as Peter pounded again and again into Lewis's feeble and weak frame. And it was shocking to witness; perhaps because despite Peter's strength I hadn't thought he was capable of such violence. Maybe it wouldn't have been as bad if Lewis hadn't kept trying to get up and beg. If he'd just stopped, lain there and played dead, surely it wouldn't have been as bad. Evelyn eventually commanded Peter to stop. And he did, taking a step back to catch his breath before spitting on Lewis, who lay curled in the foetal position, trembling, but no longer asking to stay.

21

When we finally got invited into Bobby and Sam's cottage, it smelled foreign and sterile, Evelyn no doubt having worked her magic with some Dettol wipes. Mum shuffled into the open-plan behind me, while Peter took up space in front of the fireplace, and Evelyn sat comfortably in Bobby's chair. Rebecca and Noah were out of sight – hidden away in the back of the house, I presumed.

From where I stood, I could see Sam's herb and spice jars. Bobby had made him the rack they sat in, having taken a brief notion to learn basic woodwork skills. But the finished product had turned out wonky in size – too spacious for six jars, but not enough room for seven.

Things are starting to deplete, Evelyn said, nodding for us to sit. Like butter, the loaves in the freezer. I did attempt to bake a loaf, but it didn't come out right. However, I've defrosted some bagels. Would you like one with some peanut butter?

A large tub of peanut butter was sitting out on the counter, and I didn't have the heart to tell her that we only ever used that one for Rusty, squeezing his capsules and worming tablets into it on a spoon.

I nodded. Okay, thank you.

And you, Miriam? Would you like one too?

Mum nodded, while Evelyn got to her feet and made her way into the kitchen space. A four-slice toaster, she said, announcing it to room as if this was quite the revelation. Can you believe it? And a button specifically for bagels . . .

Peter walked over to Bobby's drinks cabinet and arbitrarily removed a bottle of whisky. He took a swig from the bottle as though it was nothing before coming forward and stopping in front of me, waving the bottle in my face. Feeling I had little choice, I took it and brought it to my lips, knocking back the liquid and coughing as I swallowed. A bagel popped out of the toaster then and Evelyn began scraping peanut butter across it. And as she did so, another bagel popped up.

You have this one, she said, offering me a plate, the bagel swimming in the gloppy texture of the peanut butter.

Thank you, I said.

She handed the next one to Mum. There's certainly something quite romantic about living self-sufficiently, don't you think? she said, returning to Bobby's armchair.

I gripped my plate. You think I'd choose to live like this? I said.

Evelyn paused. I wasn't trying to patronise . . .

Staring down at the oily plate, I couldn't quite bring myself to take a bite. Pre-empting the taste of it with the whisky made me feel nauseous.

Peter remained silent, once again taking a swig from the whisky bottle.

Evelyn stared at us. Look, there's no need to look so glum. Things are going to get better. I dreamed of rain last night, so surely that counts for something, right?

We said nothing.

She straightened. Are you angry with me? For sending that man, Lewis, away?

I stared at her. I'd done nothing to stop them, and I felt dirty, my insides crawling. I supposed I thought the whisky might help. Mum had barely spoken since, only to say, At least it wasn't your father.

It was cruel and inhumane, I whispered. We've essentially condemned him to death.

We have very little water now, she said.

I shrugged. What would one more mouth really have changed? I don't think he would have needed much.

Is it because you knew him? she pressed. Is it different when you know the person? Does that cause you to understand their needs and struggles better?

We took you in, didn't we? Mum countered, as quietly as a mouse.

Enough, Peter said, taking another swig, working his way through the same bottle. I can't handle this animosity, he said, manic in his behaviour.

You should eat that, Evelyn said, pointing to the bagels. We're in no position to be letting things go to waste. She jabbed her finger. Go on.

I looked from her to the plate, bringing it on to my knee. I wiped a smudge of peanut butter on to my index finger and inspected it.

We've all had the same, Evelyn said.

Mum had already taken a bite of hers.

Slowly, I licked the peanut butter off my finger.

See . . . Evelyn said. There's nothing wrong with it.

I nodded, taking a bite, hearing the noise of my chewing, everything else around me silent.

Evelyn began to laugh then, some joke she was only planning to share with herself. You're so funny sometimes, Aida. Honestly, you crack me up.

Peter found a deck of cards from a drawer and informed us that he wished to play a game, demanding that both Mum and

I play, beckoning us to join him at the dining table. He began counting out cards, forcing them across the table towards us, telling us that we were playing poker.

Don't you need money for that? I said.

He got to his feet then, rummaging around drawers again, removing an old money wallet of Bobby's, black leather and oval in shape like a little satchel. He dumped the contents out on to the table, all coppers and nothing else. It appeared to do the job and he began counting out the coins, sliding a little heap towards Mum, me and then himself.

I didn't know how to play poker and I doubted Mum did either.

No rules were explained; Peter simply started. It was my turn first, and as I stared at my cards I could see him getting irritated, waiting for me to do something. I placed two cards down and asked for two more from the deck and he snapped at me, telling me I was doing it wrong. He got to his feet, inspecting his near-empty bottle of whisky before opening the drinks cupboard again, crouching to peer inside. He stood to full height, bringing a box out with him, lifting the lid. This one looks expensive, he said, pulling the bottle out, the cork covered with a sticker seal. And I recognised it then, remembered Bobby buying it for Sam's sixtieth – how it had been too special and expensive to drink, and me not understanding why you'd buy something you wouldn't actually get to enjoy. And I wanted to cry then, because they would never taste it now. And it all seemed so fucking pointless. Everything.

No, I said. Find something else . . . Not that one.

Why? he said, quizzically.

Just not that one, okay.

He smirked, his hand creeping around the sticker, ready to tear it off.

Evelyn raised her hand. Be respectful, she warned him. She turned to look at me, a controlled smile settling on her face. Why don't we drink to them? A toast to their life . . .

I hesitated.

I'm sure they would have liked that, she said.

Slowly, I nodded, and Peter snapped off the sticker, the cork popping off with a satisfying noise. He began pouring us all tumblers of whisky, handing them out forcefully.

There was something foul about the way he threw his measure back. He didn't care how important this bottle was to the very people he was meant to be toasting. He pounded his hand down on to the table, commanding Mum now to take a turn, and it was as if the whole room was on edge, no one having any real sense of where this was going.

I could hear Noah crying but Evelyn was oblivious, her attention fixed on us and the cards. There was a tension in Peter's posture, like a pressure needing to be released. And then Mum made her move, placing her cards face up, laid out bare for everyone to see.

Peter gripped her wrist harshly and Mum winced. Please don't . . . she said. Noah's cries intensified and Peter just kept staring at Mum with what looked like real hatred, squeezing her skin.

Let her go, I said, my words firm and clear.

Why? Peter spat.

Please, I said. Just let her go. You don't want to hurt her.

Peter looked at me, a real expression of pain in his eyes, a wounded animal. Finally, he released his grip from around Mum's wrist. Sorry, he whispered.

Noah was screaming now, inconsolable wails.

Please, let me check on Noah, Mum begged, cupping her wrist. Please . . . And Rebecca . . . Let me see them.

Evelyn suddenly got to her feet, following the noise. She turned to look at us, irritated. Remember your place, she said, but to whom she was directing her words was unknown.

I got to my feet too, gesturing for Mum to follow me. I could still hear Noah crying from out in the yard as we walked back, not daring to stop until we were in our kitchen, closing and locking the door behind us.

Mum sat down in her usual chair, still cupping her wrist.

Let me see it, I said.

It's fine.

It's not fine.

He's just sprained it, that's all.

I went rummaging through the bathroom cupboard, looking for something we could use. There was an old elasticated bandage rolled up in a heap and I grabbed it, taking it back to the kitchen. It was too long so I cut it in half with a pair of scissors, before stretching it up and over Mum's hand, tucking the frayed edges in and around her wrist. I took a step back to inspect my handiwork. Do you think it will help? I said.

It could have been worse, she said.

I nodded, because it was true. We were all capable of anything, especially without water. And there couldn't have been much left.

In the early morning light, I woke, startled, to find Rebecca hovering over me as I lay on one of the sofas in the living room. Metres away, Mum was still asleep, oblivious. The curtains were drawn but not especially thick, allowing a strange glow of light to filter through. I sat up, pressing my hands into the cushions of the corduroy fabric. Rebecca's eyes were wide, and when I looked down she was holding one of Bobby and Sam's kitchen knives, covered in blood, droplets falling on to our worn and filthy carpet, her kaftan nightdress also covered in red. She looked like a piece of art. I remained completely still, an invisible weight pinning me down, my chest heavy.

What happened? I said, my words barely more than a whisper.

She brought her index finger up to her lips and reached out with her other hand, waited for me to take it. Slowly I rose, casting my blanket off to the floor, and with silent steps I allowed her to guide me out of the living room, her touch gentle, until we were leaving through the kitchen.

The door to Bobby and Sam's cottage lay open and we carried on until we were inside, the open-plan room in disarray, bottles of whisky lining the table. She wore no shoes or socks, and once again I found myself staring at her middle toe, the tip of it missing. She still gripped the bloodied knife and I feared her dropping it, slicing off another toe.

Using the knife, she pointed towards the back hall.

What is it? I whispered.

She stared at me. Vacant.

I let go of her hand and stepped forward, the door into the hall creaking open. There was a trail of thick droplets heading towards Bobby and Sam's bedroom. And inside, lying across the bed was Evelyn, still and lifeless, her body covered in blood.

I stared in shock; the image of it weirdly consuming. The blood had soaked into everything: the bed sheets, the mattress, on to the floor. Red was no doubt seeping into the springs and the memory foam underneath her. How strange that this was the second time I had witnessed death in this room, on this same bed.

Rebecca was behind me and I turned to look at her fragile frame, I couldn't quite comprehend that she was capable of such an act.

The baby . . . I whispered.

And as if Noah could sense my worry, a little whimper escaped from the corner of the room. Cautiously, I walked over to find him beginning to stir in his makeshift cot: one of Bobby's dresser drawers padded with blankets. I lifted him gently from his cot and brought him to my chest. Then, I took Rebecca by the hand and guided her out of the room.

She pointed to the closed door of the spare room where Peter slept, bringing her index finger up to her lips once again. Silently, we walked back through the living space, stopping for a moment while I prised open the fridge door, retrieving my insulin supplies, throwing them one-handed into a bag-for-life, before making for the front door.

I was aware of the gravel under my feet as we walked, of Noah nuzzling further into my chest. Mostly, I was still aware of the knife Rebecca continued to grip in her right hand. Back in our kitchen I locked the door, dropped the bag of insulin on to the table and checked the clock, realising that it was nearly seven. What time would Peter be likely to stir? He'd been up late into the night, drowning himself in whisky, shooting Bobby's gun into the darkness of the fields.

I stood there, the warmth of the baby against my body so soothing. I reached out for the knife, but Rebecca seemed reluctant to let go.

It's okay, I said.

I touched her hand and then the handle of the knife. Slowly her fingers uncurled. Carefully, with the blade pointing downwards, I placed it in the sink. Instinctively I turned on the tap, momentarily forgetting that it was redundant.

I pulled out a chair and ushered Rebecca into it before handing Noah to her, watching as she brought him upright, his little head resting over her shoulder.

Wait here, I said, using my hands in a gesture of *stay*.

As I walked down the hall I reached for the front door, rattling the handle several times to ensure it, too, was locked. I took a breath, closed my eyes for a moment. I entered the living room and could hear Mum snoring lightly, her face turned inwards towards the sofa, and I stood, hesitating, unsure whether it was fair to disturb her sleep, shatter the illusion.

I reached down and patted her shoulder. Mum, I whispered.

She tried to roll away from me, brought the blanket up past her nose.

Mum, I said, more firmly, shaking her now.

She stirred, reluctant. What?

You need to get up.

Her eyes widened as she came to, blinking several times. What time is it?

I lowered myself down into a kneeling position, so that our faces were practically touching. As I did so, I sensed her trying to pull back.

We have a situation, I said.

What's wrong? she asked, suddenly alert.

I shook my head, the reality of it all finally seeming to hit me. I clenched my hands together in an attempt to stop the trembling.

Aida, you're scaring me, she said.

Rebecca . . . I swallowed, acid rising to the back of my throat.

Just say it, she said. Whatever it is.

My breathing was heavy. Rebecca stabbed Evelyn, I said. She's dead. And as the words came out, I was aware of a flippancy to my tone, my body shrugging as if it was nothing.

What?

I nodded, aware that the shaking had taken over.

Where is she?

Who? Rebecca or Evelyn?

Both . . .

Rebecca is in our kitchen, I said. And Evelyn is on Bobby and Sam's bed. I paused, took a breath. Peter is still sleeping, I think.

Did you see her? she asked. Are you sure she's dead?

I began nodding my head, furiously, like a tic.

She sat completely upright, still.

What should we do? I whispered.

Mum was on her feet suddenly, her pyjamas looking ridiculous, and she ran into the hall, looking both ways as though she was trying to decide on the best escape route.

I've already locked the doors, I said.

I followed her into the kitchen where we found Rebecca sitting in the chair where I'd left her, her hand tapping gently and rhythmically against Noah's back. Mum stared at her blood-covered nightdress. She crouched down then and took in Rebecca's blank, expressionless face. Gently, Mum placed her left hand on Rebecca's cheek. I'm so sorry, she whispered. What awful things have you had to endure? Mum looked up at me then. Does he still have Bobby's gun . . . Or did you manage to take it?

No . . . I said. I didn't see it.

Mum stood straight, the fabric of the elasticated bandage around her wrist a grubby brown instead of cream. We should leave, she said. We need to get away from here. Wherever we can go without being stopped.

Peter has the key to the Defender, I said.

Fine, we'll go on foot.

And then what? I said.

Mum closed her eyes for a moment. I don't know, Aida. I don't know.

The ruins, I said. You should take Rebecca and Noah down to the ruined cottages . . . I can stay and get the key. You can follow the washed-up road to the village if you have to.

I'm not leaving you behind, she said. We all go together.

We can't, I shouted. This has to end, Mum. I started frantically collecting things in front of me: the scraps of rations left for us, our mug of water to be decanted into the chewed sports bottle, some spare nappies and wipes. There was a worn backpack hanging on a peg in the hall and I threw everything into it. Take my insulin too, I said. That way you know I'm coming to get you.

Aida . . . Mum said, but I wasn't willing to listen to what she wanted to say.

Okay, get some shoes on, I said, grabbing her by the arm, willing her to quicken her pace. Rebecca needs shoes too, I added, rummaging through the hall cupboard, finding a pair of my old trainers and bending to shove them on to Rebecca's feet.

Mum was trying to stop me from moving, her left hand gripping me. Please, she begged, let's all go and look for help.

There is no help, I said, staring at her. We do whatever we have to do to survive, don't we?

I can't let anything happen to you, she said.

I'll be okay.

Her lip began to quiver.

I nodded towards Rebecca and Noah. They need you more than I do. I reached forward to kiss her cheek. I love you. Now go and put on some shoes.

I watched her force her feet frantically into her boots. I handed her the backpack and she slung it over her shoulder.

Take the knife, I said, to be safe.

I gestured for Rebecca to get to her feet and obediently she followed us as we returned to the hall. You'll take the front door and avoid the yard, I said, matter of fact.

Aida . . . Mum pleaded.

Quick, we don't have much time.

Tears of panic began to run down Mum's cheeks. Promise me you'll be safe, she said. Promise that you will come to the ruins. You will come and get your insulin.

I will, I said. I'll come.

Swear it.

I swear.

We stood over the threshold of the front door, suspicious of our surroundings, the sun glistening across the empty reservoir.

I watched them leave, Mum cautious but moving at pace, turning briefly to look back at me before they were gone, out of view behind the sheds.

I walked into the yard and entered the cattle shed, taking in the empty expanse. It still smelled of livestock. How long had it been? I couldn't tell any more. There was straw and dry dung stains, the last of the hay bales, useless now. The tractor hadn't moved in so long, various-shaped pieces lying on the ground before me that Peter had disassembled. I contemplated how each of these pieces could make this huge vehicle move, doubted it would ever move again. I used to like riding up front with Bobby, driving it even, while Mum stood from a distance, hating every moment, fearing that with one misstep I could be taken under and crushed by those huge tyres. When you did something so often, you forgot the risk that came with it. All the slurry-pit fatalities, the gases taking you before anyone would have a chance to scoop you out; all the suicides. All the hazards, the terrible tragedies waiting to happen.

Quietly, I entered Bobby and Sam's cottage and stood in the open-plan space for a moment, running my hand along the mantel of the fireplace. There was a wooden giraffe staring at me, carved in South Africa and gifted to Bobby by some distant relative who had been lucky enough to travel. There were all these places I knew I'd never see; all these places no one was likely to see ever again. People had been going on their honeymoons in the Maldives until about a year ago and I wasn't even sure these islands even existed any more. Had the sea swallowed them yet? Maybe when we started removing more water from the sea to desalinate it, they'd magically appear again.

I crept into the back hall and hovered outside the master bedroom, staring at Evelyn, before closing the door. Then, taking a deep breath, I entered the spare bedroom. Peter was still sleeping soundly, oblivious. His face twitched; maybe he was dreaming. He looked vulnerable and I wasn't sure if he'd know what to do without Evelyn. Bobby's shotgun was on the floor, and I picked it up; it weighed heavy in my hands. Bobby had told me stories of his father burying pistols across the land when they'd changed the regulations of what firearms you were allowed to keep. We had no idea where they were.

There were cartridges still in the gun. I could have just shot him; he would never have known. And I tried. I held the gun up and aimed it at his face, it hovering there. I imagined what it would be like, the devastation it would cause to his beautiful face. But I couldn't do it. Evelyn was right: I didn't have it in me. And I was too pragmatic, like Mum - I was thinking that I'd then have two bodies and two lots of blood to deal with and I didn't want to deal with any of it.

The keys to the Defender were on the bedside table and cautiously I reached over for them. I left the cottage and emptied the cartridges out of the gun, before walking over to the cattle grid by the gateposts. Crouching, I dropped the gun into it, and it landed in the thick undergrowth beneath, disappearing from view. I reasoned that whatever happened now, at least no one was going to get shot.

Standing in the yard, I gazed up to the sky again. There was a breeze and all I wanted to do was acknowledge it – it was all so beautiful. I could have gone for Mum and Rebecca then, prayed for Peter not to wake until after we were away, bundled everyone and everything into the Defender. But, I thought, why should I do that? Why did he get to stay? I supposed part of me wanted to see his reaction to Evelyn too – I thought of him in the abattoir, his sense of not getting too attached – this perverseness I had, wanting to know if he suffered at all.

I walked back inside and into the spare room with purpose, opening the curtains wide. They were thick and old, a purple colour with retro green swirls, white lining, that perhaps my grandmother had made before her passing. Still Peter did not stir. I reached over and tapped him on the arm. He startled awake, confused, his eyes coming into focus, wincing from the pain of the light.

I had wanted to see him feign some form of distress at finding me there, but he only shielded his eyes from the sun, as if I were merely an inconvenience.

Your mother is dead, I said.

He sat up slowly, glancing down at the floor to where the gun should have been. He stared at me, a strange, almost pleasing expression settling on his sun-kissed face. I've had dreams about this happening, he replied.

I saw her . . . I said. I'm sorry.

Was it you?

I shook my head. Rebecca.

He started laughing, it rolling through him, before he slumped back down on to the bed. Where is she – in there? he asked, nodding his head towards the door.

Do you want to see her?

She's not my mother. Well, maybe she is, but not biologically. I've been with her since I was seven. I was one she couldn't sell – the reason she shifted to babies.

We were both silent for a moment.

Why did you stay with her?

It's all I've known. Sometimes, when everything is a bad choice, you try and take the least bad option.

Better to help capture new fish than be gutted yourself? I said.

When you're a kid, you have no say in what happens to you. It's sheer luck who you end up with, whether that be biological parents or otherwise.

I nodded. Luck, I said.

He cleared his throat. How long where you watching me for?

Not long.

Why didn't you just finish the job? You could have. Wouldn't that have been easier for everyone?

I did think about it, I said. But if I had killed you . . . I shrugged. I don't know. I wouldn't have been able to to reverse it, and what if I'd liked it . . . ? That probably scares me more than anything else.

He laughed. Push someone far enough and they'll do anything . . . he said.

It's just you and me now. Everyone else is gone. So, you have nothing to threaten me with.

I killed them, he whispered. Bobby and Sam. Suffocated them in their sleep. Evelyn said it needed to be done – that it was the only way to be sure we could stay.

Everything seemed to stop then, a woozy feeling, my heart pounding in my chest, and I wondered if that was what would kill me – a panic attack, my body unable to function. A broken heart. I had always been so consumed by my own inevitable death. I remained perfectly still; it seemed like the only thing I was capable of.

Peter gripped the duvet, pulling it towards him in comfort. I liked them. Don't think I didn't, he said, shrugging. So, if you were looking for a reason to kill me, there it is. I've thought before about ending things myself, but I've never quite managed.

I remained silent.

Is that cowardly? he asked.

When did it all get so barbaric? I said. When did this become normal?

Some of us have been living barbarically for longer, he replied, and he reached over then, causing me to flinch. Don't worry, he said. I won't hurt you.

He forced his hand under the mattress, fumbling, before removing something. It was Bobby's signet ring and he offered it to me.

I took it from him, placing it on my thumb, the size of it so large. I didn't realise it was missing, I said. I just assumed we'd buried him with it.

You think there's something wrong with me, don't you? he said.

I don't know what I think any more.

He pulled the covers back and got to his feet, eclipsing me with his height, only a worn pair of boxers clinging to his body. I should probably see her, he said, stepping around me then, walking out of the room and towards Bobby and Sam's bedroom. I followed him, watching as he came close to where she lay, hovering over to inspect her. I can't believe Rebecca managed this, he said. There was no emotion in his voice as he spoke, as if he were merely inspecting a painting, trying to understand how the artist went about creating their masterpiece.

Can you get rid of the body? I said. Will you do that?

He took a step back, distancing himself from Evelyn. Yeah, okay, he said. Where?

Where the livestock are buried.

★

Between us we managed to heave Evelyn's wrapped-up body into the Defender and we worked almost mechanically, so well versed were we now in moving bodies. I drove, manoeuvring the vehicle over the uneven terrain until we were back to the same place he'd shown me before, the livestock fresh in the ground. There was a stench, but we didn't bother to articulate this to each other; it was something to be endured, perhaps something we both thought we deserved to suffer. He dug, the ground and soil softer than up by the forest where Bobby and Sam lay. And for the entire time I thought about Mum and Rebecca, wondered what they were thinking.

Afterwards, we sat staring at the heap of displaced earth.

For what it's worth, he said, I don't think we ever really meant to stay longer than was initially agreed. The plan had been to push on once the baby arrived. Get our money. We wanted to get to that big loch that everyone talks about.

Loch Ness, I said.

He nodded.

What changed?

He shrugged. I'm not sure . . . I think Evelyn liked the idea of being here. It felt safe. Like you had everything in the entire world you'd ever need. He closed his eyes, brought his hands up and let the wind ripple over them, the little hairs on his arms standing up.

You have to leave, Peter. You need to take your campervan and go. Take some supplies, enough to see you on your way. But you can't come back here. There is nothing here for you now.

He looked at me. Why would you do that for me?

I don't know . . . Maybe because I want to be better than you.

He smiled. Okay.

He had to use the Defender to jumpstart the campervan, its engine finally coming to life after so long. And I was generous with the supplies I offered, more because it made me feel good. Righteous. Afterwards, I stood by the gateposts and watched him leave, waited until he was past the deserted waterworks and out of view.

And as I made for the path towards the ruins, I played out the reunion with Mum in my head, pre-empted the words we were likely to exchange, tried to invoke real emotion. But I felt empty, just like the reservoir, just like Rebecca. There was nothing left to give.

22

We did our best to remove any trace of Evelyn and Peter, and as a continuation Mum suggested we start going through Bobby and Sam's things too – apparently that was what people did when their loved ones died. And in a way it was comforting, getting to know Bobby and Sam in a way we perhaps hadn't before. Inside Sam's bureau we found stacks of paper: deeds to the land, farming documents among other things, all of which meant little now, and I showed them to Mum. It was a relatively small stack and it saddened me to realise that everything we had could be summarised down to almost nothing. In their bedroom I opened a dresser drawer and lifted out one of Bobby's checked shirts, bringing the collar to my nose and inhaling. They're still here, I thought. In one way or another.

Mum moved with purpose through their other drawers, pushing contents around, no sense of sentimentality.

Is there something specific you're after? I said.

Where's the money? she replied. I've no idea where they kept it. They never told me.

Why would it be in the house?

It was all in cash. Bobby didn't believe in banks, she said.

What? He didn't have a bank account?

We still have a business account for the farm, where all the money from incentives, sales and subsidies went. But Bobby and

Sam personally preferred to deal in cash or trades. When money got divided up, they always took their share in cash.

I sat down on the empty bed frame, Bobby's shirt clutched to my chest. What do you need the money for? I said.

I want to give it to you.

Don't you think if there was any money to be found, Evelyn or Peter would have already taken it?

Why don't we try the other bedroom? she said.

You haven't told me why you want to give me money . . .

Isn't it obvious?

I stared at her. No, it's not.

I suspect, at some point, you'll want to leave this place, she said. You've never really had any intention of taking on the farm, and now there isn't really a farm left. So, I want you to have whatever might still hold value.

Mum, I don't think there's anywhere left for me to . . .

She held her hand up, silencing me. There needs to be hope, she said. And when it comes, I don't want you to feel like I'm holding you here.

I nodded. Okay, we'll see.

In the spare bedroom, I stared at the two small antique wardrobes sitting side by side. Inside the first I found Bobby's *good* clothes – suits worn only a handful of times a year – and as I flicked through the hangers I suspected that he'd been wearing these same suits for decades, that he'd believed right up until the end that everything to be purchased should have a longevity about it – last longer than him. The ritual of being meticulous with one's possessions was intriguing to me – nothing in my own world seemed sacred. The occasions when Bobby had sported these suits would have been important to him. I wondered if he and Sam ever dressed up for each other, maybe on a Saturday evening, as if they were going on a date. I was told Bobby had liked barn dances in his youth; that his moves had been some-thing to behold on the dance floor. Had he serenaded Sam with them? I hoped so.

I opened the other wardrobe and there were more hangers and clothes, the cut and size obviously Sam's. I'd never seen him wear these garments and I let my fingers glide across the differ-ent fabrics. I sniffed the sleeve of a blazer, but it smelled only of stale cupboard. On the bedside table there was a picture of a prize cow and I wanted to laugh. Why would either of them have looked at this? To lie in a bed and admire a picture of a cow who had sold particularly well seemed ridiculous. Pictures of Rusty I could understand, but this . . . I hoped they were watching us from wherever they were, laughing too.

Check under here for me, will you? Mum said, pointing at the single bed, its dated and discoloured mattress on top.

I crouched down sticking my head under the frame. There was a wooden box at the top end, and I had to stretch quite far to get a handle on it. When I opened it there was a picture of Bobby and Sam sitting out on a stretch of grass, their arms around one another. Behind them was the same forest where they lay now. I traced a finger over their faces. They looked happy, and I tried to harness the image of them. Underneath the photo, I found some pornography and I burst out laughing. Dirty fuckers, I said, and Mum peered round to see what I was talking about it.

Eh, no, Aida, I don't want to see that, she said, taking a step back. That's private . . .

And I was smiling as I turned it over. They would have been mortified at the idea of me finding this, the same way they'd been mortified when I'd accidentally walked in on them once, and we'd all had to act as though nothing had happened. If it had been me that had died, I thought, what would they have discov-ered when going through my possessions? Maybe I would have purged my belongings of anything suspicious before departing this world. Although most people never got the opportunity to organise their life so neatly for others.

At the very bottom of the box, I found rolls of banknotes, held in place by elastic bands. But their appearance and texture were unfamiliar. What currency is that? I said.

Mum peered over me. Don't tell me . . . she said. They wouldn't have been so stupid . . .

I unrolled some notes and held them tight in my hands.

It's old money, Mum said, exasperated. It's out of circulation now.

The texture was like paper that could be torn.

These are completely defunct, she said. They might as well have set the money alight. You would think they could have at least told us where the money was before they . . .

I rubbed my forehead, and realised this was the moment to tell her that Bobby and Sam hadn't killed themselves. But I couldn't do it. We'll keep looking, I said. They must have something more current than this stuff.

What if you're right? she said. What if Evelyn and Peter already removed any money that was stashed away? What if he has it all?

I walked into the kitchen area and opened the fridge. There were some uncooked lamb chops in clingfilm that were turning, their colour a darkening brown instead of red like open flesh. And I remembered that the soldier from the border still hadn't come to collect the cuts of lamb he'd bargained for; perhaps he himself had tried to flee to another part of the country. Or maybe he would still come. In the breadbin was the last of Sam's banana bread, stale and wrapped in tinfoil. Had he ever written down the recipe? It was one of my favourites and I'd never thought to ask him how to make it. When I looked up, Rebecca was staring at me, from one of the armchairs, Noah to her breast. I'd almost forgotten they were there.

With no money to be found, we settled Rebecca and Noah into the spare room, finding clean bedding and a makeshift cot, while Mum and I shared Bobby and Sam's bedroom, dragging Mum's mattress in across the yard. It was old but comfy and familiar. Our whole world existed no further than this now, nothing to contemplate past the gateposts.

There were too many chores, particularly now that Evelyn was gone. In the open-plan, I stood surveying the space, losing all sense of what it was I'd planned to do, before retreating to the bedroom, needing to lie down, exhausted from doing nothing. The afternoon sun shone in through the window, blinding me, but I couldn't be bothered to get up and close the curtains. I shut my eyes instead, not moving, letting the sun warm my face. I must have stayed there all day and when the sun set, it didn't seem late enough. The door opened and Rebecca walked in, turning on my bedside lamp before sitting down on the floor. She'd found a thousand-piece jigsaw of a tractor in one of the cupboards and the beginnings of its frame were now materialising on the floor.

I got up, coming to sit down on the floor beside her, crossing my legs. I found a piece I thought fitted and slotted it into place.

Rebecca . . . I whispered.

She stopped and looked up.

I smiled. Maybe she understood every word we said. Perhaps it was just easier to pretend otherwise.

I couldn't remember what it was I wanted to say. My mouth was parched, and I licked my lips several times, trying to force myself into thinking that I did not need water.

She turned her attention back to the jigsaw pieces laid out before her and I was envious at her ease of detachment. I climbed

349

back into bed and fell asleep, comforted by her presence. Dreams came then but nothing tangible, just the notion that my mind was racing, never at peace. When I woke, it was pitch black outside. I could hear Mum's voice coming from somewhere in the house; she started to laugh, and it was lovely. I walked into the open-plan space to find Mum and Rebecca huddled around Noah, who lay flat on his back, while Mum rubbed her head gently against his belly, prompting him to giggle, real, little honest chuckles that couldn't have been ignored.

Later when the house was quiet, I stood at the large kitchen counter, staring out at the full moon. It lit up the sky. Stars were everywhere, and to look at them was to momentarily forget all that had happened or was happening. There was one star flickering low and I'd read somewhere that when a star did this it was because it was dying out, and would soon no longer shine, gone forever.

I heard footsteps and looked over to see Rebecca staring at me. I poured her a glass of water from one of the last remaining containers.

You've always reminded me of someone, I said.

She cleared her throat and began to speak slowly in a language I did not recognise.

I wish you could tell me what to do, I said, bringing my face down on to the cool granite surface, laying my cheek against it.

She stared blankly at me before reaching out and wrapping her arms around me, her face briefly resting against my back. She lifted the glass of water and began to drink.

I watched her drain the glass and place it gently down on the table.

The girl you remind me of, she drowned, I said. She was a strong swimmer. No one expected it. It happened in the lake at the American summer camp where I was working. It was horrific.

People searched the lake for hours; some of us had to swim under the pontoon. They closed the camp early and I didn't tell anyone here. I used the money I'd earned to bum about until it was time for my flight home.

She just smiled at me.

Maybe we should watch a DVD or something, I said.

And she followed me to the sofa, settling in next to me. I pressed play on the DVD player and the disc came to life, prompting me to choose to play the whole film or the first sequence. It was something random – an old comedy with Arnold Schwarzenegger. The cosiness and cheapness of it brought me comfort while Rebecca fell asleep, her head resting against my shoulder. And as my eyes began to droop Mum came in carrying Noah, slumping down on the other side of me.

He's a good wee boy, she said, nuzzling him to her chest.

I hesitated.

Rebecca spoke to me, I said.

Mum turned. What did she say?

I shrugged. It was in a language I couldn't understand.

I don't know if I could bear to hear what she had to say, Mum said, snuggling closer, while Noah continued to sleep soundly across her chest.

Do you think she'll be okay? I asked. Do you think we'll ever be able to make things better for her?

I don't know, darling . . .

There was a strange noise suddenly coming from outside, like a light patter echoing off the windows. Mum sat up, careful not to wake Noah, and peered out.

Aida, she whispered. Look.

It was faint, nothing more than a drizzle, but the drops were there, clinging to the window. I got to my feet and ran, flinging the door open and sprinting out into the yard. I had to feel it;

I had to be reminded of the sensation. I closed my eyes and stuck my tongue out. The moisture was surreal, and I was laughing, just laughing and laughing, walking around in a circle like a parade, a celebration of rain. The noise of it continued in a steady rhythm for what must have been hours, while we set out buckets and cups to gather what we could. And we just watched it fall, the sky a stunning murky grey.

By the browning conifer trees, I stood beside the rectangular patch of earth where Bobby and Sam lay. Little green shoots were sprouting in the disturbed soil, and I realised that it didn't take much for things to find the urge to grow. It reminded me of being a kid, of growing seeds inside damp paper towels.

Is it weird that sometimes I wonder how your bodies are decomposing? I whispered, my voice directed to the ground, my skin damp with the finest drizzle. I imagine your skulls as fine props in a play.

Perhaps I could now scatter seeds over them, let a miniature wild meadow be their tribute.

I don't really know what to do now, I said, crouching down to pat the earth affectionately. Every day I find myself wanting to ask you both questions, wanting your opinions . . .

I drove back down the hill and parked up in the yard, the drizzle still falling around me. Inside, Mum and Rebecca were huddled together on the sofa, shivering a little under the blanket as they watched another DVD.

I can build a fire if you're cold, I said.

Mum nodded.

I crouched down to open the metal box by the hearth that housed the kindling.

Do you think the farm could be something again? Mum asked.

I turned to look at her. I don't know if livestock is the way to go any more, I said, suddenly feeling quite certain. But yeah, there might be grants, and subsidies to use the land in *greener* ways. I paused. This land should be used, I said. Shared, even. So many people will be displaced. We don't need it all.

Mum nodded. That's what I think too.

I positioned the kindling in the grate, reaching for the box of firelighters that had fallen beside the hearth. That was when I saw the cut-out section of wooden skirting board, wedged into the wall but sitting ever so slightly squint. I reached out, lowering my face, looking closer. It was stiff, but finally I managed to pull the wood away from the wall. And behind it was a small recess, a space no wider than Bobby's hand. Peering inside, I could see it all – rolls and rolls of money. It was a wonder it hadn't burnt or caught alight, its proximity to the fire uncomfortably close.

I drew a roll of money out and held it up for Mum.

Oh, my goodness, she said, standing to take it from me. How on earth . . . ?

Outside, the reservoir was gathering the little water it could – the rocks would hopefully once again be covered in algae sludge, a sign of life. It was in these tiniest markers that we would per-haps notice life slowly attempting to return.

The DVD was coming to an end, the credits rolling. Can I pick something else? I said.

Mum nodded, too busy staring at the money.

I pressed a button, turning the DVD player off, to discover the news on.

I stopped, my head tilting to one side. Is this real? I said, pointing to the screen.

Mum took the remote from me and started flicking through the channels to find more news outlets. There were warnings of floods, not because the rainfall was about to intensify, more because the soil was so baked and dry that the water wouldn't penetrate, it would simply bounce off, and gather at low-lying levels.

We stood in silence, watching the screen. There was a cautious conversation between environmental experts, no one willing to offer huge reassurances, but there was a glimmer of optimism. They were stressing how imperative it was that we continue to preserve and recycle our limited supply. One more year, one of them said. And then desalination plants would begin to alleviate the global burden we've been putting on our existing water infrastructures. And we pray, we hope, we adjust . . . That's all we have.

Our life before was gone but there was still life.

Another year, I said. Until something else crops up . . .

Rebecca was staring straight ahead, Noah sleeping in her arms.

We can do another year, Mum replied. We keep going, keep pushing.

I walked into the kitchen area and flicked the switch, turning the power from the generator back on to the mains. The TV went blank only for a moment before surging back to life. I ran, then, out and across the yard and into our cottage, switching the lights on, needing to be sure that the power really was back on. Everything came to life before me, the clock on our oven flashing. In the hall, I gathered the slimline telephone in my hand. When I brought it to me ear a dial tone had returned. It rang eight, nine, ten times and I nearly hung up, with a heaviness in my chest. But then Dad picked up and I wanted to weep with relief. The phones are working again, I said.

It would appear so.

Are you okay? I said.

Just about, darling.

I'm so glad to hear your voice, I said.

There was silence on the other end of the line, then an intake of breath and I realised he was crying.

Dad . . . it's okay, I whispered. It's okay.

Afterwards, I placed the receiver back in its cradle and stood there, pressing my back up against the wall. A spider ran across the carpet and I smiled at it, nodded hello. When the phone rang again, I picked it up immediately, assuming it to be Dad. Did you forget something? I said.

Aida? the voice said.

I stood straight. Aaron . . . ?

Did you mean what you said? About us coming . . .

Come, I said. Please come.

Back in Bobby and Sam's, another expert on the television was reiterating how best to wash and clean yourself as efficiently as possible. Use a sponge or flannel to wash, and wring it back into your basin, he said. Do not pour the water down the plughole. Instead, use it to flush waste down your toilet. If we all pull together, he said, we *can* make this work. And we *will* get through this. The army is being used to distribute supplies and medicine, he said. Travel is still restricted so emergency services can reach those in need. Share what you can. Look out for each other, check on your neighbours . . . There was no news on the wider world; an acceptance that it was best to focus only on our little pocket of earth.

I looked at Noah, still sleeping in his mother's arms. He had it all ahead of him – an uncertainty that would never leave. But, for the time being, within these walls, on this land, surrounded by us, he had what he needed. And that was enough; that was enough for now.

ACKNOWLEDGEMENTS

Thank you to Joanne Dickinson, Eve Hall and Sorcha Rose for your exceptional editorial insight and for your collective belief in this book; to Steven Cooper, Niamh Anderson and Katy Blott for publicity and marketing; and to the whole team at Hodder & Stoughton for continuing to champion me and my writing.

To my passionate and dedicated literary agent Cathryn Summerhayes, as well as Jess Molloy and everyone at Curtis Brown. Thank you.

To the Scottish Book Trust for their continued support; and to Moniack Mhor, Scotland's National Writing Centre, for offering me a residency and where a large proportion of this novel was re-written.

A big thank you also to Creative Scotland for providing me with funding, allowing me undisturbed editing time.

An abundance of people generously offered their time as I grappled with the research for this story – for their expertise on trafficking and human rights, thank you to Felicity Keefe, Angela McLaughlin and Carolann Nesbitt. For their midwifery knowledge and honesty, thank you to Sheila Atalla, Louise Reap and Gillian Spence. With regards to the climate emergency and our relationship to water, thank you to Marie-Sophie Beier and Rebecca Simmonds for their expertise and frank discussions on the realities of our water consumption. I am also incredibly grateful to the farmers who agreed to help me; to Fiona Robertson and Ian Robertson for engaging with my ideas and for being enthusiastic when I decided to write a novel set on a livestock farm; to Jim Black for being so open and receptive to my questions; and to Catriona Gemmell and Sandy Kirkpatrick for being early readers, and for their patience when I continued to pester them about niche farming details. Any inconsistences or errors in this novel are mine, and mine alone.

Thank you to the generous writing community I'm grateful to be part of, in particular to Liam Bell who read the beginnings of this book and to Leyla Josephine for listening to my rambling thoughts. Also, a big thank you to my local book group for their support and to Hazel Maxwell for stepping in to offer childcare when the deadlines got too tight.

To my parents, thank you for your love and unwavering belief in me; to my family and friends, thank you again for your endless enthusiasm and encouragement. To Fraser and Phoebe – it's not easy having a writer for a mum. Thank you. And finally, as always, to Angus, for everything.